FLASH WAS ONLY THE BEGINNING

FLASH WAS ONLY THE BEGINNING

The creators of Pure Storage® who reimagined
data storage and built the fastest growing
enterprise technology company in history

Pure Storage, Inc.

Author: Pure Storage, Inc.
650 Castro Street, Suite 400
Mountain View, CA 94041
https://www.purestorage.com/

Title: Flash Was Only The Beginning
Published by: Pure Storage, Inc.
Identifier: ISBN 9780-578-48373-3
Design & Illustrations: LMA Communications
Photographs: Roland Dreier, Patrick Lee, and Taher Vohra

FSC
www.fsc.org
MIX
Paper from
responsible sources
FSC® C136333

Contents

"Whenever I describe Pure to someone who doesn't know the company, I begin by saying everything about this company is an A+."

"I met with Coz and Mike Speiser for the first time on July 20, 2009 to discuss a new company they planned to start. I don't remember whether Coz was wearing shorts, although I'm sure he must have been. What I do remember very vividly is that Coz and Mike impressed upon me that everything about this new company was going to be an A+. They told me they were going to recruit an A+ group of employees, and they were going to assemble an A+ group of board members and investors. And they were now looking for A+ legal counsel. Fortunately for me and Cooley, I was able to convince them that we could make the grade. To this day, whenever I describe Pure to someone who doesn't know the company, I begin by saying everything about this company is an A+."

Mark Tanoury, Cooley LLP

"Every day I realize how lucky I am to work with some of the brightest minds and most passionate individuals in the industry."

Foreword

Y ou hold in your hands the culmination of ten years of hard work. Work that started with the vision of making flash storage available to organizations everywhere. More than a recitation of the last decade, our history is an integral part of Pure Storage lore and culture. From the naming of the company (twice) to the color orange and the five values we've held as core to the company since the early days -- this book details the very essence of the company I am honored to lead.

We're fortunate to have so many long-serving employees at Pure. Paul Massiglia, the primary author of this book, is one of those people. As our 15th employee, he is one of the best people to share our history, having been front and center as it unfolded. He was here when we could hold a company meeting in a hallway. Some things have changed. Less than 10 years after our founding we are now over 3,000 employees.

I was drawn to Pure by the company's vision and potential: the opportunity to continue to disrupt the storage market, to build more game-changing products, and to help build a multibillion-dollar, industry-leading public company,

Every day I realize how lucky I am to work with some of the brightest minds and most passionate individuals in the industry. I pass engineers in the hallways who were responsible for our very first product and collaborate on the incubation of new innovations to lead the next generation of computing. I work with the most passionate sales, support, and marketing teams and regularly visit with highly enthusiastic partners and customers—customers who have conferred on Pure an almost unbelievable 86.6 Net Promoter Score.

This book is more than our history. It's the story of technology and how we were founded on the principle of relentless and pervasive innovation. It's the story of the thousands of customers who have believed in Pure since the beginning. And it's the story of the people who work hard every day to make this the best technology company in the world. At Pure, these stories are absolutely intertwined.

Charlie Giancarlo—Chairman & CEO

"I'm glad I answered that email

from Coz."

Preface

I joined OS76 in October 2010 as employee 15. In the (only) conference room, I learned about flash from Michael Cornwell and FlashArray architecture from Coz and Hayes (you'll read about them). From Kix's masterful market requirements, I discovered how all this technology was going to create products that would upend data storage as we then knew it.

I drafted what became the first FlashArray User Guide. There was no user interface yet, so I started by describing the architecture. As several colleagues have observed, it was very much a "do what needs to be done" environment—I participated in a variety of distinctly non-writing projects—defining the CLI, designing labels to minimize cabling errors, photographing installation and repair steps, and others. Having spent most of my career with large companies, I thought being involved in so many things was pretty cool, and sometimes wished that I had "done the startup thing" earlier in life.

The company (now Pure Storage) has obviously grown and prospered and has evolved from storage vendor to forward-looking provider of data-centric information technology products and services. In mid-2018, with the 10th anniversary looming, Coz decided we should capture the story of how Pure Storage came to be. This book developed over nine months, including 80+ interviews with some of the key people who made the history, and a lot of review. I am grateful to everyone who contributed, and especially to my editors, Kim Austin and Diane Craig, whose suggestions improved readability immensely. I feel guilty, though, because so many contributors to the company's success aren't mentioned. To them, I apologize—my only defense is, "so many heroes, so little time."

Although I've been with Pure Storage almost from the beginning, doing this book taught me a tremendous amount about the company and how it works. I also learned that when our recruiters boast that "we hire rock stars," they aren't joking. Pure Storage is a collection of truly remarkable individuals who team up to deliver the most advanced, reliable, easiest to use storage products and capabilities the IT world has ever seen. I'm privileged to have been part of it, and I'm glad I answered that long-ago email from Coz that said, "Call me. Let's talk about how you can still afford new cars after you retire."

Paul Massiglia—Colorado Springs, 2019

Acronyms

Information technology is rife with acronyms, both the common ones that everyone knows—SCSI, DBA, etc.—and the more arcane ones—FTL, MLC,.... Rather than expand them in place throughout the text, the acronyms in this book are expanded at first occurrence, and used thereafter. This table lists the acronyms used and the pages on which the expansions appear.

Acronym	Expansion	Page	Acronym	Expansion	Page
ABAP	Advanced Business Application Programming	231	DBA	DataBase Administrator	91
AE	Account Executive	42	DBMS	DataBase Management System	225
AIRI	Artificial Intelligence-Ready Infrastructure	270	DICOM	Digital Imaging and Communications in Medicine	228
APJ	Asia, Pacific, Japan	100	DRAM	Dynamic Random-Access Memory	xxiv
ASIC	Application-Specific Integrated Circuit	244	EBC	Executive Briefing Center	86
ASP	Authorized Service Partner	125	EDA	Electronic Design Automation	254
BIOS	Basic Input/Output System	217	ELT	Extract, Load, and Transform	266
CAD	Computer-Assisted Design	194	EMEA	Europe, Middle East, Africa	99
CAM	Channel Account Manager	83	EMR	Electronic Medical Record [keeping]	225
CBS	Cloud Block Store	281	ERP	Enterprise Resource Planning	108
CEO	Chief Executive Officer	37	ES2	Evergreen Storage Services	280
CI/CD	Continuous Integration/Continuous Development	21	ETL	Extract, Transform, Load	265
CLED	Channel-Led	84	F2F2C	FlashArray-to-FlashBlade-to-Cloud	256
CoLo	Co-Location [site]	16	FPL	Flash Personality Layer	110
CRM	Customer Relationship Management	109	FIPS	Federal Information Processing Standard	151
D2D2T	Disk To Disk To Tape	256	FRU	Field-Replaceable Unit	175

Acronym	Expansion	Page
FTL	Flash Translation Layer	xxvi
GAAP	Generally Accepted Accounting Practices	73
GC	Garbage Collection	129
GDPR	General Data Protection Regulation	216
GUI	Graphical User Interface	29
HANA	High-Performance Analytic Appliance	231
HIPAA	Health Insurance Portability and Accountability Act	227
IOPS	Input-Output Operations per second	79
IP	Intellectual Property	68
IPO	Initial Public Offering	10
ISV	Independent Software Vendor	225
IVR	Interactive Voice Response	119
LBA	Logical Block Address	110
LDAP	[Open] Lightweight Directory Access Protocol	166
MLC	Multi-Level Cell	xxvi
MRAM	Magnetic Random Access Memory	7
MRD	Market Requirements Document	27
MVP	Minimum Viable Product	40
NAND	Not AND [flash]	285

Acronym	Expansion	Page
NDA	Non-Disclosure Agreement	55
NDU	Non-Disruptive Upgrade	15
NEMA	National Electrical Manufacturers Association	228
NFS	Network File System	172
NPI	New Product Introduction	111
NPIV	N_Port ID Virtualization	166
NPS	Net Promoter Score	177
NTFS	New Technology File System	220
NVMe	Non-Volatile Memory express	15
NVMe-oF	NVMe over Fabric	15
NVRAM	Non-Volatile Random Access Memory	28
NVTP	Non-Volatile Transfer Protocol	244
ODX	Offloaded Data Transfer	166
OLTP	OnLine Transaction Processing	225
P/E	Program/Erase	141
PACS	Picture Archiving and Communications System	228
PBX	Private Branch Exchange	19
PDA	Personal Digital Assistant	xxv
PoC	Proof of Concept	62

Acronym	Expansion	Page
PRB	Patent Review Board	76
QLC	Quad-Level Cell	284
RAID	Redundant Array of Independent Disks	xxv
REST	Representational State Transformation	159
RFP	Request For Proposal	252
RoCE	Remote Direct Memory Access over Converged Ethernet	272
RPO	Recovery Point Objective	167
RSG	Right Size Guarantee	136
RTO	Recovery Time Objective	280
SaaS	Software as a Service	134
SAS	Serial-Attached SCSI	15
SATA	Serial Advanced Technology Attachment	55
SCSI	Small Computer Storage Interface	58
SDR	Sales Development Representative	86
SE	System Engineer	23
SKO	Sales Kickoff	44
SLC	Single-Level Cell	xxvi
SMB	Server Message Block	218
SMI-S	Storage Management Initiative Specification	166

Acronym	Expansion	Page
SoC	System-on-Chip	245
SSD	Solid-State Device	xxv
SSRC	Storage System Research Center	13
STaaS	STorage as a Service	280
TAM	Total Addressable Market	80
TCO	Total Cost of Ownership	93
TDI	Tailored Datacenter Integration	234
TED	Tokyo Electron Device [Limited]	101
TSIA	Technology Service Industry Association	125
VAAI	vStorage API for Array Integration	64
VASA	vStorage APIs for Storage Awareness	162
VDI	Virtual Desktop Infrastructure	100
VLAN	Virtual Local Area Network	165
VPN	Virtual Private Network	217
WFS	Windows File Services	222
WWN	Worldwide Name	28
XCOPY	[SCSI} eXtended Copy	64

Dramatis Personae

This book mentions but a few of the people who have contributed to Pure Storage's success in the decade since the company's inception. The table below lists those who are mentioned. Photos of current (at publication time) employees (and a few who've left the company) appear in sidebars throughout the text. Most ex-employees and consultants are mentioned by name. This table lists page references everyone who's mentioned in the book. A few are referred to predominantly by the nicknames in the third column.

"Over the past 60 years, computing has become

more pervasive— computers are used to record,

track, and analyze more and more types of data."

Introduction

There's a Reason It's Called DATA Processing

Ever since there have been digital computers, they have been used to extract value from data. From early machines that calculated artillery firing tables from parameters laboriously input by "operators" flipping switches[1], to supercomputers that perform trillions of computations to forecast weather, to commercial servers that keep track of billions of electronic transactions every day, to smartphones that hold address books, mail, texts, photos, music, and video, digital computing has been about deriving value from data.

Data takes many forms, from notches on a stick to writings on paper, and many between, but this book is concerned with *digital* data. Very early in the computer era, users realized that transcribing human-readable data into computer-friendly form every time it was processed was simply not viable. There had to be a way store it in computer-friendly form for later use.

I Want My Data and I Want It Now!

So digital data storage technology was born, based largely on permanent magnetization of metals, initially on rotating cylinders ("drums"), followed by much less expensive flexible tape with metallic coatings. It didn't take long for users to realize that even though data on tape was computer-readable, searching for a specific record in a large data set took so long that random access was impractical. Technologists then developed rotating magnetic disks with radial arms that could move directly to any record in a data set. In short order, disks supplanted tapes for online processing, largely relegating tape to a backup role.

Over the years, computing has become both more pervasive—computers are used to record, track, and analyze more and more types of data—and more interactive—records are modified randomly, with immediate effect.

Meanwhile, computers have become thousands of times more powerful and the software that controls them has become more sophisticated. Today's typical data center computer contains one or more processors, each with multiple cores, and is often part of a virtual machine cluster, controlled by a hypervisor that balances resources among tasks and enables the overall system to continue to function if one of its computers fails.

---

[1] https://en.wikipedia.org/wiki/ENIAC

With storage, the story is similar. Over its 60+ year history, some disk drive metrics have improved by thousands (e.g., smaller size and lower weight), others by hundreds of millions (e.g., higher bit density and device capacity). In data centers, disks connected directly to computers have largely been replaced by storage arrays— semi-autonomous systems that coordinate concurrent operation of many disks. Today's storage arrays outperform individual disks by a wide margin, and can survive failures of individual disks, electronics, and the storage network paths that connect them to host computers.

One key disk metric has lagged, however: the time it takes to access a randomly selected block of data. It has decreased by a factor of about 200—a little more than 1% of the improvement in typical disk capacity. Put differently, today a disk filled with data can deliver only about 1/100th of the number of random accesses per second per megabyte (or gigabyte, or terabyte) of stored data compared to a disk of a half century ago, although the computers that process the data are millions of times more powerful than their predecessors of the same era. Storage system advances like cache and parallel data striping improve performance somewhat, but the gap continues to widen.

Thus, as computer systems become more powerful, the gap between their ability to process data and the ability of storage devices to deliver data for processing has become a frustrating impediment to advancement.

The reason for the increasing performance gap is obvious: whereas computing and networking are all-electronic, accessing data stored on disks has an inherent mechanical component. Access arms move and platters spin to locate data for reading or media areas for writing. As compact and lightweight as disk components have become, these motions take milliseconds, compared to nanoseconds for computations. As long as data storage has a mechanical component, the gap will inevitably widen.

Information Technology Situation Report: 2009

In 2009, when the Pure Storage story begins, the theme in enterprise computing technology was more of just about everything:

- Processor technology was improving by orders of magnitude. When clock speeds hit a wall at around 3GHz, developers pivoted and began to produce multi-core dies containing four, eight, or more independent processors. Software adapted to the more powerful machines with virtualization that subdivided a physical computer into several virtual machines that operated independently.

- *Dynamic random-access memory* (DRAM) size and bandwidth were increasing to deliver the needed instructions and data to processing cores. Servers with hundreds of gigabytes of DRAM became common.

- Network data transfer speeds were also on the rise, data centers were beginning to deploy 10Gb/s Ethernet, and 40Gb/s and 100Gb/s parts were on the horizon. Fibre Channel speed was doubling every three or four years. Falling inter-system communication latencies were making more flexible cluster and distributed system designs feasible.

- Storage device capacities were increasing geometrically, but—and here's the core issue—random access speed was only improving in tiny increments. Ten times as much data on a disk that spins and seeks at the same speed means one tenth the random accesses per second per gigabyte. Intelligent storage systems tried to mitigate the mismatch but could not eliminate the effect of mechanical motion.

Accessing stored data had become the main limitation to more responsive computing and development of new applications like analytics and artificial intelligence. A breakthrough in accessing stored data access was needed, particularly for random access. Spinning disks and moving actuators were the main contributors to latency, so software alone could not solve the problem. A storage technology that didn't require mechanical motion was a must.

Moreover, by comparison with computing and networking, the storage systems of 2009 were embarrassingly difficult to deploy and use. Servers and network switches were becoming more autonomous, but 'intelligent' storage systems forced administrators to micromanage—to partition disks, define RAID (*redundant array of independent disks*) groups, designate spares, juggle data sets to balance load, and so forth.

To improve storage performance and reduce complexity, the breakthrough would have to use hardware and software to create high-performing systems that would be reliable, flexible, and above all, easy to deploy, manage, and use. The first challenge was to identify a storage technology that was a quantum leap faster and at least as reliable as disks, but affordable in the amounts needed by the ever-growing masses of digital data being accumulated.

Enter Flash

In the 1980s, microelectronics researchers had developed flash memory. Commonly called simply flash, the memories store bits of data as electrical charges coupled to otherwise conventional transistor cells. Flash had potential as a storage medium because unlike DRAM, it retains data when powered off. Vendors specify conservative powered-off data retention times of upwards of a year for mature devices.[2] Moreover, when flash cells are overwritten, the data retention clock restarts.

One type of flash, inverse AND (Not AND, or NAND) logic, is particularly attractive as a storage medium. It is non-volatile (retains data when powered off), can be read randomly in microseconds, resists shock and pressure and temperature changes much better than disk drives, and can be manufactured relatively inexpensively in large quantities. NAND flash is read and written in pages, typically of 2-16 kilobytes, so it could be used by storage systems that address data in blocks.

Crossing the Flash Chasm

By 2009, NAND had been in use for some time in several applications—digital cameras, *personal digital assistants* (PDAs), digital media players, and most importantly, *solid-state devices* (SSDs) for personal computers.

From the mid-1990s, flash had been available for personal computer storage, in forms such as USB "thumb drives" with disk emulation firmware. But use of large quantities of flash in

---

[2] For example, https://www.micron.com/about/blogs/2015/may/addressing-data-retention-in-ssds

Google's data centers, and the mass adoption of "smartphones" by consumers created the real inflection point. Smartphones are produced by the million, at a cost constrained by consumer economics. The need for low power consumption and physical robustness made NAND an obvious choice for gigabytes of storage in devices carried in people's pockets and other environments hostile to delicate electronics. Manufacturers produced flash in huge quantities, with a consequent decrease in cost.

A Few Flies In the Flash Ointment

NAND is read and written in pages of 2-16 kilobytes. But most computers depend on reading and writing 512-byte sectors, so the addressability mismatch is a minor obstacle. To overcome it, SSDs have *flash translation layer* (FTL) firmware that maps sector addresses to flash pages and places incoming data dynamically to optimize performance and minimize wear.

The earliest flash devices used *single-level cell* (SLC) technology, in which each cell stores a single bit. Because SLC cells have only two possible states, output current can vary over nearly half its total range and without affecting data correctness.

To improve density, developers created *multi-level cell* (MLC) flash, in which each cell stores two bits. Per cell capacity doubles, but because MLC requires discrimination among four output levels, it is more prone to errors. Early MLC devices had lower endurance (useful lifetime measured in number of overwrites) than SLC ones, some by an order of magnitude or more.

Thumb drives, PDAs, and smartphones make good use of flash's low power, fast access, and reliability. They are largely unaffected by limited endurance and unpredictable write performance. Data center storage is another matter. Duty cycles can approach 100% and five-year lifetimes are common. Some records are overwritten millions of times, so fast, consistent write performance is critical. Thus, while flash is an obvious choice for personal devices, in 2009 its suitability for use in data centers was by no means assured.

MLC-based "consumer grade" SSDs were starting to appear in personal computers. They cost more than magnetic disks, but low power consumption and high performance made them attractive for premium laptops. Endurance and variable write performance are not problematic in the personal computer space. Most personal computer storage is overwritten only a few hundred times during its lifetime, and most human users do not discern a difference between five and 50 millisecond write response.

A few companies were producing data center-class storage systems based on SLC technology. Endurance was good, but the low data density and high per-gigabyte cost made the systems unaffordable for all but performance-critical applications for which storage cost was unimportant.

It was high time for a breakthrough in data center storage technology.

PART I

Building a Company

The Pure Storage Story

In This Chapter...

Venture capitalist Mike Speiser introduced technologists John Colgrove and John Hayes, who came to the realization that the time was ripe to disrupt the enterprise storage market with flash and that they were the ones who could build a company to do it. They agreed that they were in it for the long term and sought investors who would not only provide funding, but would also contribute expertise to help the company grow and prosper over decades.

Beginnings

What to Do for an Encore?

John Colgrove ("Coz")
"We are going to radically simplify the storage user's experience."

I t was 2008, and John Colgrove, known throughout Silicon Valley as Coz, was looking for his next challenge. For nearly two decades, he had been a driving technical force behind the phenomenally successful Veritas Storage Foundation—the suite of file system and volume management software that persuaded commercial Unix users to adopt storage and data management technology from a "third party" (Veritas) for its robustness and performance, even though it was an extra cost item. The revived startup[3] that Coz had joined almost two decades earlier had made a name for itself in data centers, become a billion-dollar powerhouse in the software world, and merged with IT security giant Symantec.

While some saw the merger as synergistic, it had a couple of not-so-positive unintended effects from the Veritas perspective. It diminished corporate attention on storage-related projects, and in addition, suffered the usual disruption that occurs when two dissimilar company cultures attempt to meld.

Taking a Breather

Oleg Kiselev
"Coz has a remarkable ability to synthesize better solutions from 'almost-right' ones that people bring to him. On several occasions I have seen engineers with ideas that were 90% 'there' come to Coz, explain their problems and ideas, and he'd suggest the brilliant 10% that would bring it together into something far better than the original."

With the software he helped create reaching a plateau of maturity, and with the family responsibilities of two young sons, Coz left Symantec and spent about a year designing and supervising the construction of a new house in the valley. By his own admission, he went months "without even thinking about computers." But an email from former colleague Oleg Kiselev asking

---

[3] Veritas was a "reboot" of Tolerant Systems, an unsuccessful startup firm that had made fault-tolerant computer systems based on microprocessors.

Mike Speiser
"In 2001, Coz and I worked on strategy for Veritas. His technical acumen was matched by an appreciation of economics. People would argue that some new fad in storage was going to replace disks, and Coz would calmly ask what would drive enough volume to make it price competitive. There was never a compelling answer, so the company continued to invest in the Veritas Storage Foundation, which retained its dominant market position well into the new millennium. With flash, I think he finally found a compelling answer."

for advice on a software design problem started Coz thinking about storage technology, and about getting back into the game.

Getting Back Into the Game

As his house approached completion in early 2009, Coz began having conversations with another former colleague, Mike Speiser, now a partner at Sutter Hill Ventures in Palo Alto. Within a few months, he joined Sutter Hill as an entrepreneur in residence—a position unique to the high-tech venture capital world, in which individuals with demonstrated imagination and ability to turn their ideas into money-makers scan the technology horizon looking for the proverbial "next big thing" to advise their VCs to invest in.

The career trajectory Coz had in mind was to help Sutter Hill evaluate the proposals they were constantly receiving for one related to his skills and experience that they felt would have a high probability of success. He would join the venture in an advisory capacity for a year or two, and then rotate back to Sutter to do it all again.

Scouting the Tech Landscape

For several months, Coz reviewed proposals from aspiring entrepreneurs. With his background in robust, high-performing storage, and his appreciation for the first law of enterprise data storage ("Don't lose data—ever—no matter what happens"), he found flaws in every proposal. One would grossly overestimate the potential market, another underappreciated the effort required to develop robust software, a third failed to appreciate the sea change that was taking place in the enterprise data storage world.

After reviewing dozens of proposals and not finding any that merited investment, Coz and Mike began to toy with the idea of creating their own company. But what would it do?

They observed that while the solid-state arrays on the market were priced so high that they were only affordable for the most cost-insensitive applications, personal computer SSDs made from consumer-grade flash were within three to four times the cost per byte of high-capacity disks. They began to explore the possibility of using advanced software to remove redundancy before storing data to bring effective cost per byte close to that of disk-based arrays.

Of course, there were challenges to be overcome with consumer-grade flash. Its low endurance meant it wouldn't last in data-center environments. They would have to devise ways to make SSDs last for 3 to 5 years under data center workloads. Similarly, while a human generally can't distinguish between five and 50 millisecond I/O response, multi-user applications in data centers certainly can. Ways would also have to be found to make SSDs deliver consistently fast write response, regardless of workload.

Finally, even if the technical challenges could be conquered, there was the challenge of gaining a foothold for an unproven technology in a mature, conservative sector of the IT market dominated by large, well-established vendors. They believed that this could be done by attacking a long-standing Achilles' heel of data center storage—administrative complexity. An array with solid-state performance that was as easy to deploy and use as a consumer product would get the attention of executives who were sensitive to administrative costs as well as capital expenditures.

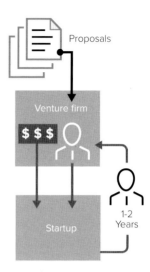

A Flash of Insight

Coz and Mike were not the only ones to see the need for much higher performing storage systems. Laboratory research was occurring on several solid-state persistent storage technologies—*magnetic random-access memory* (MRAM), phase-change memory, molecular memory, and others.[4]

One stood out from the rest, though: flash. It wasn't as fast as phase-change memory; it wasn't as durable as MRAM; but it had one overwhelming advantage: it was already in high volume production. Flash was already being used to store data in several types of consumer devices. It got an enormous boost when smartphones became popular. Apple Inc. used it to replace disks in its MacBook computers. Google used it in some of its servers. Wide deployment meant volume production—billions of gigabytes of flash were being manufactured for millions of products. Manufacturers who embed millions of components in their devices demand low cost and high reliability, so component producers look hard for ways to improve reliability and production efficiency. Volume creates a virtuous circle of improvement, which begets more volume, which leads to further improvement, and so it goes.

Coz and Mike converged on the idea that the breakthrough in enterprise storage would be an affordable flash-based array with an order of magnitude higher performance than any disk-based array, and no sacrifice in reliability or flexibility. Such an array would have an enormous addressable market—*every* data center has storage and its needs for capacity only increase.

Flash was the obvious storage medium, but there's a long distance between flash and a system that could succeed in a mature market with a conservative customer base, particularly one that was well-aware of both the advantages of flash (low power consumption, high density, high speed), and its shortcomings (high cost, limited endurance, unpredictable write performance).

[4] https://www.cambridge.org/core/journals/mrs-bulletin/issue/highperformance-emerging-solidstate-memory-technologies/FCA1978A4594FE65C6E58BF4FA506A55

John Hayes
"Look for a technology change wherever the common wisdom contains a lot of unproven assertions."

Coz began to apply his software expertise to an architecture for block storage arrays[5] based on solid-state devices—*solid-state* as opposed to specifically flash. Flash was, and remains today, the obvious media choice, but in technology, nothing is forever. Coz recognized the need to design for flash while remaining flexible in case a more attractive technology emerged. This led to a two-layer software architecture with a lower layer that optimized the performance, reliability, and longevity of the physical media, and an upper layer that implemented the storage system's externally visible properties—virtualization, communication with hosts, data reduction, scheduling internal I/O, RAID protection, and overall array management.

Meanwhile, Elsewhere in the Valley…

John Hayes had been living and working in Silicon Valley for about five years when a mutual acquaintance introduced him to Mike, at the time CEO of a startup that needed a video and Internet-savvy engineer. Soon the two were working together.

The startup was acquired. About 18 months later, Mike left to join Sutter Hill, where he would occasionally engage Hayes to consult on proposals that came their way. It was there that Hayes and Coz first met.

At first, the contact was casual—Coz and Hayes would occasionally attend the same presentations but didn't say much to each other. Moreover, Hayes had planned to take a six-month hiatus from technology to travel and consider his "next big thing." He had been leaning toward the consumer space, where his interest lay in infrastructure—central services for endpoint devices developed by others who were better equipped to generate demand.

In mid-2009, Hayes quit his job, but continued to consult for Sutter Hill. In August, Mike mentioned to him that Coz had been disappointed by the proposals he'd seen and was considering starting his own company to develop and manufacture storage arrays. He suggested that the two discuss the possibility of combining their interests.

When Coz and Hayes began serious discussions, they discovered quite a bit of common ground. Hayes had believed for some time that flash would have a disruptive impact on computing, but because of the cost, he had been thinking in terms of low-volume niche applications. In 2009, however, MLC flash hit the market, and suddenly cost was lower, so there was potential for broader applicability. He started fleshing out ideas for using flash in large databases and analytics applications. For his part, Coz was mapping out ways to adapt his storage and data management software expertise to enterprise-class arrays that would be affordable for any data center.

---

[5] Block storage arrays present their storage capacity to host computers in the form of sector-addressable virtual disks. They contrast with filers, which abstract the physical nature of their storage and present hierarchical file systems or namespaces.

The pair gradually became convinced that they were onto something. In the meantime, Coz and Mike were introducing selected contacts to the concept of affordable all-flash storage arrays based on what were then perceived as "consumer-grade" devices and looking for a few "angel" investors (Sutter Hill had agreed to provide the bulk of the seed funding for a new venture). In contrast to proposals they had been reviewing, the two recognized that the hard part of the solution was in software rather than hardware. Could they devise software to reduce incoming data in real time and make consumer-grade SSDs last for five years in data center environments?

Coz and Hayes continued to brainstorm during August. By September the rough outline of a two-layer software architecture that could be implemented using off-the-shelf hardware had emerged. On October 1, 2009, a company called OS76 Inc. opened for business. They quickly engaged two software engineers, as well as "go-to-market" expert Matt Kixmoeller and experienced flash architect Michael Cornwell. Initially, they operated from Sutter Hill's Palo Alto office, but soon moved to premises at 650 Castro Street in Mountain View. 650 Castro is still the seat of the company's headquarters.

A Big Break

When entrepreneurs form a "startup" company, their first few months are typically spent making the rounds of venture capitalists seeking funding. Because of their association with Sutter Hill, Coz and Hayes weren't burdened with that. Sutter Hill had agreed to invest a significant portion of the startup funding and encouraged them to enlist a few "angels" to provide additional capital. This gave them the luxury

Mark Leslie
First Board of Directors Member
"When John Colgrove asked me for advice about the all-flash storage company he was proposing, I was struck by its similarity to the tape-to-disk transition that had taken place decades ago.
Although disks had direct access capability, people initially treated them like faster tapes, running files of new items against old master files to output new master files.
As software management of storage advanced, however, John recognized that direct access made it possible to manage storage in fundamentally new ways.
It was obvious to me that something similar was happening with flash— people were treating flash devices as faster disks. John made me realize that not only was flash faster, it made new ways of managing data possible, like eliminating de-populated disks, compressing, and deduplicating.
I was confident that John's idea would lead to another major storage management paradigm shift, so I was happy to advise and invest."

of choosing which investors to approach. They targeted individuals who would not only invest, but who would also be useful as business advisors, and might eventually serve as members of the board of directors, as company executives, or as attention-getters on the public stage. In the latter category, former San Francisco 49ers stars Ronnie Lott and Harris Barton became early investors in the company.

Aneel Bhusri
Early Board of Directors Member
"Aneel often told me that to be a
successful CEO, you need to build both
above (the board of directors), and
below (the team)."
—**Scott Dietzen**

Frank Slootman
Early Board of Directors Member
"[OS76]…was going to do a 'Data
Domain' for primary storage."

The Right Investors

Careful selection of investors became a guiding principle in the five subsequent funding rounds. It wasn't just about the money—for every round there were more investors willing to invest than the stakeholders were willing to accommodate. They chose carefully—investors with international presence when expansion outside the United States was imminent, broad-based financial firms when the time came for *initial public offering* (IPO). The leadership team boasts that they never accepted an investment offer solely based on price, and that only one firm had ever declined to invest.

Mark Leslie, founder of Veritas, became the first angel investor and board member, followed by Workday founder Aneel Bhusri. Aneel introduced the company to Frank Slootman, who had recently completed a highly successful tenure as CEO of Data Domain, a pioneer in the use of data reduction in backup systems. Frank immediately perceived that the new company's goal was to create the kind of upheaval in primary storage that Data Domain had caused in the backup sector and became an investor. Others invested as well, including VMware Inc. co-founders Diane Greene and Mendel Rosenblum.

Technical Advisors

Many technology startups engage outside technical advisors early in their existence. Technical advisors provide impartial perspective on how a new company's technology and anticipated products will fit into the environment and market. They can suggest alternate directions that may prove fruitful. They can be a source of contacts for building industry relationships and for recruiting. Startups typically compensate their technical advisors financially or with stock, or a combination of the two.

The obvious technical advisor candidates are individuals well-known for their experience and expertise in fields related to the new company's mission and future plans. While operating out of Sutter Hill's offices, Coz, Hayes, and Mike created a short list of candidates, developed a recruiting pitch, and planned to embark on a series of meetings.

The University of California at Santa Cruz has both a tradition of innovative research in computer science, particularly in data storage, and close ties with Silicon Valley. The university's Jack Baskin School of Engineering and its SSRC have long been sources of engineering recruits for large and small technology companies in the valley and beyond.

Coz had long-standing ties with the SSRC, stemming both from recruiting graduates and from representing employers that sponsored the center. Early in the technical advisor search, he approached Professor Ethan Miller about becoming a technical advisor to the new company. Ethan was enthusiastic, as were Hayes and Mike upon meeting him, and he became the company's first technical advisor. Shortly thereafter, he also became a part-time employee (with the University's approval—UC faculty are allotted a budget of time to pursue outside interests). He is still a Pure Storage employee and is a named inventor on several of the company's most fundamental patents, as are some of the students he helped recruit.

With Ethan's engagement, the urgency of recruiting technical advisors waned, and no additional ones were recruited. Inasmuch as he is still primarily a professor, his perspective remains somewhat external. He is effectively the company's one-man technical advisory council.

Professor Ethan Miller, UCSC
"Watching the company grow from a half dozen people to over 3,000 in weekly snapshots has been a great experience. Especially at the beginning, the pace of change was dizzying—big changes seemed to happen every week. I've taken lessons from Pure Storage back to classes at the university, helping to better prepare students for careers after graduation."

In This Chapter…

Coz and Hayes had a pretty good idea of what they wanted to do, both technologically and in the approach to the market. They laid down principles for both and set about creating and organizing the company. There were thousands of details, from where to locate, to office design, to ordering and managing equipment, to arranging for administrative services. They needed both skilled engineers to keep the work progressing while they tended to the details of creating a company, and self-starting administrators to run the office and computing infrastructure. The down-to-earth decisions made at this stage were the germ of a unique company culture.

Enter Pure Storage

There's a lot involved in creating a company—incorporation paperwork, finding and leasing space, contracting with payroll and benefit service providers, and so forth—none of which furthers the "great idea" that was the basis for the company. In Silicon Valley, the great idea is almost always a technology breakthrough. But to go from idea to prototype to saleable and supportable product takes manufacturing, supply chains, a sales force, marketing, a support organization, and a whole lot of administration.

Bo Hong
Pure Storage Employee #3
" 'Check your ego at the door' was a vital ingredient of the early engineering team, which was highly challenging, but at the same time, supportive and aspirational."

Coz and Hayes realized that while they were both fundamentally technologists, they would have to spend a lot of their time on the mechanics of getting the company up and running. So even before the formal founding, they began to think about recruiting. They agreed that they wanted a company of "rock stars;" that skills and expertise would be the primary hiring criteria.

Each of them planned to take primary responsibility for developing one of the software layers, so they began by looking for two engineers, one to partner with each of them. The search criteria were brilliance, some data storage experience, and ability to focus on development while the founders took care of the hundreds of details of forming and operating the new company.

Feng Wang
Pure Storage Employee #5
"Do it NOW!"

Fortunately, Coz had been a sponsor of the *Storage Systems Research Center* (SSRC) at the University of California at Santa Cruz during his earlier tenure. He knew the students well, and had recruited some in the past, so he was able to quickly identify two candidates—Bo Hong and Feng Wang, both SSRC graduates who had worked as software engineers in the storage sector after graduation. Bo and Feng became the first two engineers hired by the company. Both are still with Pure Storage today.

Fleshing Out the Big Idea

The founders realized that while it's easy to keep two people in sync, as more employees joined it would be harder to keep everyone aligned and pursuing the same goal, so they articulated a concise company mission statement:

> *To create high-quality, affordable block storage arrays with performance an order of magnitude higher than anything else in the market.*

Simplicity in Action
Coz's then-7-year old son installing an FA-320.

They had definite ideas about how to accomplish the mission, and about the resulting products:

- Start with the proverbial "clean sheet," unconstrained by the maxims of conventional disk array design, and design exclusively for solid-state media. Make no provision for mechanical disk drives.
- Design for consumer-grade SSDs. The low cost would help meet affordability goals but the founders also expected the high volumes in which consumer flash was manufactured to result in faster technology improvement than with lower-volume devices.
- Minimize startup cost and time to revenue by utilizing readily available hardware wherever possible and investing the company's intellectual capital mainly in software. The first array generations were built entirely from purchased components; only after a revenue stream had been established did the company begin to design its own hardware.
- Build arrays that are much easier to install, configure, and operate than anything on the market. Eliminate routine administration wherever possible and reduce what can't be eliminated to the barest essentials. Make the arrays *self-tuning*; do not provide "knobs" for administrators to manipulate.
- Deliver breakthrough performance and high reliability at per-gigabyte prices at or below those of the disk-based storage systems of the day.

A secondary motivation for an all-flash approach was the large number of disk storage patents on which Coz was a named inventor. The founders felt that any new disk-based technology for which he was a principal architect might invite patent infringement actions from competitors, justified or not.

Technology breakthroughs are interesting, but persuading users in a mature, conservative market sector to do business with a young company is more of a challenge. It was clear that the first products the company shipped would not be as feature-rich as those of the industry incumbents. Therefore, in addition to technical innovations, Coz and Hayes proposed to change the data storage buyer's experience in fundamental ways:

ALL-INCLUSIVE PRICING

Base pricing entirely on physical storage capacity and controller processing power. As software features are added, include them in base array pricing and make all software available to all customers.

ELIMINATING FLASH LONGEVITY CONCERNS

In 2009, many users were hesitant to adopt flash storage because of a perception that the useful media life was limited. The developers initially countered this objection with fault-tolerant software. Later, when consumer-grade flash proved to be much more reliable than anticipated, the company created its *ForeverFlash* lifetime media guarantee.

An Osmium Nugget
The new company was called OS76, after the periodic table symbol and atomic number of the element osmium.
The goal was ultra-high-density storage systems. Osmium is the highest-density naturally occurring element. It became a tradition to name major projects for high-density natural elements.

Other aspects of the product that were initially implemented to streamline development also proved to be strong selling points for the new company:

ELIMINATING PLANNED DOWNTIME

Flash failure modes made self-healing and automated alerting a necessity for handling media faults. Even when the arrays were introduced, all components were failure-tolerant, alerting was automatic, and hot-swapping was the norm. Today, arrays are expected to operate continuously without planned downtime for their entire service lives.

NON-DISRUPTIVE EVERYTHING

The developers designed hardware that could be repaired and upgraded *during operation*. Initially, software supported non-disruptive upgrades primarily to streamline transitions during beta testing. The feature was so attractive to users however, that the company decided to deliver *non-disruptive upgrade* (NDU) in every software release and hardware generation. NDU implies *perpetual forward compatibility*—each software release and hardware generation can be upgraded from the preceding one without disrupting service and without migrating data, even for major device changes such as from *serial-attached SCSI*[6] (SAS)-connected storage devices to NVMe (*Non-Volatile Memory Express*) and NVMe-oF (*NVMe over Fabrics*) ones.

Getting off the Ground

The company was incorporated on October 1, 2009, under the name OS76, Inc. Mike served as interim CEO, and Coz and Hayes were the first two employees (others had received and accepted employment offers, but for various bureaucratic reasons had not yet formally become employees).

---

[6] Small Computer System Interface

Open Plan Offices Today—(Pure1® Engineering)
*"Early in my career I had a private office, which I thought was great. When I joined my previous company, I worked in a cubicle—a step down, but not a big deal. At first, I was doubtful about the Pure Storage open office plan, but while there **is** some distraction, it's outweighed by the collaborative atmosphere it encourages. These days, I sometimes wonder how I ever got anything done back then in my private office."*
—Alex Gregory

Where to Locate?

Among the first challenges was office space. For obvious reasons, the company would locate in the greater San Jose area, but there were other factors to consider.

South Bay[7] real estate is expensive, some locations more so than others. Less expensive locations tend to be in less attractive environments with poorer commuter access. The company had to be frugal with startup capital, but it had to attract employees in a highly-competitive technology labor market. Palo Alto, with proximity to Stanford University and a vibrant downtown was considered, but rejected, partly on cost grounds, but also because it was somewhat less convenient for the founders.

The founders chose downtown Mountain View. It wasn't the least expensive option, but it had modern office space in pleasant surroundings, and easy access from throughout the Bay Area. Located at the confluence of major commuting arteries, the location was practical for commuting from virtually anywhere in the Bay Area, including the city of San Francisco.

The company's offices were in an iconic building at 650 Castro Street that had housed Netscape in an early stage, and later the Mozilla offshoot.[8] There was space for a small lab but the founders understood that most test and development hardware would eventually be located remotely at a multi-user *co-located data center* ("CoLo"), and that when production started, volume manufacturing would be outsourced to a contract manufacturer.

---

[7] Roughly, the US highway 101 corridor between Redwood Shores and Morgan Hill.
[8] The company's headquarters, administration, and most engineering are still located on Castro Street, where they now occupy space in five separate buildings.

The Office Floor Plan

The next step was outfitting the offices. In Coz's previous workplaces, private offices for engineers had been the norm. Privacy helps concentration when there is deep thinking to be done. But individual offices are expensive, both in terms of square footage per engineer and in terms of outfitting. Moreover, they tend to encourage isolation.

Hayes had worked mostly in open environments, so he favored an open plan, even dispensing with the cubicles that seem to be ubiquitous in modern offices. He argued that all a software engineer needs is a fast computer, a decent monitor, and a pair of earmuffs or headphones to block background noise. Open plans are space-efficient (about 20% less square footage per engineer than cubicles; about 40% less than private offices), cost less to outfit, and perhaps most important, encourage real-time collaboration—it's easier to talk across a monitor than to walk down the hall and knock on someone's door.

Coz was concerned that in an open plan, engineers might be distracted, either by work issues or by casual conversations within earshot. He and Hayes debated the subject repeatedly in the weeks leading up to the office opening.

The final decision was for an open arrangement, with a 6-foot work table and under-desk credenza for each engineer. Until it was time to build hardware prototypes, work was done on company-supplied laptop computers, usually docked while in the office, but portable for carrying to meetings or working offsite. To minimize distractions, space was reserved for conversation areas outfitted with sofas and comfortable chairs, where people could converse without distracting others. In the early days, the areas did double duty as impromptu meeting rooms. Today, headquarters has more meeting rooms, but some of the conversation areas still exist, and holding impromptu gatherings in them to avoid distracting colleagues has become common practice.

The open plan arrangement conserved startup capital. Candidates did not shy away from it as had been feared. The company supplied headphones and noise blockers to employees who requested them. Even today, headquarters facilities are open plan, even for executives. When Coz talks about office space, he invariably says, "I'm really glad Hayes won that argument."

What About India? What About Eastern Europe?

For about a quarter century, technology startups have been minimizing software engineering cost by establishing offshore offices in countries where engineers are in ready supply and labor cost is lower than in the United States. The trend began with India and has since expanded to eastern Europe.

With previous employers, Coz had observed offshore development firsthand. He concluded that for self-contained projects, remote development could be successful and was even desirable, provided there was strong communication with the center. But splitting a team that required a lot of interaction was not a recipe for success. Experience suggested that savings would inevitably be outweighed by project delays and high communication and travel costs.

The founders considered both offshore and domestic remote development, and ultimately rejected it because FlashArray™ development wasn't cleanly separable into well-defined parts with clear interfaces. To this day, most FlashArray and FlashBlade core development occurs at the company's Mountain View locations.

That is not to say that the company is opposed to remote development in principle. In fact, it took a step toward remote development when it established a separate site for FlashBlade™ development, and a larger one with an engineering center near Seattle. Granted, the FlashBlade site was only a few blocks away, for the very good reason that many of the software techniques developed for FlashArray were adaptable to FlashBlade, so there was cross-pollination between the two teams as the product matured. But FlashBlade had its own engineers, labs, budgets, schedules, and management, all distinct from those of FlashArray. Based on the success of this model, the company is poised to further distribute engineering as future opportunities emerge.

The Care and Feeding of Engineers

Engineers are hired to do engineering. There's little value in their spending time and energy coping with the details of working life. Even before there were employees, the company founders concerned themselves with making the work environment smooth and stress-free.

"The first Platinum lab was a repurposed conference room next to the 4th floor kitchen. When our systems in the lab and the toaster oven in the kitchen were both powered on, the circuits would blow." — **Pete Kirkpatrick**

In the United States, one common source of employee angst is health insurance. In the technology sector, employer-subsidized health insurance is considered a standard part of the compensation package. But for a young company trying to conserve cash, health insurance is a major expense. After identifying a provider with a good service record, the company leadership settled on a compromise package—they chose a second-tier plan rather than the provider's "Cadillac" option, but "split the difference" by subsidizing employees directly to defray the deductible costs of the selected plan. This cost the company less, but effectively insulated employees from large out-of-pocket expenses for unplanned health care needs.

Some companies in the Silicon Valley technology sector provide meals during working hours. Employers and employees agree that the cost of meals is far outweighed by not having to interrupt the work day with a lunchtime commute, and the continuity of team interaction fostered by on-site breaks. But again, for a startup trying to conserve cash, on-premises catering is a substantial expense.

Downtown Mountain View office space wasn't the least expensive, but the location was convenient, and had a useful side benefit. With a dozen or more restaurants within a few minutes' walk (a couple just an elevator ride away), the company did not need on-premises catering. "Snack islands" in the office sufficed. Moreover, the location encouraged team cohesion, because teams tended to walk to restaurants together, continuing to interact during breaks from the office.

Open-plan offices struck a balance between conserving capital and providing an adequate working environment. But with individual productivity the primary goal, engineers had to be well-equipped, so money was spent on flexible, high-quality furniture rather than on setting up and outfitting cubicles.

Fortunately, software engineers' needs are few—powerful workstations, large displays[9], central servers with code management systems for preserving their work, and in open plan environments, ambient noise blocking.

Coz researched equipment options extensively and settled on a couple of high-performing "standard" server and laptop models, the latter configured with the most processor cores and largest amount of DRAM obtainable, and of course, SSDs rather than disks. One important selection criterion for workstations was ready availability. An engineer reporting for work could not wait a week or more for the tools of the trade to be delivered.

Like any craftspeople, software engineers are individualistic in their tool preference, so the standard was a "soft" one—if an engineer wanted a different computer, the company would provide it (within reason).[10] The same was true for personal storage devices, noise-suppressing headphones, and other auxiliary equipment. The philosophy was to spend money wisely, but not inhibit productivity by forcing people to use inadequate equipment.

Both Windows/Linux computers and MacBooks were on the standard menu. Interestingly, nearly all engineers chose to use Linux or Windows, largely because of development tool availability, whereas other employees overwhelmingly chose MacBooks—the opposite of the usual Silicon Valley norm.

Every company needs an office telephone system so that any employee can reach out or be reached conveniently. But *private branch exchanges* (PBXs) are expensive, and in an open plan office they can be distracting. The company ordered a few telephone lines for corporate and conference use and encouraged employees to use their mobile phones for business with a subsidy to defray personal mobile phone cost. The company still follows this model today, with over 3,000 employees in dozens of offices around the world.

Finally, despite being founders, Coz and Hayes "paid" themselves relatively low salaries. This set an implied norm for salary offers, which were relatively low by Silicon Valley standards, but generously augmented with stock grants.

An Office Doesn't Run Itself

Even in a tiny operation like OS76, there is a steady stream of "administrivia" that aren't trivial at all. Supplies and equipment to be ordered, invoices to be paid, appointments to be arranged, new employees to be brought on board, cleaning services to be contracted,

---

[9] Coz believed, and continues to believe, in a high correlation between "lots of glass" and software engineer productivity. Today, his own "monitor" is a monster 55" 4K television connected to a laptop computer, and 40" and larger monitors are becoming common.

[10] With over 3,000 employees' equipment to manage, the company's internal IT department has necessarily become somewhat less flexible with individual equipment requests.

Emily Kay

*"Sure, I'm happy to help. Just ask!"
Following her time as office manager,
Emily managed human resources for
the company, and briefly, finance as
well. When field offices were being
opened at a rapid pace, she served
as Cultural Ambassador. Reporting
directly to the CEO, she visited new
offices, ensuring that they were
equipped for success and being
a conduit between them and the
executive committee. Following a 2018
maternity leave, Emily resigned to
devote herself to motherhood.*

kitchens to be stocked, and so forth. None of these help the technologists make progress on the big idea, but if they don't get done, chaos quickly ensues. Even before they moved from Sutter Hill's Palo Alto offices to Mountain View, Coz and Hayes realized they would need an office manager from day one. Recruiting one was an early priority.

With no existing administrative infrastructure, the office manager would have to create day-to-day operating procedures like on-boarding new employees, processing expense claims, and so forth, deal with vendors as disparate as Paylocity and Starbucks, and present a professional company image to callers and visitors, all with little or no supervision. An ability to work autonomously was a must. There was no substitute for experience in this position.

Fortunately for the fledgling company, Sutter Hill was able to come to the rescue. Prior to joining Sutter Hill, Mike had himself founded a startup, and in that capacity, had had to find someone to create a functional office starting from essentially nothing. He was able to enlist Emily Kay, office manager for his former startup, for a six-week part-time engagement to help Coz and Hayes get off the ground.

Six weeks became 12; part time became full time, and eventually Emily became OS76 employee number 4. She did everything from setting up payroll and benefits systems, to ordering a refrigerator for the kitchen, to contracting for office waste recycling. As new employees were hired, she developed the procedure for getting them up and running— procuring their equipment and supplies, familiarizing them with the way the company worked, and fielding just about any request that came her way. She became the "go-to" person for whatever people felt they needed, with an innate sense of what to do on her own authority and when to seek guidance. She made the office function smoothly so Coz, Hayes, and a steadily growing number of employees could devote more of their energy to the company's mission.

Creating a Work Environment

Silicon Valley computer engineers are a picky bunch. Companies tend to be lavish with amenities—on-site meals, exercise centers, commuter buses, and so forth—and with compensation—high-tech stock options are the stuff of legends. It's not easy for a young company without a revenue stream that's trying to conserve capital to recruit talent.

Fortunately, there's a correlation between technical brilliance and willingness to take risk, especially among younger engineers with few outside responsibilities. They can often be persuaded to work for lower fixed compensation against the promise of a big payday when their company "goes public" or is bought and they can "cash out."

But in the meantime, engineers expect comfortable, supportive work environments that help them be productive. Having opted for open plan offices, the company outfitted them inexpensively, but adequately, with individual work spaces and ample areas for impromptu meetings, casual conversations, and general relaxation.

The interview process aimed to identify people who were not only "brilliant" (a favorite Silicon Valley characterization), but energetic

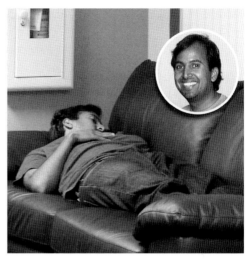

"…ample areas for general relaxation"

and predisposed to dedication to a mission. Long distance commuting, although not a disqualifier, was generally discouraged—two hours on the road every day are two hours that aren't available for work or personal pursuits.

Like most software development operations today, the team adopted a *continuous integration-continuous deployment* (CI/CD) methodology. Among the first bits of infrastructure set up was a Jenkins automated test management system that scheduled tests every time a developer checked code into the central software repository. Planning was dynamic, using the well-known Agile Method with brief biweekly "sprints" that kept developers focused on near-term goals as they made progress toward long-term ones.

In the early days, the dozen or so employees reported progress in daily *standups*. Everyone, including CEO Dietz and office manager Emily, would stand in a circle with a soccer ball in the center.[11] Someone would kick the ball to one of the standees, who would summarize what he or she was working on, highlight issues and request assistance, and kick the ball to the next person. Standing up kept the meetings short.

It is easy to keep a dozen people synchronized and aware of what's happening. Company-wide standups eventually fell victim to growth, but to this day, someone passing through engineering areas in the late morning is guaranteed to encounter circles of standing engineers keeping each other up to date on what's going on in their teams.

Keeping Up with What's Happening

Very soon, several teams were developing separate pieces of the Purity//FA FlashArray software, some of which were internally complex. Management felt it was important to keep engineers abreast of the entire scope of development.

---

[11] Originally, an American football was used, with each person passing it to his or her designated next speaker. However, when an overenthusiastic engineer passed the ball a bit too hard, narrowly missing an entire bank of filled coffee cups, the team decided to switch to kicking an easier-to-control soccer ball around the floor.

Patrick Lee
Performance Engineer, Scheduler of Tech Talks & ad hoc Company Photographer
"This is my second startup rodeo so I knew there were going to be incredible highs and funny setbacks. My goal was to document it all because if lightning were to strike twice, I wanted more than fading memory of war stories in the 'Glory Days.' "

They instituted a weekly series of lunchtime *Tech Talks* in which volunteers would describe their work to their peers working on other projects. In the company's early days, talks were delivered when and wherever it was convenient—usually in office conversation areas. As the engineering team grew, Wednesday lunchtime became the standard, and the talks were held in the newly-acquired company break room, with Patrick Lee taking over scheduling. Eventually videocasts were added because the company had no space large enough to accommodate the entire engineering team. As remote engineering and support teams were added, the videocasts served them as well. Talks were also recorded for later viewing by people who couldn't attend. Eight years later, Tech Talks still occur weekly, with most of the engineering community attending or viewing.

The original intention of the talks was keeping engineers aware of work going on in other teams and imparting an appreciation of the totality of FlashArray, and later FlashBlade, software and hardware. In part, they are a morale builder, but they have also been synergistic—people often draw on outside experiences to suggest alternative approaches and solutions. The talks have also help further the goal of rotating engineers through different projects to develop a cadre of people with broad knowledge of the company's technology. An engineer is more likely to feel comfortable moving to another team if he or she understands that team's work and how it fits into the overall product development scheme.

Managing Our Equipment

A computer engineering organization needs computers. The engineers' primary task is to *create*, not to manage the development environment and their own workstations. By late 2011 Pure Storage had about 50 employees, each with a workstation, as well as servers for software development and testing, code and document management, and in-house IT. As the FlashArray introduction approached, more development and test machines and more personal equipment for the growing number of employees would be needed. It was time for dedicated IT management.

Like many in the Bay Area, Ken Zachmann, then managing engineering IT for a major software developer, knew that "Coz had a stealth project going on." Ken was comfortable with his situation, which allowed him to work from home, avoiding the Silicon Valley daily commute. In 2012, however, former colleagues Patrick Lee and Marcus Padro asked him if he'd be interested in managing the Pure Storage engineering labs.

Ken met with Coz and Bob Wood (page 67), who described the opportunity that the company represented. Impressed that the founder and the engineering VP had given him so much of their time, he stopped at the offices for a tour. He found the atmosphere vibrant—an ingredient missing in his then-current situation—and felt it had fantastic potential for growth and personal development. After a long day of interviews he received an offer, and in May 2012, became the 61st Pure Storage employee.

Ken Zachmann
"Don't underestimate the value of a strong infrastructure team—the work they do makes engineers more efficient. Hiring an automation developer, a lab person, and 48 development engineers will yield far better long-term results than just hiring 50 engineers."

The year 2012 was a time of "doing what needed to be done." Although Ken had been hired primarily to manage the engineering labs, revamping the company's own IT was a more immediate need, so his early days were focused on that. He managed the phone system and business applications for which Kix (page 27) had contracted, administered the company's internal network and servers, developed backup strategies and self-help documentation, and created standard laptop images so that new employees didn't have to set up their own systems (which often required his assistance). In addition, he greeted new employees on arrival and "showed them the ropes." For his first nine months, he *was* the company's IT department.

The improvements Ken made paid off as the employee population grew—slowly at first (the next 50 employees were hired over 15 months)—but then at an increasing rate. Growth from 100 to 150 took four months; from 150 to 200, two months; then he stopped tracking it. He would often be so busy that he'd miss the last train home and sleep overnight in the one conference room with a long couch, a door with a lock, and no interior-facing windows—key requirements when certain coworkers are inveterate pranksters.

From Desktop Support to the Labs

About a year after Ken's arrival, Ricky Kamfolt joined the company and took over most desktop user support, giving Ken more time to concentrate on the labs. But both he and Ricky preferred lab work, so in late 2013, they persuaded the company to hire additional IT staff to support employee needs and oversee business computing and applications. This freed them to manage the engineering labs more proactively. Prior to that, Udy Gold, another engineering employee, had dealt with lab needs on an ad hoc basis.

In 2012, Pure Storage was leasing eight racks at a CoLo for equipment used primarily by *system engineers* (SEs) to refine skills and demonstrate FlashArray to prospects. Engineering's development and test systems were located at the company offices. By late 2013, engineering systems had moved to the CoLo, where leased space was increased by twelve racks to accommodate it. Today, Pure Storage engineering labs occupy over 500 extended height racks of development and field SE equipment located at CoLos in California and Utah.

Ken and Ricky created standard rack layouts that balanced power and streamlined cable management for common combinations of equipment. They instituted naming conventions that enabled developers, SEs, and support engineers to quickly identify and locate equipment they might never have seen. Their layouts eliminated most of the equipment relocation and relabeling that had consumed a disproportionate share of lab management time (their layouts are still in use today). In addition, they configured "torture" and performance stress testing scenarios. And they did all this within the company's engineering budget, which at the time was quite limited.

Realizing that shell scripts they had developed were less effective at automating system management than their design and process improvements were at simplifying lab work, they argued that engineering needed dedicated lab tool development. Mitch Nibbelink joined the company in May 2014, and gradually assembled a team of talented developers whose network, configuration management, and virtual machine provisioning skills greatly improved the operational efficiency of the engineering labs.

Phoning Home Isn't Easy

During the FlashArray alpha phase, engineering had developed rudimentary automatic reporting for arrays to eliminate the need for constant monitoring. Arrays would send hourly configuration and state information and comprehensive daily activity logs to a server at company headquarters. Reporting was soon expanded to include performance and utilization reports, called *frequent diagnostic* messages, sent every 30 seconds.

The facility was dubbed *phonehome*, and proved to be extremely useful, especially with products deployed in remote locations. The support organization had constant visibility to customers' arrays, and in many cases was able to anticipate problems and prevent them from occurring (a facility later formalized as *automated fingerprinting*—using profiles of problematic arrays to identify others that could experience the problems at some future time). With frequent diagnostics, engineering could track the reliability and performance of the entire installed base (except for a few arrays located in data centers whose policies disallowed Internet connections).

As the number of installed arrays grew, so did the amount of data they sent to headquarters. Engineering and support used it to great advantage but hosting it in-house was not affordable. Moreover, as the amount of data increased, analyses became unacceptably time-consuming. Something had to change. Either the company had to curtail the service, which it had come to regard as critical to customer satisfaction, or a different means of storing the exploding body of data would have to be found.

With a 2013 Purity//FA release, arrays were able to send phonehome data to a public cloud storage service. That solved the storage capacity problem, but analysis of the collected logs was still slow and expensive. Lab tools engineers Corry Haines and Phillip Pollard developed distributed cloud-based log analysis tools so engineering and support could use the scripts developed for in-house data. Over time, both storage and processing of phonehome data moved to the cloud and evolved into CloudAssist, which later formed the basis for Pure1 Manage consolidated monitoring, analysis, and management of customers' entire fleets of Pure Storage products.

In This Chapter…

Companies with excellent technology often fail because they don't bring it to the market effectively. "Go-to-market" strategies encompass everything from defining the target market to naming the company to creating a public image and a self-image to getting attention from the media and prospective customers to arranging the "launch" to ensuring that there are technical resources to back up the messaging. The company was fortunate to be able to recruit Matt Kixmoeller who built the marketing and product management functions that endure today.

Creating an Image

I n the fall of 2009, Matt Kixmoeller ("Kix"), then vice president of product management at a security software firm, got an invitation to join Mike Speiser, with whom he had formerly worked, for coffee. Upon arriving, he was surprised to find Coz, with whom he had also worked previously, in Mike's office. Later that day, he met with Hayes. In his own words, "…[Hayes] asked me a bunch of questions, but I didn't realize I was being interviewed at the time."

Matt Kixmoeller ("Kix")
"Look at the tech company logos on this slide. What color don't you see? We'll be THE ORANGE!"

The recruitment continued—Coz, Mike, and Hayes explained their all-flash array concept. For Matt, who had observed the backup technology transition from tape to disk, hearing that they proposed to create all-flash primary storage was "like a light bulb going on." He was instantly sold on the idea. His confidence in Coz and Mike was the swing factor—he accepted their offer and became the company's first non-engineering employee.

Kix took on product management. His first priority was to write a *market requirements document* (MRD) which would define the capabilities needed to make the eventual product successful. Technology users generally had positive perceptions of flash as a storage medium, fueled by the broad acceptance of smartphones and other personal appliances. So although the company was in "stealth mode," limiting what he could tell people to "we're a startup doing something revolutionary in flash storage," he expected there would be no difficulty in getting potential customers to share their experiences and needs.

Users were pre-conditioned by incumbent storage companies' efforts to use flash as performance-boosting cache for their disk arrays, so some failed to grasp the all-flash storage concept. Kix persisted, though, and eventually acquired enough market input to write a comprehensive MRD.

An MRD for a technology product specifies market requirements, not architecture or implementation techniques. Kix wrote about capacity, performance, cost points, and feature requirements such as host interfaces and fault tolerance. Realizing that the company's first product would not be as feature-rich as its competitors, he segmented the market to avoid "ocean boiling"—a broad attack on a diverse market—and homed in on specific target applications for the company's first product.

The slice of the storage market to focus on would be organizations needing reliable, affordable high-performing storage at modest capacity points, and not requiring features like snapshots and long-distance replication for disaster protection. These advanced features would ultimately be required, but reality dictated that they would have to come later.

The addressable market was circumscribed by what the company could develop and manufacture while operating on investment capital. That suggested that at least initially, targeted customers should either be smaller organizations or semi-autonomous departments of larger ones, with storage needs in the terabyte rather than petabyte range, and applications that were outside their critical paths for prosperity or survival. The first of these assumptions proved to be correct—early customers included municipalities, hospitals, casinos, trucking companies, and so forth. The second assumption, however, was not. Early customers quickly gained confidence in the product and began using it for mission-critical storage, so reliability became an even more vital product criterion than had been envisioned.

Once an MRD is agreed upon, it becomes the focal point for architecture and development. Some evolution is inevitable, but change should be resisted unless it is for overwhelmingly compelling reasons, to avoid creating a "moving target" for engineering. Once Kix's compilation of market needs—rack-mounted all-flash arrays in the 20-100 terabyte (effective) range with sub-millisecond I/O latency at price points comparable to those of high-performance disk-based arrays—was accepted, his work was done, at least until the product was close to release and the company could "launch" itself to generate market interest.

He continued to seek meetings with potential customers, expecting to refine his conclusions, but in the main, he was in a holding pattern. He took part in architectural discussions, continually reminding engineers of the MRD product requirements. But he and others, notably Mike, experienced a level of frustration, feeling that architecture was being "debated to death," and not enough progress was being made on the actual product. Things came to a head in a staff meeting where Mike announced that he had committed (unbeknownst to anyone else on the team) to deliver a prototype to a potential customer for "alpha testing" in about three months. The customer's interest was in whether an all-flash array could deliver its claimed performance while "reducing" incoming data as it arrived to keep effective cost per byte affordable. After a stunned silence, led by Hayes, the group agreed that it could be done, and set about paring down features to essentials and building a shippable prototype.

The first alpha prototype was pretty basic—an enclosure with a controller, 24 SSDs, and a *non-volatile random-access memory* (NVRAM). Data was protected by conventional RAID. There was no user configurability; the array exported a fixed number of virtual volumes of fixed size. Fibre Channel was the only host interface, and the company pre-configured the *worldwide names* (WWNs) presented by the array. There was no user interface.

Despite its limitations, the alpha system demonstrated that an all-flash array could reduce data in real time and still provide breakthrough performance. It provided a much-need confidence boost for the company.

The first alpha array was followed by second and third alphas, each more capable, and each going to more users, who were becoming easier to find as word spread among the data center technologist community. Alpha hardware gave way to beta hardware with production components.

What to Do Until the Product Is Ready

While the product was being readied, Kix kept busy with fund raising (he was instrumental in all five of the company's funding rounds), refining the MRD, developing the company's "look and feel," and participating in product design tradeoffs. In addition, realizing that the product would eventually need a *graphical user interface* (GUI), he contracted with experienced GUI designer Chuck Clanton. Together the two designed the first FlashArray GUI. Over time as the product became more feature-rich, the GUI has evolved, but Kix's original conception remains intact.

"Launching" the Company

After eighteen months, with the software running on production hardware and nearly all software features complete, it was time to "launch" the company—to increase its public visibility. The leadership team set VMware's August, 2011 VMworld conference as the target launch event, contracted for exhibit space, and engaged a public relations firm. The selected firm was also a startup, chosen partly for that reason, but also because its principals had prior storage experience. With his product management background, Kix was taken a bit aback by the vagueness of the PR contract.

The company's challenge was to gain user attention in a conservative space dominated by incumbents with large marketing budgets. By chance, Kix had recently seen a launch video from a company in a completely different market.[12] The video was brash and irreverent, but in 90 seconds it introduced the company's value proposition and positioned it against its larger, established competitors in a way that was difficult to forget.

With some difficulty, he persuaded Dietz that Pure Storage should make a similarly irreverent video to drive home a single point: groundbreaking I/O latency at affordable prices, and to establish a contrast between the company and "big storage." Kix found a production firm with a comedy writer, auditioned actors (all but one of the eventual cast were company employees) and engaged the services of a monkey—*yes, a monkey.*

The video[13] appeared on the company's web site a few months after launch. It was phenomenally successful in several dimensions. First, it went "viral," gaining more publicity by word of mouth than the company could have hoped to purchase. People with no connection to storage told their friends about it. Overnight, name recognition increased a thousandfold. Second, it positioned the company as an upstart, clearly differentiated from

---

[12] https://www.youtube.com/watch?v=ZUG9qYTJMsI
[13] https://www.youtube.com/watch?v=-lhKQrweaFw

E Pluribus Logo
"…one morning I was making breakfast and pulled out a tub of honey, with 'pure' on its label. … From this I went to bees, then to hives, then to hexagons, then to speed and agility, to organization, to intelligence, to workers…pretty much everything to do with bees could be attributed to this company"
—**Graham Smith, The Logo Smith**

"To many engineers, the lighted bezel on FlashArray is simply a potential source of issues. But it has also become a powerful representation of our brand.
In the early days of Platinum we didn't have much time for 'extras,' but I made a prototype logo with parts from home. It was a disaster. The second attempt was worse—you couldn't even tell it was turned on. We finally found the right design, and today the bezel represents Pure Storage all over the world. People even wear the lighted logo on chains—'FlashArray bling.'"
—**Pete Kirkpatrick**

the stodgy "old school" storage vendors that dominated the market. Third, it boosted employee morale, giving people a sense of identity as "the new kids in storage-town who were going to shake things up" that became a pillar of the internal culture. For a time, it even became a recruiting tool. Engineers would view it and decide they wanted to work for a company with that attitude. And finally, the "we're different" attitude became part of the company's brand. Every product and program introduction has featured a "here's how we're different from what you've experienced in the past" component.

Pure Storage and "The Orange"

Initially, the company was called OS76, and used a rather plain maroon logo. OS76 appealed to technologists but was too "nerdy" for long-term brand recognition in the wider IT community, so the leaders felt that a different name would be preferable for the company's public launch. Various candidates were discussed. The team finally converged on Pure Storage as the name by which the public would know the company. The name had several advantages. In the near term, it connoted the company's focus on storage and nothing else. 'Pure' suggested Coz's ongoing passion for ease of use, which was to remain a company mantra. Perhaps more significantly, though, the name was general enough to encompass additional storage-related technologies that the company might pursue, such as FlashBlade and the data-centric IT strategy. So Pure Storage became the name.

With the name in hand, the next challenge was a logo. Getting this seemingly trivial symbol right is harder than it sounds. A logo must be instantly and unambiguously recognizable. Ideally, it should somehow create a positive impression of the company. Kix collected the logos of dozens of companies with "pure" in their names (thankfully none in the storage sector), largely to avoid inadvertently creating a similar logo. He engaged a professional graphic artist who tried many concepts without success before serendipitously hitting upon the hexagon motif. With one edge removed, the hexagon formed the company's first initial (P). The shape suggested efficiency, industry, and simplicity all at the same time.

The logo's color was a different story. Initially, it had been maroon, but that was thought to be too stodgy for the company's upstart image. Kix assembled dozens of technology company logos on a slide for a staff meeting, and asked, "What color do you **not** see here?" Orange was conspicuously absent, so it became the company color.

The choice of orange had an important, if unintended beneficial side effect. Employees began to wear orange shirts, socks, hats, and so forth to work. The trend intensified—office walls were painted orange; orange posters, notebooks, coffee cups, and other paraphernalia appeared. Executives would wear orange on public stages. Eventually, Pure Storage came to be identified by the color in much the same way that blue and IBM had been synonymous in earlier times.

Emerging from Stealth

The company had an image (the upstarts), a logo (the hexagonal P), a color (orange), and a target market focus (storage for virtualization and databases). The next challenge was to present itself to the public in a way that got attention, underscored its value proposition, and focused on its targets. As always, there were financial constraints. The only large expense would be a booth at the 2011 VMworld conference. Other activities would be aimed at generating interest among storage users attending the conference.

Employees were urged to use social networking to publicize an interesting storage announcement that would occur at VMworld. But the real attention-getter was the company's web site, where the home page was a "teaser" showing an equipment rack covered by a drape and hinting that Pure Storage was all about flash. The page contained "call to action" links for the curious, for potential beta users, and for prospective employees.

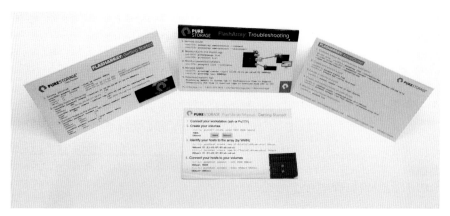

FlashArray Instruction "Manuals"

Little Things Mean a Lot

Like the color orange, small things often acquire greater significance than expected. One such was Coz's contention that if FlashArray was really easy to use, it should be possible to illustrate setup and operation on a business card. Kix was dubious but agreed to produce a business card-size "micro-manual" with the commands for FlashArray setup on one side and volume management on the other. Kix himself coined the slogan at the bottom of the card to underscore the point, "*Come for the performance, stay for the simplicity.*"

Much to everyone's surprise (possibly except Coz's), the business cards were a tremendous hit. At trade shows they were conversation starters. They often wound up in people's wallets or pockets. Rediscovered after the event, they would remind people that they had talked with this upstart company that was making affordable all-flash storage arrays. On sales calls, the cards helped drive home the Pure Storage value proposition. One employee even claims to have joined the company because he "wanted to work for a company that could make storage that easy."

The cards have become a standard marketing tool. As features were added to the products, the format changed to tent card, but new developments are still accompanied by these pocket-size mementos.

Another seemingly trivial item that took on outsized importance was the term "Evergreen™" that described the company's perpetual upgrade business model. From the beginning, the team had intended to change the way organizations managed storage lifecycles as well as the technology. Different business models were proposed and debated, and the company eventually settled on its current program with *free every three, ForeverFlash*, flexible upgrades, and capacity consolidations.

Various names for the business model were proposed, but Coz insisted on *Evergreen* to underscore the perpetual nature of FlashArray—an array's components might be replaced, but the array and most importantly, the data stored in it, live continuously. The team grudgingly let him have his way on this apparently trivial point. Again, to everyone's surprise, the Evergreen name "went viral." It gained instant market recognition, and the concept behind it became so popular with the user community that competitors attempted to imitate it—not easy with legacy products and business models.

The general point is that in marketing as in technology, details matter, often in unexpected ways. Even the smallest things—a logo, a color scheme, promotional items—deserve attention and forethought, because one never knows what impact they will eventually have.

Building a Marketing Team

With the company launch imminent, marketing had to expand. Kix was doing double duty with both product management and marketing, and there weren't enough hours in his day to handle press and analyst interviews, conference attendance, trade show appearances, and the many other activities that surround a launch. In addition, as engagements with potential customers increased, technical marketing expertise was needed.

The recruiting philosophy was the same throughout the company—look for energetic, motivated people with skills in their areas of expertise, and don't be bothered by a lack of storage credentials.

The first addition was Luanne Dauber, whom Kix describes as a "marketing machine." Intelligent and aggressive, but with little storage background, Luanne took over both demand generation and branding. She managed trade show participation, designed giveaways, and encouraged employees to use social media to create "buzz" at every opportunity. She curated the Pure Storage "disruptor brand." Under her leadership, the company portrayed itself as "the antidote to Big Storage," taking every opportunity to showcase its innovation and throw competitive punches in the marketplace.

From its early days, the company's marketing team became the envy of the industry. John Koo, Mike Kim, and Katie Abbaszadeh built a creative digital demand-generation function. Ali Page managed a steadily growing presence at events like VMworld. Megan Polhemus, Regina Soller-Gould, and Lesley Rubin developed a field marketing organization.

The company focused on storage for structured databases and for virtualization, especially the virtual desktop infrastructures that were coming into vogue at the time. By chance, Ravi Venkat, then working as a solution architect for a networking giant's server business unit, saw an announcement of a Pure Storage funding round that piqued his

Ravi Venkat
"I visited a customer who 'complained' that when he replaced his disk arrays with our arrays, he got a spate of environmental alerts from his data center. It seems that our two arrays generated so much less heat than the four racks of disk storage they replaced, that the data center was falling below its minimum allowable operating temperature!"

Different for Different's Sake?

Despite the upstart image it cultivated, Pure Storage resisted "being different for the sake of being different." The company's leadership initially considered a "this is the product, this is the price" selling model similar to that of former automaker Saturn, but was eventually persuaded that users expected "high price, high-discount" for IT purchases. An unknown company was unlikely to be able to change that expectation.

interest. The announcement named Coz and Kix as company executives, both of whom he knew from previous associations. He contacted them by email, and Kix responded, inviting him for an exploratory chat. Subsequent meetings with other team members convinced Ravi that Pure Storage was onto something interesting, but when Coz made an offer, he hesitated. He enjoyed "rock star" status with his current employer. Giving that up to join a company with uncertain prospects was not an easy decision. What finally swayed him was a long-standing desire to join a startup early enough to have a visible impact on its success and incidentally, to make a name for himself. After considering the offer for a week, he accepted, and was immediately thrown into the maelstrom of launch preparations.

Ravi started by creating a virtualization demonstration for the VMworld conference. Using 10 rack-mounted servers, he demonstrated a single FlashArray hosting 1,000 virtual machines running VMware test workloads. Attendees who saw his demo were generally amazed that such a compact array could support that many virtual machines with sub-millisecond I/O latency, and with how quickly they could be started up. The enthusiastic reception dispelled any hesitancy Ravi might have felt about having joined Pure Storage. He embarked on a months-long campaign of presenting the advantages of FlashArray for virtualized computing at conferences, to potential customers, and to the company's growing cadre of field employees. He was the company's first *solution architect*, combining domain expertise with an ability to present concepts clearly and persuade potential users of their advantages.

Kix soon added Oracle experts Bryan Wood and Charles Dye ("Chas") as database solution architects. Today, solution architects develop and test mechanisms that demonstrate the advantages of Pure Storage products in major application environments and evangelize the techniques they devise in solution briefs and public presentations. The solution architecture team has become a mainstay of Pure Storage technical marketing.

In This Chapter...

The individual who perhaps has greatest impact on a startup's success is its first chief executive officer. On the one hand, the CEO must present the company credibly to the media, to potential investors, and to prospective customers, usually in advance of having a product. While doing that, he or she must also create policies and procedures and most importantly, what is usually called a company culture—the values, expectations and behavioral norms that guide employees in their interactions with customers, partners, vendors, and each other. CEO Scott Dietzen worked to instill a team-oriented open culture that made the company a light-hearted fun place to work, but at the same time was quite serious, about being the best and about making customers paramount in everything the company did.

When products shipped and the company began to be known, demands on Scott grew. The search began for a president to manage current operations and give Scott the freedom to focus on the longer term. David Hatfield became the company president in 2012, but demands for executive involvement were so great that the two became twin public faces of the company.

Someone to Be in Charge

The initial role of a startup *chief executive officer* (CEO) is to help make it into a real company. There are board members and leaders to recruit, investors to be sought, contracts to negotiate, introductions to industry players to arrange, go-to-market strategy to be defined, morale to be boosted, and so forth. During OS76's first few months, Mike served as interim CEO. He was well-suited to the role, but the three principals agreed that Mike's tenure would be temporary, and that a permanent chief executive was needed as soon as one could be recruited.

Scott Dietzen ("Dietz")
"There's no 'I' in 'team.'"

Coz and Hayes realized that neither of them was the right choice for CEO. As the company progressed and awareness increased, it would need a "public face"—someone with a technology background who could represent it convincingly to investors, partners, prospects, and customers, as well as to the media—all of which would be a distraction for people trying to create a breakthrough technology. Mike led the CEO search, relying heavily on his own network and contacts he made through board members.

In the founders' view, a company planning to disrupt an established market with radically different technology, needs a technically-oriented CEO—one who can effectively represent its as-yet unproven technology credibly. A new company's CEO necessarily starts out as an evangelist, for both the technology and the company. Until products are shipping, there's less need to focus on operations and sales. There are no large customers, established partners, inventories, receivables, debt, investor relations, or any of the other issues that occupy CEOs of established firms. As Coz observed at the time, "The goal is to reach the first $10 million in sales. If we don't do that, we will never have the opportunity to reach $100 million, $1 billion, and beyond." Each plateau requires different CEO skills and interests. OS76 needed a CEO who could help the company reach the $10 million and $100 million plateaus quickly.

A startup doesn't have an established culture. The CEO's second mission is to formulate a company culture and inculcate it in employees so strongly that they in turn instill it in newcomers as the company grows.

Finally, the early members of a startup are inherently a tight-knit bunch. The CEO must be able to meld with an essentially technical group, trust them, and persuade them by action to trust him or her.

Finding Dietz

In mid-2010, board member Aneel Bhusri introduced Scott Dietzen ("Dietz"), whom he had known previously, to the OS76 team. Dietz had recently completed a stint as president and CTO of a startup that had been acquired and had been taking the proverbial breather for nearly a year. Like Coz, he was ready to "get back in the game." He'd been evaluating opportunities—"kissing frogs" as he puts it—but hadn't encountered anything compelling enough to entice him.

Dietz wasn't a "storage guy," nor had he previously served as a CEO, but he had launched and ramped three companies, so the board felt he was a good choice to lead the fledgling OS76. He appeared at about the same time as a second candidate, a veteran CEO who was less technical, but who had run a larger, more established company. While both candidates' profiles were attractive, the search team decided to pursue Dietz aggressively based on his computer technology background (he holds a doctorate in computer science from Carnegie Mellon University) and his experience with startups. Mike and other mutual acquaintances further bolstered his credibility with the team.

Throughout his career, Dietz had seen users frustrated by complex, fragile, slow storage, so he was excited by the opportunity to disrupt a market badly in need of innovation. He joined the company to do just that, with the mutual expectation that he'd take it to around $100 million annual revenue and then bow out in favor of a more operationally-focused CEO. In fact, he remained CEO until the company achieved $1 billion in annual revenue, one of the fastest in the industry ever to do so. In keeping with his "There's no 'I' in team" philosophy, he credits the entire company with that success.

Hitting the Ground Running

Dietz felt that his first task was setting a tone for the company, both by clearly defining its mission and by setting norms for day to day conduct. An early opportunity to clarify the mission arose in defining target markets for the upcoming product. One school of thought felt that concentrating on a single market sector would get the most from scarce marketing resources. The alternative, which Dietz favored, was a "full frontal assault" on the storage market, positioning the company as a metaphorical David to the incumbents' Goliaths. Dietz argued hard for his position and eventually prevailed. Pure Storage went to market as a broad-spectrum storage vendor (page 31), although the majority of early sales were in virtualization and database applications.

The frontal assault approach had a few beneficial side effects. As FlashArray started to win against much larger competitors, they would strike back. At conferences and trade shows they would present feature comparisons of their products to "The Orange Mystery Array." The net impression on audiences was that the unnamed (wink, wink) upstart was credible in competitors' eyes—publicity Pure Storage couldn't purchase at any price.

Occasionally, the team's brashness nonplussed even Dietz. When Kix proposed to spend a significant part of the marketing budget on an irreverent comedy video (page 29) to boost the company's visibility, Dietz wasn't sure it was the kind of image that would attract data-center equipment buyers, and he doubted that it would be funny. But seeing the script completely changed his mind, so production went ahead. Not only did the video go viral overnight, it ultimately became a recruiting tool; several candidates expressed desires to work for a company that would do something like that.

> **The Pure Storage Values**
> - Persistence
> - Creativity
> - Teamwork
> - Ownership
> - Customer first

Setting the Tone

The founders agreed with Dietz's philosophy of openness and sharing information to the greatest extent possible. They felt that being open with employees about setbacks would empower and motivate them to strive to improve products and processes, whereas managers who only disbursed good news would eventually lose credibility. Moreover, they believed that compartmentalizing information fosters an inward focus that can lead to "information is power" office politics.

Dietz was a strong proponent of "measuring what matters." He insisted that the company measure its success by customer and partner *Net Promoter Scores* (NPS) rather than internal metrics. He felt that customers' view of the company was the best indicator of success and would keep people focused on what really matters—being customer and partner-driven rather than driven by engineering or sales. He encouraged employees to view the company from the perspective of customers and competitors, rather comparing one internal department to another.

Openness breeds trust, which the company builds by communicating openly with employees. For example, salary negotiations are rare, because people trust their managers to treat them fairly. When hiring, Dietz would tell candidates that they need not negotiate compensation. He would explain that any offer would be commensurate with company's expectations for the person. He would go on to explain that exceeding expectations would reap rewards, both financial and in increased responsibility, and close by asking if the candidate did not trust the company to be fair, why they would consider joining. Openness is a powerful trust-builder because it places a burden on the company's managers to treat their employees fairly.

Doing Whatever Needs to Be Done

Dietz devoted much of his early effort to recruiting. He was usually the "closer" who sold candidates on the opportunity after they had passed the other hurdles. He followed a principle learned from Frank Slootman (page 10): "favor the up-and-comer's hunger over the 'been there, done that' experience that hints of complacency." With two equally qualified candidates, enthusiasm and tenacity often turn out to be more valuable over time than long experience that can fall into the trap of trying to recreate the past.

In interviewing, he tried to set realistic expectations. For example, if he felt that a candidate manager was ideal for a current need but might lack the experience to grow apace with the company, he would make it clear that the candidate might find his or her manager being hired if growth required more organizational depth. He would observe that he was in the same situation.

Dietz describes himself as a stubborn recruiter, observing that he spent the better part of a year pursuing Hat (page 49) and Bob Wood (page 67), who fit the desired profiles for company president and engineering vice president respectively. Fortunately, the managers hired earlier—Evan Driscoll and Dan Decasper in engineering and Matt Burr in sales—gave him the space he needed to pursue and close the optimal candidates.

Creating a Company Culture

A company's *culture* is a difficult concept to define, but it quickly becomes obvious to anyone immersed in it. It has an ethics dimension (How do we treat our customers and suppliers?); it sets the tone for employee interaction (openness and honesty); it establishes norms for individual responsibility and initiative (do the right thing, think out of the box); and perhaps most importantly, it is the (often unwritten) rules that define the company's and employees' expectations of each other.

As Dietz settled into the CEO role, he held a series of leadership meetings to codify behaviors that had already become the norm into a statement of company values. He uses the well-known "stone soup" metaphor[14] to describe his contribution to what became the core of the Pure Storage culture—the company's five core values:

PERSISTENCE

means sticking with a situation until it's resolved, even if, as in many cases, it's not a Pure Storage issue. Emphasis is on the "long game"—doing the

Dietz on Persistence
"If we're not uncomfortable, we're probably not 'leaning in' hard enough."

right thing for customers and partners, anticipating and preparing for technology and market trends, and so forth. Dietz often observes that Pure Storage is "a marathon, not a sprint," and that it welcomes competition because it drives innovation and ultimately, customer value.

CREATIVITY

is the bedrock of high-tech, but Pure Storage is a business, too. Employees throughout the company should "think out of the box," and strive to improve products and processes. The watchword is, "we can do better."

TEAMWORK

reflects the reality that technology and business are both so complex that individuals working alone

Dietz on Teamwork
"We're here to win the Super Bowl of Storage, not to field the most MVPs."

can seldom accomplish meaningful things on a large scale. Pure Storage is a "leave your ego at the door" culture, where teams accomplish things—standing ones for long-term projects and ad hoc ones for one-time events.

[14] https://en.wikipedia.org/wiki/Stone_Soup

OWNERSHIP

is about doing what needs to be done, regardless of organizational lines. It follows from hiring individuals who think and operate independently. As Coz puts it, "Being at Pure Storage means that you're very good at what you do, and what you do is important to the company's success."

Dietz on Meetings

"In the early days, I would often tell groups of employees, 'if you're ever stuck in an excruciating internal meeting, you have the CEO's permission to get up and walk out.' "

CUSTOMER FIRST

is the sum of the other values. Companies thrive when their customers are satisfied; customers value a company that values them and treats them well. Pure Storage employees are expected to take ownership of situations, work creatively in teams, and persist until customers are satisfied. The company measures its success by NPS, not by sales or production quotas, support case closure rates, or engineering schedules.

Of course, partners are customers, too. Pure Storage does not treat negotiations as a zero-sum game. The company tries to make every sale a "win/win/win"—for the customer, the partner, and the company.

Dietz and Coz had roughed out the Pure Storage values. After Hat joined, the values were codified in a document that one of the executives presents to every class of incoming employees. While the values statement codifies it, the culture is really defined by how the company and its employees act, not by what's written. Pure Storage employees are expected to act in accordance with the values and are encouraged to intervene constructively when they feel the values are not being adhered to.

Expanding on the Values

From the beginning, the company strove for a meritocracy that recognized and rewarded individuals for contributions rather than for position on the organization chart. The philosophy was, and is "hire the best and expect a lot from them." Individuals are expected to be creative and to consider ideas on their merits, not on their sources. Open debate is encouraged but expected to end with decisions. Stakeholders are expected to support decisions and implement them faithfully unless revisiting them is justified.

"Make it easier" is a company mantra that applies both to products and to operations. Recognizing that with growth, process can stifle progress, the company encourages "just enough" process to maximize progress. The organization is relatively flat, but more importantly, the culture encourages "any to any" communication and information sharing. Pure Storage measures what matters, for example, NPS, array-days between disruptive events, and service calls averted by anticipating customer issues.

The culture favors the long-term over the immediate. For customers, this means developing lasting relationships, even if at the expense of a quick sale. For employees, it means maintaining a healthy work-life balance. Occasional extraordinary commitments are necessary but should not be a way of life. For managers, it means mentoring new generations of employees. For products, it means anticipating technology and market developments and continually evolving products, services, and business practices accordingly.

The culture encourages team over individual success. Occasional failures such as lost sales and missed deadlines are accepted and learned from rather than hidden. The catchphrase is, "**We** succeed but **I** fail." Bad news is shared rather than suppressed. Stakeholders should be aware that something has gone badly, learn what can be learned from it, and move on.

Pure Storage does not try to offer the least expensive products. It does, however, strive to deliver the greatest value in many ways—all-inclusive pricing, high quality products, lifetime flash guarantees, breakthrough ease of use, excellent support, non-disruptive repair and upgrade, Evergreen's "free every three," Pure1 user-accessible fleet management, and so forth.

With its customers, the company strives to "under-promise and over-deliver." Individual and organizational needs and desires are subordinated to serving customers and partners. Employees understand that the negative impact of an unhappy customer outweighs the positive impact of many happy ones. Every sale should have a positive outcome for the customer, the partner, and the company. *Account executives* (AEs) compete hard but lose gracefully and preserve relationships for future engagement. Everyone is keenly aware that regaining a lost customer or partner is far more difficult and expensive than losing a single sale.

A Culture of Openness

Dietz and Coz felt strongly that openness led to employee satisfaction and ultimately, business success. Any company has certain information that must be restricted to those with legitimate needs—financial status, employees' personal information, sensitive negotiations in progress, and so forth—but the team felt that communicating as openly as possible across the entire organization would make employees feel involved and committed to the company's success. Coz often observed that "We should have a good reason for *not* sharing any piece of information." Every employee is encouraged to know and understand the company's goals, roadmap, and strategy.

One important way to motivate people is to keep them informed about happenings in and around the organization. The open office environment inherently encourages communication. In the early days, daily 10 a.m. standups (page 21) kept everyone informed and involved.

> "Having spent most of my career with big companies where information was closely held and distributed on a 'need to know' basis, seeing Hat talk about sales figures and projections in weekly company meetings open to all employees was awesome. It made me feel like I was really part of the team."—**Brian Gold**

With growth, daily company-wide standups became unwieldy and the concept morphed into team events. This became particularly important in the engineering organization, where it dovetailed with Agile methodology. Daily team standups continue—wandering through engineering spaces at 10 a.m., one can observe small groups of standing people in earnest discussion. The practice is an important part of the engineering culture.

In keeping with the spirit of openness, from the beginning Dietz chaired weekly "all hands" meetings to which all employees were invited and encouraged to attend. The meetings communicated internal and external events of company significance and gave employees an opportunity to ask unfiltered questions. Prior to IPO and the restrictions it imposes, these meetings shared sales results and forecasts. Growth eventually made it impractical to assemble everyone in one room, especially as the field organization developed. The meetings became webcasts, still open to all employees, local and remote. Like team standups, weekly company-wide webcasts continue today.

The first Butt Kicker award went to Taher Vohra and Joe Hasbani for successfully bringing up the Purity//FA platform component.

Recognition

The desire to be recognized for one's accomplishments is human nature. Nowhere is that more true than in technology. Inventors bask in the recognition that comes with publishing—in journal articles, as conference talks, as mentions in the press—but what's most important to them is peer recognition.

Dietz felt the need for ways to make the entire company aware of individuals' extraordinary achievements, whether in engineering, marketing, sales, or operations. He proposed instituting ad hoc awards for individual achievements beyond the expected high standards. The awards were called "Butt Kickers" and were symbolized by a statuette of a kicking donkey. Any employee could nominate a colleague for a Butt Kicker at any time. A committee chose winners and awards were announced at company meetings. To symbolize the fleeting nature of achievement, the trophies were lent to recipients for a few weeks as desk ornaments, and then recycled. But their real significance lay in the peer recognition of individual achievement.

A companion to the Butt Kicker, the Razzie, was also instituted. In the spirit of openness and sharing bad news, Razzies were "awarded" for obvious missteps, like rebooting the wrong server and causing the entire test infrastructure to fail (engineering), allowing a faulty component into production (operations), or making a grammatical error on the public web site (marketing). Their purpose was to openly acknowledge missteps, use them as learning experiences, relegate them to the past, and move on. As the company grew, Butt Kicker and Razzie proposals became departmental, with awards given at departmental all-hands meetings.

In addition to individual recognition, the company realized the importance of recognizing collective achievements to mark progress toward a product and to build a sense

"Shipping" the first Beta Array (2011)

Celebrating after the Shipment

of camaraderie. This was especially important because it was not yet able to celebrate public announcements of quarterly financial performance.

The company made a point of celebrating each major milestone it reached. Celebrations were typically unassuming—most were afternoon beverage and snack parties in the office. The important thing was to recognize the group accomplishment.

The company also encouraged holiday celebrations, employee birthdays, and other significant personal events. On Thursday afternoons, everyone would stop work an hour early and convene in the break area for drinks and conversation. All relatively low-key, but all aimed at creating a feeling of belonging to a close-knit team with a common goal.

Going Global with Recognition

As the company expanded internationally, the emphasis on team building expanded with it. Semi-annual *Sales Kickoff* (SKO) meetings brought AEs and SEs to headquarters for several days of business and social interaction with engineers, marketers, and executives. Team building became regional. Area managers were encouraged to recognize milestones and to instill a sense of community in their employees. One notable example has been annual long-distance bicycle tours by groups of employee cycling enthusiasts in EMEA to raise money for charities.

Following the Pure Storage *"there is no I in team"* ethos, top performers from throughout the company were (and are) invited to its annual *Pure Performers Club* award conference along with their partners, rather than just AEs and SEs. Not only is this a very visible token of recognition, it builds cross-functional relationships, fosters a sense of performance through teamwork, and avoids a potential sales-engineering cultural divide.

Pure Performers Club events often include surprise videos in which family members and friends congratulate award winners, resulting in laughter, applause, and occasional tears from audiences. Employees greatly appreciate the personal recognition and effort put forth by the company to recognize their achievements. It is one of the important ways in which the Pure Storage culture is unique.

Hackathons: All Work and No Play...*Not!*

Software engineering is essentially creative, but software engineers are almost always creating something that was assigned to them. Seldom do they have opportunities for free expression. In mid-2015, Chris Golden (page 63) proposed that the company sponsor its own *hackathon*—a two-day event in which ad hoc teams of volunteers could prototype solutions to problems entirely of their own choosing. Hackathons were not a new idea; the concept had taken hold in a number of other areas,[15] like science and music.

---

[15] https://en.wikipedia.org/wiki/Hackathon

Chris believed that a hackathon would benefit engineers…

- With no restrictions on project content, it would be an opportunity for free expression.
- The brief duration would train participants to focus intensely, a vital software development skill, and also give them a feeling of accomplishment that might take months to achieve in "day jobs."
- Small ad hoc teams would help people get to know each other and foster a sense of community.

…and the company…

- It would help re-energize participants and onlookers who might be bogged down in lengthy projects.
- It would be an opportunity to prototype product features that somehow never made it above the "cut line" on the priority list.
- It might spawn novel ideas that would eventually find their way into products or improve processes.

Chris proposed the idea to his manager, and then to Bob and Coz. All were enthusiastic, and he got the go-ahead to try it. The timing was fortuitous, because it coincided with the company's first group of summer interns, who were able to enjoy the festive atmosphere along with full-time employees.

Any group of three to six employees could form a team and define a project. They would work primarily on the project during the hackathon. Company resources—computers, networks, servers, and storage—could be used, except where key projects would be affected. Work would cease after two days, and each team would present its project goals and results in an open meeting. Judges were appointed and several categories of prizes were awarded.

The idea was a resounding success. The first hackathon in the summer of 2015 attracted about 60 participants in 20 project teams. Today, hackathons occur quarterly, typically attracting upwards of 50 participants. Project ideas have ranged from ridiculous (programming a FlashArray bezel to blink in time with music to create a data center discotheque) to extremely useful (evaluating a new library that led to a revamp of FlashArray compression). Others included a warning system that alerted the sales department when a customer's array was approaching full utilization and a mechanism for compressing phonehome log data that was eventually used to reduce CloudAssist storage requirements.

An adage states that, "Success has a thousand fathers." As the value of hackathons became obvious, the company's business units engaged more directly, suggesting project ideas and motivating participants with tangible rewards. For example, to encourage ideas for FlashBlade object store applications, the business unit once offered a special prize for the most creative use of objects by an application.

The Nerfinators
"They had all answered the interview question, 'What do you do when a nerf dart hits you on the side of the head while you're working on an important project?' correctly."—**Marcus Padro**

Drew Bernat and the Kegerator
"It holds 20 gallons…5 non-alcoholic and the rest home-brewed."

Don't Take Yourself Too Seriously

From the beginning, the company's work environment was lighthearted. To some extent, this was the Silicon Valley norm in which technology giants like Google and Facebook are unabashedly youth-oriented, and even mature firms like Oracle and Adobe cater to their younger employees.

The challenge for Pure Storage was to create a "fun" environment on a startup budget that would also be motivational. In the early days, with alpha systems nearly a year off and FlashArray general availability over two years in the future, keeping engineers enthusiastic was particularly important. Motivation came partly from celebrating milestones but also from an enjoyable day-to-day environment.

For a company intending to break in to a mature market with a technology it hopes will be disruptive, an occasional gentle poke at incumbents can be an employee morale builder. For Pure Storage, an opportunity arose when a future competitor's obsolete storage system became available for resale at a bargain price.

The company acquired the system and gutted it, saving only the cabinet. Led by Andrew Bernat ("Drew"), employees filled the cabinet with refrigeration units and pressurized beverage kegs and installed taps on the front door. The result was the "Kegerator," a source of much early-day mirth.

Wire frames designed for mounting disk drives were removed from the cabinet and mounted on walls. Fortuitously, their dimensions were perfect for use as wine racks, creating opportunities for "101 uses for…" jokes.

"Gus's Galaxy Grill"—**(Castro Street Headquarters).** Arcade games courtesy of Panos

Today, the wine racks are gone, fallen victim to the growing employee population's space needs. The Kegerator survives, tucked unobtrusively in a corner of the engineering break area at headquarters. It still dispenses beverages to employees on special occasions.

Stress Relief in the Office

Silicon Valley work environments are a world apart from the buttoned-up three-piece suit atmosphere of the east coast. From his experience in a previous startup, Dietz felt that a bit of playfulness in the office could be both an outlet for stress and a morale builder. When the office grew to the point the it could take two or three minutes to walk from one end to the other, he bought a few Razor scooters and Hoverboards that employees allegedly used to get from place to place faster, but were really just fun. Both have since largely succumbed to growth and office population density, but in the early days, it was common to see engineers zipping from place to place, parking a scooter against a pole or table, and getting on with their business.

By far the most visible office toys were spring-loaded plastic guns that launch foam-tipped darts 20-30 feet. The so-called *nerf darts* are harmless but having one land on a keyboard or bounce off a screen is sure to get attention, if not invite a response in kind. Like the Razors and Hoverboards, nerf dart guns were a low-cost diversion from work that demanded meticulous attention. They provided impromptu breaks from unrelieved concentration. As with the scooters and Hoverboards, nerf dart use has diminished with higher employee population density, but the plastic guns can often be spotted in unused corners of the offices.

Fast forward to 2012. FlashArray was shipping, and occasionally support issues arose, some of which the support organization "escalated" to a dedicated team of problem solvers in the engineering organization.

In any technology company, customer escalations are high-pressure situations, with the field and engineering having different perspectives on resolution. Keeping escalations under control needs an experienced manager who can *triage*—determine how each one

Hat and Assistant
Raising Funds for Charity

should be handled—and manage interactions between the field, engineering, and the customer.

Pure Storage was able to recruit such a person in Panos Koutsoyannis (page 122) to manage the escalations team. In the context of the working environment, the company was doubly fortunate, because Panos was a long-time collector of arcade-class electronic games. Hiring him worked out well for him as well as for Pure Storage. He needed housing for his extensive collection, and Pure Storage was happy to acquire a superb means for development engineers to unwind with a round of pinball or foosball right in the company offices.

During an expansion, the company had outfitted an employee break room, dubbed *Gus's Galaxy Grill* after the diner in the popular movie "Spaceballs." Panos installed a selection of games. Today, he periodically rotates in different games from the warehouse that houses the bulk of his collection.

Giving Back to the Community

From the company's earliest days, its employees have actively engaged with their communities. From donations to worthy causes to sponsoring and participating in volunteer events, the general employee attitude is one of expressing gratitude for being associated with a prosperous company in a prosperous industry. During each SKO event, an evening is devoted to raising funds for a worthy cause, with David Hatfield (page 49) as master of ceremonies, on one occasion assisted by a monkey. Over five years, the evenings have raised nearly a million dollars, with upwards of 50% of attendees participating.

In 2015, the company took an even more active role in community outreach by establishing the *Pure Good Foundation* to "continue and deepen employee engagement in communities around the world." The foundation's mission is to "accelerate positive change by harnessing the power of people, technology, and community to uplift youth through education-based initiatives." It has funded initiatives to expand opportunities for low-income middle school students and teachers through a free summer learning program in the United States and to help young people who are unemployed or struggling at school to transform their lives.

The Foundation is active in three areas:

INVESTMENT IN INNOVATION

True to the Pure Storage innovation core value, the foundation invests in innovative solutions to the pressing problems of youth.

GLOBAL INTEREST GRANTS

Demonstrating the teamwork core value, the foundation funds initiatives consistent with its mission selected by teams of employees.

Volunteerism

The foundation pairs Pure Storage employees with youth organizations around the world based on organizations' needs and employees' skills.

The foundation has broad-based employee backing. It was funded by a grant of company stock taken from the employee compensation pool with the approval of a majority of eligible employees.

Expanding the Executive Suite

In a previous engagement, Matt Burr (page 81) had reported to David Hatfield ("Hat"). Through Burr, with whom he had remained in contact, Hat learned more about the company (by then renamed Pure Storage) and followed its progress with interest. He already knew Burr, Mike, and Coz; upon meeting Dietz, he was favorably impressed, both by the man's intellect and by the "do the right thing" attitude with which he had imbued the company.

Hat had long since set himself a long-term goal of becoming CEO of a company able to have an impact on technology, early enough for him to have an impact on the company.

He had no shortage of opportunities, but he continued to be intrigued by the potential of Pure Storage—the size of its addressable market, the disruptive nature of its technology and business practices, and its culture of openness with customers and employees. His conversations with company leaders gradually shifted from "How should we set up our sales operation?" to "Don't you want to be part of something that could

David Hatfield ("Hat")

"From the early days, we have been 100% committed to building a company culture that we all wanted to be part of. It starts with hiring the very best people at what they do, who are as passionate about our shared vision and values as we are. Then it is about being honest, open, team players who are obsessed with challenging the status quo to make our customers, partners, colleagues, and the industry better. We're missionaries, not mercenaries. We care.

Finally, it's about having fun and enjoying the ride, while we transform the industry. I love all of our orange, our Kegerator, Panos' classic arcade games, our gongs, Halloween parades, holiday parties and being surrounded by people who love what we do. Despite all we have achieved in such a short period of time, the best is yet to come!"

—2013 & still true

really shake up information technology?" He began to realize that the company was young enough for him to have a personal impact on its development, and through that impact, to change the trajectory of the enterprise storage market.

Meanwhile, it was becoming clear that the combination of CEO duties and being the company's "public face" was overwhelming Dietz, so more executive talent was needed. Thus began what Dietz half-jokingly describes as "nine months of dating." In late 2011, Hat was persuaded—he rethought his resolve never to work for a CEO with an engineering background and joined the company, which at the time had fewer than 100 employees and a tiny revenue stream, as its President. Hat strongly emphasized a "culture of caring," for example by including families in award ceremonies. He later became a prime mover in establishing the Pure Good Foundation.

Pure Storage est Omnis Divisa in Partes Tres

When Hat joined, Bob Wood (page 67), Dietz and he divided executive responsibilities, with Bob managing engineering and support and Hat taking charge of the "go-to-market" sales and marketing functions in conjunction with Kix. Operations reported to Dietz, in part to bolster his experience with hardware company operations.

Dietz and Hat became the combined outward face of the company. The informal rule was that with the exception of executive staff meetings, they should never be in the same place at the same time. Hat wore multiple "hats"—he was one of the company's executive "closers" of sales, overseer of the "pipeline" that stabilized forecasting for operations, and cheerleader in chief for employees. He reinforced the "culture of caring" in many ways, for example by including employees' families in award ceremonies.

For Hat, the appeal of Pure Storage lay in the company's potential to radically streamline information technology—to "accelerate possible" as one slogan had it at the time. He realized that FlashArray technology could fundamentally alter IT, but was also keenly aware that to succeed, excellent technology must be accompanied by an effective "go-to-market" strategy. He made it his goal to move the company toward a business model that encompassed packaging, pricing, promotion, and sales to augment the technology and fulfill its promise of market disruption. He emphasized customer outcomes rather than the "speeds and feeds" that were endemic to storage at the time.

"How would eliminating a million hours of I/O latency per year change the way you operate?" became a common theme of sales engagements. Presentations were likely to emphasize better patient care, more responsive public sector services, faster time to market, more competitiveness, improved customer satisfaction, and so forth, rather than IOPS and throughput.

Hat subscribed completely to the all-inclusive pricing strategy, which undercut competitors' revenue with FlashArray base prices that included features that others sold as extra-cost options. He pushed hard to extend pricing to encompass what eventually became the Evergreen model whose "free every three," "ForeverFlash," and "flat and fair" service provisions that exploit "data in place" NDU to position Pure Storage products as decade-plus investments. By his informal estimate, each Pure Storage sale cost the competitor five times the amount of revenue it had failed to capture.

He reinforced the company's early decision to place all sales through channel partners rather than selling directly. Selling through partners has had multiple benefits, perhaps the greatest being partner loyalty—today, partners introduce over half of new customers. For the partners, working with Pure Storage helps them gain access to very large organizations to which competing vendors sell directly.

He figured prominently in AE recruiting, which everyone felt would be the most important factor in getting the company "off the ground and into the air." Sales recruiting is based on candidates' track records, attitudes, and leadership potential. He insisted that candidate AEs not only have stellar sales records but also exhibit values and attitudes that would mesh well with the Pure Storage team-oriented, "customer first" culture. He insisted too, on recruiting SEs who could promote a vision of transformation, and on treating and compensating them as peers of AEs, rather than as assistants.

Hat hired to accommodate the company's anticipated growth and allow promotion from within. Several early recruits were nominally overqualified for their positions. For example, Kevin Delane joined in 2014 to lead a Global Accounts Program, progressed to managing International Business, and became Sales Vice President in 2017. James Petter joined to manage EMEA and later took over all International Business. Dan FitzSimons established Enterprise Sales Segmentation and eventually became manager of Sales for the Americas.

The results of this philosophy speak for themselves. Ten years since its founding, Pure Storage not only enjoys outstanding success in the market, the company also has one of the technology sector's highest sales-employee retention rates.

In This Chapter...

The first order of business was creating an engineering team to build what Coz and Hayes had conceived. The core of the invention was software, but the company's products would be complete storage systems, so both hardware and software teams would be needed. Early recruiting relied on personal contacts and, to a lesser extent, recruiters. After a couple engagements, they found Doug Mohr, who was the proverbial recruiting machine. Doug introduced the majority of early hires to the team. The key to recruiting was finding individuals who were both smart and creative. Emphasis was on problem-solving abilities; less so on candidates with the "right" resumes. Even as the employee population passes 3,000, this continues to be the company's recruiting philosophy.

Engineers brought different skills and interests. Some concentrated on the underlying operating environment, some on the core array functionality that would become Purity//FA, and some on the pieces that would round out the product. Throughout the development, close attention was given to product reliability.

The Engineering Team: Beginnings

With the first engineers and a CEO in place, the founders next turned to recruiting an engineering team. Coz and Hayes agreed on hiring "rock stars"—people they judged to be skilled in their areas of expertise, energetic, and motivated, rather than people with long lists of storage experience or programming languages on their resumes. In the early days, Coz was reluctant to recruit from his former employer, because of past association, and because he didn't want the Pure Storage to become a "v2.0," technically or culturally.

Initially, they prioritized hands-on "doers" over managers. Managers could wait until there was something to manage. This jump-started development. Today it creates growth opportunities for individuals who are already familiar with the company and its technology. Later, as the organization took shape, the focus shifted. Where possible, the company recruited senior managers for its major functions and expected them to build their teams.

To produce flash-based storage systems, the company needed both flash memory and storage system hardware expertise. Coz and Hayes were conversant with both, but they considered themselves fundamentally software people. They wanted managers with extensive hands-on experience to handle hardware design and development.

"Experience" means not only a thorough knowledge of and a history of working with a technology, but also well-established contacts with the technology's ecosystem. It can be difficult for a tiny startup to get the attention of suppliers who deal with the industry's biggest companies. Employees with credibility can lend that credibility to a fledgling company.

Just when the company needed flash expertise, Michael Cornwell was in search of a new challenge. Michael had twice led other firms' transitions from magnetic disk to flash-based products. He joined OS76 in late 2009 as its flash technology expert. His industry credibility helped the company gain entry to the community of major SSD and raw flash memory suppliers.

While the company's primary value would be in software, the software would run on hardware, which, at least initially, would come from OEM vendors and have to be thoroughly tested before it qualified as part of a product carrying the Pure Storage name.

Again, the timing was fortuitous. An acquaintance suggested Ko Yamamoto to Coz as a potential source of advice on dealing with vendors and qualifying hardware components.

Ko Yamamoto
"Go fast. Save money. But make sure it's going to work well, because high reliability is easy to say, but hard to do and even harder to prove you've done it."

Michael Cornwell
"[…for APJ] we needed to have a Pure [Storage] face on everything we did."

Ko had experience as a hardware engineering director with other storage companies and had dealt extensively with both external suppliers and internal developers. An initial conversation with Coz during a walk under the headquarters building portico to avoid rain was followed by others. Ko eventually joined the company as a hardware engineering director. Along with his storage system hardware expertise, he brought personal credibility with enclosure, processor, network interface, storage device, and other component vendors.

Ramping up Recruiting

Once Michael and Ko were hired, the company engaged professional recruiters. Recruiters were directed to look for individuals who demonstrated intelligence, energy, initiative, and adaptability, and not to worry too much about claims of storage or programming language experience. They were advised to inform candidates that OS76 was a long-term proposition, and to avoid individuals who were obviously interested in the (usually illusory) high-risk-quick-payback model commonly imputed to the technology sector.

In a startup, recruiting is critical, particularly for engineering. An engineer who can't perform or can't work in a team retards overall progress and consumes precious operating capital. Every recruit must be able to do the job and to meld with the team. The challenge for a small company is to determine whether a candidate has these qualities based on references and a few interviews. References help in the beginning because most are team members' personal acquaintances, but that only scales so far. As hiring increases, there is necessarily more reliance on interviews.

Coz and Hayes devised a method for interviewing software engineers using a collection of data structure and algorithm problems from which interviewers would pose a random selection to candidates. The problems were designed to expose thought processes and test adaptability. Interviewers would observe candidates' approaches, ask them about possible optimizations, and would sometimes alter the parameters of a solved problem to assess mental versatility. This interviewing style has become common among technology firms and is still the norm in Pure Storage engineering. Today, interviewers are formally trained in the method and observe experienced interviewers in action before interviewing on their own.

Engineering candidates typically undergo three or four problem-solving interviews in addition to a few general background discussions. Afterward, all interviewers gather to discuss their findings. In principle, a single interviewer can disqualify a candidate, but in practice this seldom occurs.

With a Little Help from Our Friends

The company engaged the services of several recruiters with mixed results. Finally, they found Doug Mohr, who understood the type of people needed, and had an extensive international network of contacts and an outgoing personality that helped him extend his network while he searched for recruits.

Doug took pains to impress on candidates that building a world-beating storage company would take a decade or more. Individuals in search of overnight success and cash-out need not apply. He consistently succeeded in recruiting the right type of talent— Coz estimated that he was the source of 60% of the company's first 100 engineers. Effective technical recruiters may be difficult for a new company to discover, but they are a necessity for acquiring qualified resources quickly to accelerate development and realize its vision.

Adding to Hardware Engineering

As hardware engineering director, Ko's mission was to integrate the servers that would be array controllers with *storage shelf* chassis, SSDs, Fibre Channel interfaces, and other components to create reliable platforms for Purity//FA. His two key challenges were server reliability and integrating single-port *Serial Advanced Technology Attachment* (SATA) SSDs with dual SAS networks.

"I had always thought that algorithms and data structures were the most interesting topics in grad school. As I learned Purity//FA internals, however, I discovered that its algorithms and structures were way beyond anything I had previously encountered. The company's problem-solving interviews were the right way to test people's ability to deal with the kind of software they would work with as engineers."

—**Eric Seppanen**

Tom Holland
"The alpha hardware was…shall we say…interesting. We bolted the NVRAMs to custom-made plastic sheets to hold them in place. The boot drives were jammed between two pieces of enclosure sheet metal and often came loose. I fixed that with some adhesive-backed Velcro. This stuff was clearly not going to go into production."

In the fall of 2010, Tom Holland, then managing a new storage system introduction for a Bay Area vendor, had grown weary of business travel. His employer had development sites, vendors, and factories around the world; introducing the new product meant face-to-face contact with all of them. When he heard from a recruiter about a startup opportunity, he was mildly interested, but felt obliged to complete his current assignment.

That assignment completed, Tom learned that his next one would mean more of the same—frequent global travel. He contacted the recruiter and was pleased to learn that not only was the opportunity still available, but the hiring manager was Ko Yamamoto, whom he knew. He signed a *non-disclosure agreement* (NDA), learned about the project, feeling that not only could he handle the technical challenge but that that there was an

Yi Ding

"I'll never forget the first time I heard of Pure Storage. In 2011, a colleague asked me to help with our silicon for a 'hot new storage startup' she was supporting.

This company was different, she said, 'it's a bunch of CompSci geeks in an office coding their brains out but they have surprisingly good supplier relationships (a shout out to Ko and MC for that!).' I was sold immediately; the rest is history!"

Alan Driscoll

"I knew Coz from a former life as a Veritas OEM. That made OS76 the right choice for my relatively late entry into the startup world."

opportunity to help build the company as well as the product. Over the course of several weeks, he became convinced, as he (under)states it, "that I could envision myself working there." In early 2011, he accepted an offer from Pure Storage .

Tom arrived during the FlashArray alpha phase. It was already understood that the alpha hardware was not suitable for production, so his task was to develop relationships with vendors whose products *could* be part of production arrays. The most significant difference between the alpha hardware and what would become the FA-320 was redundancy. All hardware components and interconnects in the product had to be redundant.

For consumer-grade SSDs, redundancy required *interposers* to connect each one to both controllers via two SAS networks. At first, the storage shelf vendor delivered boxes of empty carriers, interposers, fasteners, and cables for Pure Storage to assemble. Tom laid the parts out on a conference table and asked engineers to help assemble shelves for beta systems. Several took occasional breaks from development to assemble carriers for an hour or two at a time. Eventually, the component vendor was persuaded to pre-assemble carriers prior to delivery.

In the company's early days, the hardware engineering team was quite small. The FA-320 and FA-400 series arrays were built from off-the-shelf components; there was no actual hardware development. But the team had to completely understand the components and adapt to their idiosyncrasies, usually with software workarounds. A case in point was that controller hardware did not log power failures. The workaround was to examine the controller's boot drive, which recorded every boot time persistently.

Interposers were new to the market, so working with them was an ongoing learning experience. Each one's firmware had to be upgraded and power-cycled before first use. Upgrading a shelf of 24 carriers one by one was tedious in the extreme and would be out of the question for production. Tom devised a procedure to automate concurrent upgrade of a full shelf of carriers, which became a company manufacturing standard.

The seemingly trivial part was an ongoing challenge, in part because information was sparse. Ko realized that to meld SAS interface cards from one vendor, network expanders from a second, interposers from a third, and SSDs from still other vendors into a reliable array "back end," he would need I/O expertise both "on the wire" and at the operating system level. His next two hardware engineering recruits were Yi Ding and Tim McLeod, who filled those roles respectively.

Growing Software Engineering

In the early 1990s, Hewlett-Packard had assigned Alan Driscoll to lead the integration of the Veritas Storage Foundation with its product line. He had met Coz and been impressed by both the product and the people. Fast forward almost two decades to 2009. Unaware that Alan already knew Coz, a mutual acquaintance told him about an opportunity with a startup called Pure Storage. He was interested, in part because of the Coz connection, but also because the timing was fortuitous—with their son's graduation from college, Alan and his wife had recently become "empty nesters." Despite his having spent his entire career with established companies, his wife was able to persuade him to try the "Silicon Valley startup experience." In early 2010, he joined the company.

Cary Sandvig
"It's amazing what happens when you actually try!"

Alan soon became a frequent interviewer. He typically ended his interviews by explaining his three reasons for joining Pure Storage—the inevitability of solid-state storage (at the time, flash was not yet the clear winner), the advantages of a clean start (compared to an established storage vendor), and his confidence in the company's leaders. The "it was right for me; do it if it's right for you" tenor of his pitch helped candidates evaluate offers objectively.

Taher Vohra
"I didn't know exactly what OS76 planned, but I knew that if Coz was involved, it would be something significant."

Cary Sandvig had previously worked with Hayes on virtualization software for applications as diverse as medical treatments and counter-terrorism training for the military. The two had developed an architecture for asynchronous event-driven programming. Their company ran out of money and was acquired, and they went separate ways, but stayed in occasional contact.

Hayes contacted Cary, excited about a new storage project he was working on and asked if he'd be interested in joining. Cary's initial reaction was to wonder why he'd want to be part of a project in "the second most boring part of computing." Hayes refined his pitch and talked about "a high-performance metadata manager that happened to store bits." That sounded better, so Cary agreed to an interview.

A few conversations with Coz convinced him that flash storage could become viable in mainstream data centers. He joined, after being the first candidate to experience the

Roland Dreier
"I thought their plans were a little grandiose."

Neil Vachharajani
"While Alan Driscoll was interviewing me, someone wearing shorts and a t-shirt (who I assumed was the food delivery guy) stepped into the room and told us lunch was here. After lunch, I went back to the interview room, and the food delivery guy walked in! I was convinced this was a sign the interviews weren't going well until I realized that the interviewer was Coz.."

still-evolving interview process (page 54). Using ideas from their previous association, he and Hayes developed the asynchronous programming model for Purity//FA. Over time, Cary contributed to most components of the software before moving to the FlashBlade object store team in 2015.

In 2005, Taher Vohra had relocated from Pune (India) to Mountain View to help integrate his company's backup and online storage software, which had been developed in separated locations. Although he was an engineer, Taher had reported to Kix. He became intrigued by OS76 when Kix left to join Mike and Coz in the new venture.

Taher's extensive Solaris experience made him attractive to the company; in mid-2010 he interviewed and joined. His first assignment was to integrate SCSI target software with Purity//FA's Solaris underpinnings.

Roland Dreier was one of the first Doug Mohr (page 55) recruits. Doug contacted Roland around the time of his 40th birthday and described a fascinating opportunity with a company that had a "super-high hiring bar with a mandatory programming quiz." The challenge intrigued Roland, and although he was comfortably employed, he agreed to talk. His initial reaction was that the company's plans seemed quite grandiose, so he declined an offer. The company, especially Dietz, "wouldn't take no for an answer," and after further discussion, Roland was convinced. He joined in January 2011.

The nascent Purity//FA was based on OpenSolaris. Linux was being considered as an alternative, partly because of the moribund OpenSolaris community. The viability of OpenSolaris concerned Roland, so he pushed consistently for conversion to Linux. His first assignment was with the conversion team. The conversion was successful; beta array software was Linux-based. Roland became the FlashArray I/O expert, guiding other developers through the intricacies of SAS, SATA, Infiniband, Fibre Channel, and iSCSI.

Roland had previously known Bill Cerreta (page 153) and had helped introduce Bill to Pure Storage. Eventually he joined Bill's hardware team and his I/O expertise has helped guide the company's evolution to NVMe and NVMe-oF interconnects.

Neil Vachharajani had moved to the west coast after graduation from college to "become part of the startup ecosystem," but had joined a large company. In 2010, Doug Mohr approached him with "an interesting opportunity at a startup." Neil found Pure Storage attractive but felt obliged to consider other options as well. He identified a second possibility and began negotiations with both. Initially, he was somewhat skeptical of Pure Storage's late entrance in the flash storage arena. He found it difficult to believe that one of the giants would not emerge as leader of the "flash revolution." But the people he met—Coz, of course, but also Burr, Kix, and Dietz—convinced him of the potential for success, and he joined the company in time to contribute to the second alpha release. In time, he became a key contributor to most Purity//FA components. Today, he leads the company's advanced software development.

Mark McAuliffe
"A couple months after I joined Pure Storage, we celebrated an office expansion with a party. In front of a group, Doug asked me if I remembered the shuttle ride where we had first met. That piqued people's interest, so I told the story, after which Doug somewhat sheepishly admitted that when he asked my name on that bus, he had already figured out who I was from the conversation!"

Over the years, Mark McAuliffe had become accustomed to fending off electronic overtures from Doug Mohr, whom he had never met in person. One day in 2010, as he rode a shuttle to retrieve his car after servicing, a fellow rider struck up a conversation. One topic led to another, and the fellow finally asked his name. Upon learning it, he began to recite Mark's educational and work history, finally revealing that he was Doug Mohr, and knew Mark's history because of his recruiting attempts. They shared a laugh and went their separate ways.

But meeting Doug affected Mark. He began to wonder whether a startup might be an interesting change. When Doug next proposed an opportunity to him, he accepted an interview with Pure Storage. He was positively impressed with the company, as was the company with him. An offer was tendered immediately. After a brief hesitation, Mark accepted, and joined the engineering team in 2011.

Like others on the software team, Mark "learned by doing," developing his understanding of Purity//FA as he contributed to it. At first, he felt that his learning was piecemeal—he understood the pieces he worked on but lacked an overall picture of how the whole thing fit together. Finally, he took time to study the code intensively and the light dawned. Over time, he became the reigning expert in Purity//FA "databases"—the in-memory and persistent structures that the software uses to track the constantly changing locations of stored data and metadata. Although he works on advanced development projects today, he is still regarded as *the* Purity//FA database expert and is frequently consulted by new engineers.

Richard Hankins ("Rich") was another Doug Mohr recruit. Having spent most of his career in the research departments of large companies, he wanted to move into product development. When a project he had been working on was cancelled, he decided to consider other options.

At around that time he got Doug Mohr's semi-annual "how are things" call. Doug asked if he might be interested in a company called Pure Storage run by John Colgrove. Rich's

Richard Hankins ("Rich")

"On my first day, a guy with spiky hair stopped at my desk and gave me my passwords. Only later did I find out that it was co-founder John Hayes.
One day, I asked Joe Hasbani who made the coffee. Answer: 'We do.'
We all got together to set up desks for new hires.
It was, and is, very much an 'if it needs doing, do it' culture."

"Coz posed the usual problems in my interview. He looked so bored as I worked them that I was sure I had failed, but apparently I made the cut. In the early days, he would go home in the evening for dinner with his family, and return to the office at 8 or 9 p.m., when he would typically talk to people about any number of topics—from data compression to CPU performance to the best grilled cheese sandwich or hot chocolate to be found in the Bay Area. It took me a while to realize that this was part of his way of team building."
—**Rich Hankins**

initial response was, "Who's John Colgrove?" But he was intrigued by the idea of a company in its formative stage.

Doug had described the Pure Storage interview process as "quirky," but Rich recalls it as fun. Interviewing in the morning and receiving an offer that afternoon floored him, but out of an abundance of caution, he asked for time to consider it. A few days later, he met with Dietz ("the closer") and had lunch with some of the engineers. Within an hour, he sent an email accepting the offer.

Like all software engineers joining Pure Storage, Rich spent his first few weeks understanding Purity//FA. His first contribution was a backstop to the metadata consolidation mechanism to protect against corruption. In the lead-up to product shipment in 2012, he, like the rest of the team, was absorbed by bug fixing. His impression of the company's culture was continually reinforced by people's desire to "get it right"—when a significant bug was encountered, development would essentially cease until the root cause had been identified and the bug had been fixed.

The apex of bug fixing is rooting out and eliminating errors that cause data corruption, particularly of the sort that is only discovered long after it occurs. No storage company can survive a data corruption that escapes into its installed base; they must be identified and fixed before a product or upgrade ships to customers. Pure Storage quality assurance teams subject new hardware and code releases to extensive testing to make sure that the products store data accurately under all conceivable circumstances.

As the time for FlashArray general availability approached, Rich found himself increasingly analyzing data corruption bugs, to the point that he became known informally as the "corruption king." After four years on the Purity//FA team, during which he contributed to most areas of the software, he transferred to FlashBlade engineering, where he leads the team developing inter-array replication for the Purity//FB software that runs FlashBlade Systems.

In early 2011, Eric Seppanen was part of a Minneapolis-based team developing an SSD controller when a friend whom Doug Mohr had tried unsuccessfully to recruit made him aware of Pure Storage. There wasn't much public information about the company, so through a local professor of his acquaintance, Eric contacted Ethan Miller (page 11), who encouraged him to submit a resume. He was invited to Mountain View for an interview but there was a complication: with a baby due in a couple months, he and his wife had agreed to a moratorium on job changes. He accepted the invitation, expecting that in typical tech industry fashion, any further steps would take place over weeks or months. He was stunned when after a day of interviews, he returned to Minneapolis with an offer in hand.

The company, its people, and the technology were interesting, so Eric accepted with the proviso that he would work remotely until the baby had been born and was able to travel. The company agreed, and he began working on Linux kernel customization, participating in daily engineering standups (page 22) by email. On one occasion, he visited a site in Minneapolis to copy alpha system logs for transmission to Mountain View (obviously prior to the implementation of phonehome).

Eric Seppanen
"Other companies make the same kind of claims we do—'customer first,' 'five nines of availability,' and so forth. The difference I've found is that Pure Storage doesn't just articulate the claims; it really lives by them."

The baby didn't quite cooperate; delivery was two weeks late, but three weeks thereafter, Eric packed up his family and two cats and relocated to an apartment adjacent to the Castro Street office. The location proved to be fortuitous—he could make the 100-foot "commute" when he was needed at home and return quickly to the office, where everyone was working hard on beta systems that would shortly replace the alpha ones.

The engineering team was not satisfied with the devices available for beta system NVRAM. Some had poor performance, others were unreliable, and one did not even fit into the device carrier. A marginally satisfactory device was eventually identified, but the consensus was that the company would eventually have to find a better solution. That idea came to fruition with the NVMe-based dual-port NVRAM introduced with the FlashArray//M series, to which Eric became a principal contributor.

Reliability Really Matters

Working deep in the Linux kernel in the early days, Eric was frequently involved in chasing down and solving obscure operating system bugs that, while unlikely to be encountered in application servers, would be detrimental to the company's "six nines" availability goal. One particularly knotty case involved SSDs that would go offline and fail to return to service. The bug occurred infrequently, so the team tried to force it by repeatedly removing and reinserting device carriers and observing whether the software recognized the devices. During a month of non-stop removal-reinsertion cycles by engineers working in hour-long shifts in a chilly lab, the bug appeared about once an hour. Finally, its source was determined to be either the SAS HBA or the Linux kernel, but the drudgery of spending entire days in the lab was wearing. Evan Driscoll (page 65) and his eight-year-old son came to the rescue. They used a Lego kit to build "Yanky," a robot that removed and reinserted an SSD carrier in a storage shelf. Yanky was about as fast as an engineer, but it didn't get cold, didn't take breaks, and worked around the clock. With it, the team was able to isolate

The Yanky Robot in Action

"FlashArray is fast, recovers gracefully from hardware and software failures, and makes flash last a long time. Flash by itself isn't very reliable or long-lived, so a lot of clever software engineering went into solving all three of those problems simultaneously."
—**Eric Seppanen**

"I was skiing with my kids when I heard that we had caught a trace that might isolate a failure we had been chasing for months.
We left the hill and drove several hours straight to the data center with the test systems.
Security wouldn't let the kids come in with me, so they trashed the lobby while I collected the trace. It turned out to be the one that led to fixing the bug."
—**Pete Kirkpatrick**

Steve Hodgson
"I don't think I'd ever met anyone as confident as Coz."

the problem and develop a workaround, which Roland fed back to the Linux community.

Eric is quick to point out that the SSD recognition problem might never have been discovered, let alone remedied, were it not for the extremely rigorous automated testing regime that Evan had instituted. Not only is the number of tests large, and continually being augmented, but every failure is diagnosed to its root cause and remedied, even if it requires delaying product shipments or software updates.

Many failures have nothing to do with Pure Storage-developed hardware or software but they must still be diagnosed and remedied before products are shipped. A case in point occurred during FlashArray//MR2 development. Approximately once in 60 machine-days of operation, a system would fail in a way that strongly indicated a hardware fault. The team contacted the hardware manufacturer, who was skeptical, since its product was widely deployed with no apparent problems. Pure Storage devoted about 60 systems full-time to an attempt to reproduce the failure. There were almost daily occurrences, but a trace with enough detail to determine the root cause was elusive. Eventually a trace was obtained and a workaround devised, but the episode delayed FlashArray//MR2 availability by over three months. The company insisted on identifying and eliminating a rare component failure rather than shipping a product susceptible to it. The rigor of Pure Storage testing is a primary reason for its products' "six nines" of availability. High reliability gives the field the confidence to routinely recommend competitive *proof of concept* (PoC) trials that include device removals, cable pulls, and simulated controller failures to demonstrate the resiliency of the products relative to those of competitors.

In late 2011, Doug Mohr emailed Steve Hodgson, then working at a network company in the United Kingdom, about an opportunity with a small flash storage startup.[16] Steve ignored Doug's first contact, but he was eventually persuaded to visit Mountain View and meet with some of the company's key engineers. He found the people uniformly smart, but also

---

[16] To this day, Steve doesn't know how Doug found him.

companionable. He decided to join the company and relocate to the United States, resigned his then-current position and accepted the Pure Storage offer.

His company countered with an attractive proposal that included relocation to southern California and a work visa for his wife. He decided to accept the counter-offer and made the awkward call to Coz rescinding his acceptance. Coz was understandably disappointed, but rather than trying to persuade Steve to reconsider, he asked if he would meet with Mike Speiser before making a final decision. Steve agreed; Mike applied his full-court recruiting press, and the deal was closed. In late 2011, Steve joined the company.

Chris Golden

"Pure Storage is clearly no longer a startup, so why am I still here? It's simple. During my five plus years, I've grown apace with the company. In the early days, I could personally have a big impact on the product, but the product had a relatively minor impact on the industry. Today, our development teams are more structured, so my role is more about coordinating across the organization. My technical contributions aren't as deep, but the impact of efforts where I'm part of the team is much greater. For example, relatively few customers used our first snapshot capability. When ActiveCluster was introduced, however, over 200 arrays were using it within three months."

He arrived as hardware was being readied for release to selected beta sites. Getting the beta software ready involved lots of late hours, which for a while was fine with Steve, since his wife was still in the UK and he was living in a hotel. His dominant impression of the software team was one of passion—there were plenty of heated discussions among the engineers. On almost every issue, it seemed that everyone had an opinion and was willing to defend it. It convinced Steve he had made the right choice professionally. In his former position, passion for the job had been distinctly lacking.

At the same time, the work atmosphere was enjoyable. Everyone seemed capable of separating technical biases and opinions from personal interactions. After a protracted argument, participants were as likely as not to convene for an after-hours drink or meal. Home life was a bit more difficult in the beginning, but eventually, permanent resident ("green card") status made it possible for his wife to resume her career, which relieved most of the tension.

Over time, Steve contributed to most aspects of Purity//FA, including high availability, NDU, FlashRecover, and ActiveCluster™. Like most of the company's senior software engineers, he "did his time" with the escalations team. His deep knowledge of the software, both in overall perspective and in detail, led to his appointment as FlashArray Chief Architect in 2017.

Arrays Need More than the Core

In 2007, the startup for which Chris Golden worked was acquired by a network giant. Chris had enjoyed the small company atmosphere; over time he became less enchanted by the more bureaucratic large firm environment and decided to look for another startup opportunity.

His circle of friends included Pure Storage employee Joe Hasbani, from whom he learned about the company. Having experienced a successful startup, he appreciated the Pure Storage environment—its flexibility, its "do what needs to be done" attitude, its expectation of individual responsibility, and its recognition of accomplishment—all of which contrasted with the attitude at his large company.

Chris had interviewed with several startups in various stages but was impressed by Pure Storage for several reasons. First, the business model was solid—every data center needs storage, and storage needed a shot of technology adrenaline. Second, being young and unencumbered, he favored early-stage startups, and in 2011, Pure Storage was certainly in that category. Third, there was opportunity for professional development—the work involved big data, complex algorithms and data structures, and combined hardware and software. Fourth, he was drawn to the idea of a tangible product—one that could impart the satisfaction of creating something more significant than a web application or video game. Finally, the company's interview process convinced him that its people were the "cream of the cream of the crop"—the "A+" that Coz had described to Attorney Mark Tanoury (epigraph).

Chris joined in mid-2011 during the third alpha deployment. He was the first engineer with prior Python experience, which made him the obvious choice to develop what he describes as "non-core" array functionality. One of his early projects was *phonehome*—an array feature which evolved into CloudAssist, and later became the Pure1 data store. He developed the original FlashArray alert generator that warned of marginal and failure conditions, as well as an application for internal use called *Awesomeboard* that displayed performance data from installed arrays in real time.

Chris was a key contributor to the Purity//FA port from OpenSolaris to Linux. The port had run-of-the-mill aspects—installation packages and file location conventions differed—but came with two substantial benefits: Linux had a superior C++ language and vendors made driver software for new devices such as Fibre Channel and Ethernet interfaces available sooner.

Perhaps Chris's most important contribution was the Purity//FA snapshot technology. Hayes started him off with a prototype implementation. A long eight months later, a team led by Chris delivered snapshot-capability in a Purity//FA release based on Hayes' original code.

About eight months after the release shipped, Bob Wood (page 67) asked Chris to find out how many snapshots customers had taken. The phonehome logs indicated an embarrassingly small eight. Despite having requested the capability, customers were cautious and in addition, apparently wanted automated scheduling. When that was delivered (in the release that included FlashRecover replication), many more customers began to use snapshots.

The underpinnings of Purity//FA snapshots were also used to implement *SCSI eXtended COPY* (XCOPY) intra-array data replication. XCOPY had become important when VMware introduced its *vStorage API for Array Integration* (VAAI). Purity//FA support for

VAAI decreased bulk virtual desktop creation times from upwards of a half hour to two to three minutes, with the latter chiefly due to VMware limitations. User uptake was tremendous.

Getting Organized

By mid-2010, the software engineering team's growth demanded a more formal management structure, so a search for a manager was started. Evan Driscoll had previously managed both Hayes and Cary at other companies. When Cary contacted him in mid-2010 to ask if he would consider an engineering management opportunity with a young startup, he was intrigued, even though he was comfortable with his situation at the time.

Evan met with Coz, Mike, and the engineers. He was impressed, but as a veteran of several startups, he insisted on talking to the "product guy" about how the company proposed to turn the founders' ideas into money-making products. He met with Kix, who "had an answer for every question." After considering several other alternatives during the ensuing months, he joined OS76 as its first engineering director in late 2010.

Upon reporting for work, Evan observed that while the engineers were largely self-directed, the company lacked systematic quality assurance (QA). There was a build and test management system, but testing was not

Evan Driscoll
"At the time, the company clearly needed a QA lead more than an engineering director, so that's what I did first."

"Having worked at large companies, I was accustomed to frequent performance evaluations. After a few weeks at Pure Storage I got a little worried—I wasn't hearing any feedback from Evan, my manager at the time, so I confronted him.
He told me not to worry—if there were any issues, I'd be the second to know.
Eventually it dawned on me that the Pure Storage culture expects employees to be self-directed and self-evaluating."
—Rich Hankins

automated, and many failed tests received no root cause analysis and correction. Although he had no prior storage experience, Evan took over QA, learning the Jenkins build and test system as he went. He automated testing and instituted a policy of identifying every failure's root cause and fixing every bug.

He was also taken aback to discover that the software bug tracking mechanism was a hand-written table on a white board. Hayes asserted that the white board was adequate, at least for the moment, so Evan got him to agree that when the white board overflowed, a computerized bug-tracking system would be instituted. Tracking every failed test rather than just those that engineers considered significant quickly filled the white board. Evan led the implementation of a *Jira* issue tracking system which is still used today, by engineering, operations, and support.

He also observed that the company did not use its own product during development, which he felt should be embarrassing for a developer of storage systems. In short order

Dan Decasper

"The Pure Storage team was head and shoulders above all the others I had talked with."

he replaced the storage devices that stored the code base with an alpha array. The array was faster and more reliable than the devices it replaced, but Evan's real goal was to impress upon developers the importance of reliability not only in the final product, but at every stage of development. If a software load failed, development would halt in a highly visible way until the failure was remedied. The concept of using the system under development in the development infrastructure isn't new; it is widely practiced by computing technologists and is often referred to as "eating one's own dog food." In fact, the arrays that hold FlashArray and FlashBlade code during development are referred to internally as "dogfood servers."

As an experienced manager, Evan knew that he would occasionally have to make hard decisions and take unpleasant actions. As he became better acquainted with his team, he realized that there was one chronic non-performer. He negotiated a performance improvement plan with the person, and when the objectives were not met, performed the company's first involuntary termination, a procedure that has fortunately been exceedingly rare in the intervening years.

Evan saw himself as a team builder, occasionally at odds with Coz over sacrificing a short-term goal for a larger long-term objective. He helped develop a meritocratic engineering culture that demands excellence, and is characterized by honesty, open communication, direct conversations with individuals, and willingness to make difficult decisions and carry out difficult actions. He would take that culture with him when he became Vice President of FlashBlade engineering in 2015.

Expanding Engineering Management

At 25 engineers, the team was too large for Evan to manage directly, so in the fall of 2011, the company began a search for a second engineering director.

In early 2011, Doug Mohr had contacted Dan Decasper, then an executive with another startup, to assess his interest in Pure Storage. Dan demurred, but by late spring, he realized that his company was not progressing as expected, so he began to consider alternatives, both small and large. He asked Doug if the Pure Storage opportunity was still available, and was connected with Evan, followed by interviews with Dietz, Coz, Hayes, Kix, and Cary. Based on his prior experience, he was impressed by what he learned about the company— its market opportunity, its technology, its people, and especially its culture—so despite the position being a nominal come-down from his previous executive level ones, he accepted, and in late 2011 became the second engineering director.

Dan and Evan divided managerial responsibilities by creating a two-column list of projects in order of urgency. The most important went in the left column, the second most important in the right, and so forth. Dan took one column; Evan the other. This division was repeated several times in the early months, so project teams would occasionally find themselves reporting to a different director. With a small organization where everyone knew everyone else, projects transitioned smoothly. As engineering grew, a second management tier was created, first by promoting developer Marco Sanvido, and later by external recruiting that started with Vinay Perneti.

Over time, Dan gravitated toward usability and manageability projects, where he used his experience in cloud computing, user interface design, analytics, and containerization. He managed the CloudAssist team, and when it expanded to become Pure1 (page 187), he ran that team as well. When the company reorganized into business units in 2017, he became General Manager of the Pure1 business unit where his responsibilities today include product management and marketing as well as engineering.

Bob Wood

"*I was instantly impressed by Coz and Hayes, but it was over time that I came to appreciate how well they complemented each other. Hayes was the consummate idea man, while Coz, despite having been reluctant to hire engineers with storage backgrounds early on, kept us focused on the goal of revolutionizing the storage industry, both in terms of its products and in the way it conducted business.*"

A "Head Honcho" for Engineering

As early as 2010, the company realized that the engineering organization would have to grow to realize its ambitious plans. The leaders envisioned a senior engineering manager who would both manage the existing organization and build up the anticipated new product family teams.

In 2010, a mutual friend introduced Dietz to Bob Wood. Bob was a veteran of several startups, some acquired by large companies, an environment he did not enjoy. Dietz was favorably impressed, and recruited aggressively, but Bob was enmeshed in an acquisition at the time and was reluctant to make a change. They met occasionally over the course of nearly a year, during which Bob was watching Pure Storage closely. He felt that if a startup had a clearly identifiable market, its main challenge would be execution, an area in which he felt comfortable as an engineer. He believed that if

"*In addition to when to ship FlashArray, we had to decide on **what** to ship, which we called the 'minimum viable product,' or MVP.*
About three months prior to our planned ship date, some team members proposed adding a big new feature to our MVP.
Now I appreciate creativity and innovation as much as the next guy, but this just wasn't going to fly. It added to the risk, and we had already put the board of directors off once.
My counter-suggestion was that if the team really had the energy to develop an additional feature, they should invest it in hardening the MVP we'd agreed on or even in shipping a bit earlier.
We shipped the original MVP."
—**Bob Wood**

the market was obvious and he felt he could personally sell the concept, then a startup was probably viable. He though the Pure Storage "10 times the performance at a tenth the power and space for today's cost" proposition would easily sell to data centers.

If a startup seemed viable, Bob's next criterion was ability to execute, both by translating its vision into products and by bringing them to market. Coz and Hayes persuaded him

"The field organization was insisting that FlashArray needed synchronous replication, so engineering built a prototype and successfully demonstrated it to a very visible customer.

The demo convinced everyone that synchronous replication was feasible but set wildly optimistic expectations for how long it would take to ship it. There was tremendous pressure on the team to deliver.

From that experience I learned that as a manager I had to resist temptation to commit to unrealistic expectations from outside my team."

—**Ganesh Ramanarayanan**

that their ideas were technically sound; Kix and Dietz convinced him that the time was right for a disruption in data storage. Helped by advice from another friend who was familiar with the storage startup scene, in late 2011 he joined the company as its Vice President of Engineering.

When Bob joined, Evan had been engineering director for over a year, recently joined by Dan. Three senior managers for a staff of about 40 may have seemed like "managerial overkill," but the company anticipated that the organization would soon be much larger, with pieces breaking off to embark on new projects. When that time came, resiliency would be needed to maintain the culture and avoid crippling the original organization.

Practicing hands-on management, Bob began by learning how to triage failed FlashArray load tests and prioritize them for resolution. In effect, he was the company's de facto triager-in-chief for several months. In his main capacity, he assessed the state of FlashArray development. He concluded that the estimate given to the board of FA-320 general availability by the end of 2011 was unrealistic. His own estimate was that the product would only be shippable some six months later. With some trepidation, he made his first appearance before the board to announce the delay. His credibility was significantly enhanced when the FA-320 shipped within a month of his revised estimate.

Hard Decisions

During his years with Pure Storage, Bob was faced with difficult decisions and decisions involving existential risk for the company. Having survived his first difficult decision— delaying the release of the FA-320 and communicating the delay to the board—his next challenge was the growth dilemma. On the one hand, the company's ambitious product plans were going to require a rapid increase in the number of skilled engineers. On the other, however, the company had yet to ship its first product. He observed that engineers were spending a lot of time interviewing and not so much on engineering. In early 2012, he reluctantly declared a moratorium on hiring, realizing that he might be sacrificing future product momentum, but understanding that the company absolutely had to build credibility with the market and its board of directors by shipping a product on schedule. In retrospect, that was the right decision, but it was unpopular at the time.

In its early days, the company's intellectual property (IP) was almost completely in software. The FA-320 was built from off-the-shelf servers, enclosure chassis, storage network adapters, and above all, consumer-grade SSDs. It was generally understood, however, that eventually it would develop its own hardware, both to increase the in-house value in its products and to free itself from the inherent constraints of off-the-shelf components. The questions were when and what.

Bob and others had tried to attract Bill Cerreta (page 153) to create a hardware design program, but Bill had joined another company. In mid-2013, however, Bill re-engaged, saying he would like to reconsider, but there was a hitch: it would have to be a "package deal." He would join if the company would also hire Pete Kirkpatrick (page 154). When the team met with Pete, his skills and energy were obvious, so Bob agreed to the package.

"I would describe Bob's management style as the opposite of micro-management. People sometimes see him as 'hands-off,' but if you observe carefully, you will see that he puts structure in place that enables his subordinates to perform with little or no interference. He knows what's going on at all times."
—**Christopher Zang**

When Bill and Pete joined, the question of whether to base a FA-400 family follow-on on off-the-shelf hardware or on an in-house design was open. Bill and Pete favored in-house development and made a convincing case for it. They presented a long-term plan leading up to what eventually became the FlashArray//X family, which created a dilemma for Bob. On the one hand were two talented hardware developers and the need to develop hardware at some point. On the other hand, designing a complete system with mainboards, interconnects, storage devices, NVRAMs, and packaging that would last for several generations looked insanely ambitious for a tiny team in a company that had never done such a thing before.

Bob compromised. The company would develop its own integrated controllers and packaging but would use off-the-shelf SSDs and device enclosures. Development of storage devices would be deferred. The immediate result was the FlashArray//M series, a new generation of controllers with the same SSDs and storage shelves as previous FlashArray models. This minimized time-to-market (FlashArray//M series was delivered in slightly under two years), and mitigated risk—had device development been included, no fallback would have been possible.[17]

To Split or Not to Split?

Hayes had articulated the idea of an ultra-scalable high-throughput system, and the company was generally receptive. The question was when to embark upon a completely new development program. Bob felt that there were two main considerations. On the one hand, good business sense suggests that a technology company aspiring to sector leadership should introduce a new major product as soon as the buzz from the previous one starts to fade. On the other hand, the engineering organization must be capable of starting a major new activity without adversely affecting its primary mission. Hayes had been a prime mover for FlashArray. How would removing him from that team to lead a separate project affect that product's progress?

At the time, the FlashArray team was nearing the end of FA-420 development. Hayes' creativity was less in demand than the persistence to work the final details and get the product shipped. A new project would be a more valuable use of Hayes' talent. Moreover, Bob believed in "creating voids." Removing Hayes from the FlashArray team would

---

[17] Engineering did start to gain experience with NVMe. The FlashArray//M NVRAMs were designed in-house and used NVMe to connect to controllers' PCIe buses.

leave a void, but the team was resilient, so the major effect would be to create growth opportunities for other members.

A compromise was reached. Hayes became the FlashBlade architect, but the initial team would be recruited from outside. To attract talent, the company leaders conceived the *startup-within-a-startup* concept (page 239). The new team would have complete freedom, with no obligation to use any FlashArray technology unless it chose to do so. The project would have financial backing from Pure Storage, which had the beginnings of a revenue stream. The concept worked, and FlashBlade was a success. Early team members were recruited from outside the company. When the project achieved "critical mass," management began to encourage movement between the two major projects to cross-fertilize both technology and engineering culture.

Easing Off

After five years of frenetic pace, Bob was ready to alter his "work-life balance." He was discussing alternative roles with Dietz when Dietz himself decided to step down. The new CEO, Charlie Giancarlo, felt that the company had reached a stage where it needed a more business-oriented organization, so after discussion with the executive team and the board of directors, a new business unit structure was put in place. Consolidating hardware engineering, making the FlashArray and FlashBlade organizations separate business units, and consolidating the Pure1 organization gave Bob the freedom to adopt a less demanding role with minor impact on engineering. He became a senior advisor on engineering matters, and spends much of his time mentoring promising managers to prepare them for more senior positions.

In This Chapter...

The value of technology breakthroughs can be so great that others are encouraged to try to "get a piece of the action," by claiming that a breakthrough is actually their invention or by attacking the innovator in other ways. Legal representation is a necessity for a startup right from the beginning. Dietz and Corporate Counsel Joe FitzGerald agreed that the Pure Storage legal department would be an active business partner rather than a "last stop before contract." Active partnership took several forms—simplification of contracts and other documents, early engagement in the sales process, participation in formulating the company's business practices, and importantly, aggressive protection of the company's intellectual property.

Not by Engineers Alone

Engineers are vital, but a technology company needs other types of expertise as well. "Keeping the lights on" takes finance, human resources, facilities, and IT support. When production starts, operations must be built up. Just as in engineering, individuals in these areas have different skills and interests. Some prefer an early-stage startup; others are more comfortable in a more mature environment.

For example, a new company's finance director must establish banking relationships, create a chart of accounts, and closely manage the limited supply of startup capital. As a company grows and the number of its shareholders increases, financial reporting must become more rigorous. The IPO is a tipping point.

Joe FitzGerald ("Fitz")
"I told Dietz I would join if I could build a legal department that was integral to the business—an enabler for sales rather than a last resort."

Generally accepted accounting practices (GAAP) must be followed, and a reporting history developed. A chief financial officer is a must for an IPO; someone with credibility in the financial community is a definite plus. Occasionally, a startup's finance director will evolve into the CFO role; more often, that individual will move to another startup and the company will recruit an experienced CFO prior to going public.

Legally Speaking

By 2012, Pure Storage was selling products at an increasing rate. Every sale entailed a contract negotiation, which Dietz and Burr were handling for the most part. But with expansion came needs to deal with the legalities of doing business in different states and nations, to handle employment issues, to protect trademarks, and other legal issues.

Moreover, competitors were starting to notice the upstart, and were responding with legal as well as technical challenges. A law firm had been engaged to help, but Dietz and Burr were being overwhelmed. The company needed its own legal counsel. Its technology emphasis had to be augmented by an equal emphasis on business practices.

After leaving his previous employer, Coz had stayed in contact with Joe FitzGerald ("Fitz") there. Coz and Mike had worked extensively with Fitz to create robust IP programs, so as a favor to Coz, shortly after OS76 opened for business, Fitz had delivered a "lunch and learn" lecture on IP for the team.

Michele Ardizzone

"After 5+ years at Pure Storage, I still love coming to work and engaging with my smart and fun colleagues. Pure has been the best career move in my professional life, and I am proud to call myself a Puritan!"

Todd Wheeler

"When Fitz first approached me, I had little desire to join yet another startup. After meeting the team, though, I realized that Pure Storage had the rare combination of elements required to hit escape velocity and become a long-term leader—the right product, strategy, leadership and culture."

During occasional conversations, Fitz would sometimes ask Coz when his new company would need a general counsel. During a call in early 2013 he told Coz of his plan to leave his employer. Soon thereafter, a lunch invitation made him think that "something might be up." At the lunch, Coz suggested that Fitz meet the rest of the OS76 executive team, which he subsequently did. Like most recruitment targets, he was impressed, particularly by Dietz's insistence on "doing the right thing" for customers, for partners, for employees, and ultimately, for the company. Their discussions revolved around Fitz's desire to build a legal department that was integral to the business rather than a standoffish organization that others would engage with only when absolutely necessary. Dietz agreed enthusiastically. They struck a deal and Fitz became the company's first in-house counsel.

"Integral to the Business"

Fitz knew exactly what he meant by "integral to the business." He felt that a legal department should enable sales proactively rather than being the "last stop before contract." In the early days, when nearly every sale was predicated on an evaluation (PoC), delivering arrays to the field for evaluation was a top priority. Fitz's mantra became "immediate response." To demonstrate it he set about streamlining templates for the documents with which the company conducted its daily business— NDAs, evaluation agreements, end user agreements (EUAs), and so forth. With the help of IP specialist Michele Ardizzone, whom he hired as a Senior Legal Manager in the summer of 2013, business agreements were drastically shortened, largely by replacing tedious legalese with straightforward English. The resulting documents were so easy to read and understand that customers became comfortable executing them without involving their own counsel. Agreements were made directly available to account executives via the salesforce.com tool they used to manage prospect and customer interactions, making them effectively "self-service." Today, customer engagements with no exceptional terms and conditions routinely occur without legal department involvement, even those conducted through partners, as are virtually all Pure Storage sales.

As the company's business expanded, it had to operate under the laws and regulations of many domestic and international jurisdictions. The next addition to Fitz's legal team was attorney Todd Wheeler, whose previous stints with a well-known Silicon Valley law firm and with the legal department of another storage startup had made him skilled in IPO practices, in the wide variety of commercial and corporate legal issues common in fast-moving startups, and in the complexities of multi-jurisdictional corporate law.

Under Fitz, the legal team continues to be integral to the Pure Storage business. It has participated materially in formulating business practices like *Free Every Three* migration-free ("data in place") upgrades, *ForeverFlash*, and *Flat and Fair* maintenance pricing, all parts of the Evergreen™ model by which the company has revolutionized data center storage to the benefit of users.

Michael Moore
"Pure Storage considers the innovation and creativity of its engineers to be key ingredients in its success. The company makes every effort to protect its IP, as well as to respect that of other parties, and expects the same from them."

Intellectual Property: A Tech Company's "Crown Jewels"

IP is the *raison d'être* of most new technology companies. Protecting their IP is key to their survival. This is especially true with software, where patents often encompass broad concepts that combine elements of genuine invention with well-known concepts. In the storage sector, large, wealthy incumbents often try to suppress new entrants that might threaten their dominance by looking for ways in which a new entrant's technology might be accused of patent infringement. Even if they are ultimately unsuccessful, incumbents' "deep pockets" can embroil financially weaker startups in litigation that saps their resources and ability to innovate.

Thus, like it or not, a new company needs to secure its IP and defend itself against attacks from the more established players in its field. It must take steps to protect and defend its innovations immediately upon opening for business.

Defending IP requires both domain knowledge and an appreciation of the technical and legal nuances that are often encountered; there is no substitute for experience in the field. Outside counsel can be helpful in preparing and prosecuting patents, and Pure Storage did engage an outside firm in its early days. But to really identify, understand, and protect a company's IP, dedicated in-house IP counsel supported by the executive staff must work closely with engineers to develop and nurture a culture of innovation. In addition to its general counsel, a young company must also acquire in-house legal expertise in IP matters.

As competitors attempted to prevent Pure Storage from acquiring a market foothold by attacking the validity of its IP, the company needed specialists to defend it. Fitz reached out to former colleague Michael Moore, an attorney with extensive experience in both digital technology[18] and IP defense. In early 2016, Michael joined the company, where he rapidly built a team of professionals, including licensing expert Joe Kucera, with extensive

[18] Michael is a named inventor on 10 issued U.S. patents.

The TechShots Icon
"Just as with engineering project names, internal branding makes it easier to communicate—it helps with conversations and planning. The name 'TechShots' gave us a handy way to talk about our field education sessions. It became common to hear things like 'Should we do a TechShot on ...?', 'Where can I find the TechShot about ...?', and 'When's the next TechShots?'"
—**Larry Touchette**

experience in both the law and the business of IP. His team expanded and promoted the company's patenting process to bolster its defensive posture.

IP protection starts with making it easy for engineers to document their inventions for internal review. Proposed inventions should be vetted by experts with broad and deep technical perspectives so that patenting effort is focused on innovations that are both meaningful and defensible.

Ideally, the membership of the team that vets patent proposals should change slowly over time, so that most members share a common context most of the time. Pure Storage formed a standing *Patent Review Board* (PRB) to review proposed inventions against a backdrop of both domain knowledge and awareness of the company's already-existing IP. Michael's legal team converts proposals approved by the PRB into patent applications and shepherds them through domestic and international patenting processes.

IP protection isn't just about patents. As a company gains recognition in the market, its brand becomes a valuable piece of IP that distinguishes it from competitors. Brand is expressed in a few key ways—the company name, logos, Internet presence, collateral, and trademarks and slogans. Would-be competitors sometimes mimic the "look" of a successful company hoping to capitalize on its success.

As Pure Storage gained market presence, Michael's IP team acquired additional responsibilities. It became responsible for protecting the brand by trademarking key identifiers, warning off encroachers, and ensuring that employees used branding elements properly. In addition, it trained employees on handling other parties' IP appropriately, respecting the IP rights of others and conforming to relevant laws and regulations in its business dealings with customers, partners, and suppliers.

In This Chapter…

You can't just build it; you have to sell it. A startup has to start planning its sales strategy well in advance of having products to sell. That requires as special kind of sales leader, one who can buy into the vision and represent it convincingly to prospective customers and to candidate account executives during recruitment. It also requires a special kind of account executive—one who can maintain prospect interest until there is a product to deliver. This was, and continues to be, reflected in a sales recruiting process every bit as rigorous as the engineering one.

There's a fork close to the beginning of the road: a company has to decide whether it's going to sell directly to customers or through *channel partners*. Partners multiply a company's own sales force, but they must be recruited carefully and treated well. Above all, there should never be competition between partners and a company's own sales force.

Sales isn't only about being face to face with prospects. In the "back room," there are orders to track, compensation rules to determine, events to arrange, and subscriptions to manage.

Finally, when a technology is new, prospects have to be convinced. Account executives need the support of technically knowledgeable system engineers (SEs). SEs, in turn, have to be kept up to date on rapidly changing technology. Timely training is a must, as are "experts of last resort," called *solution architects* by Pure Storage.

Building a Sales Organization

A company needs a sales team to sell its products. Selling is market-specific: selling consumer products is quite different from selling to data centers.

Building a sales team is a three-fold challenge for a new company. It must choose its basic sales model, begin selling at the right time, and engage the right number and type of AEs at each stage of development.

As in other professions, technology AEs have different skills and interests. Some are more suitable for a company's early stages; others operate better in an established organization. Analogies to prospectors, hunters, miners, and farmers are sometimes made.

Pure Storage faced a barrier to market entry in that the enterprise data storage space is both mature and conservative and is dominated by a few large players. New entrants appear from time to time, but historically they have either failed to gain a foothold or have been quickly absorbed by incumbents. Moreover, the company proposed a radically new technology—affordable all-flash storage arrays capable of reducing data at production I/O speeds—to a user community not noted for taking risks.

Getting Ready to Sell

The company did have advantages. The founders, key employees, and the board of directors were "known quantities" among technology producers and users. Their contacts opened doors, and unearthed users who would be willing to test prototype arrays with real applications and data. The first *alpha* systems delivered to (non-paying) "customers" had limited capabilities. Stored data was RAID-protected, but full high availability had not been implemented. Volume configurations and storage network addresses were pre-configured by engineering prior to delivery and were not alterable by users. Their objective was to demonstrate that all-flash storage could be both faster than comparable offerings and affordable, the latter achieved by a combination of consumer-grade SSDs and data reduction.

The alpha systems delivered upwards of 100,000 *Input-Output Operations per Second* (IOPS). This convinced the company that despite a *minimum viable product* (MVP) for general availability and revenue being a year or more in the future, it was time to develop a sales force that could begin exposing the technology and its benefits to potential customers, so that when the product *was* ready to ship, early adopters would be ready for it.

Recruiting AEs for a company with no products is a challenge. Candidates must be motivated by a vision of the future rather than by "next quarter's numbers." They must be able to impart the vision to prospects who cannot buy immediately and to maintain their enthusiasm until they can.

Selling When There's Nothing to Sell

Selling prior to product availability is essentially technical—there's no installed base to reference, no public benchmarks to build credibility, no track record of reliability, and no working models to show off. Worse, as product development takes its inevitable twists and turns, dates become unreliable, and tomorrow's claims and commitments may differ from today's.

Sales activity at this stage inherently involves engineering. Nothing establishes credibility with prospects better than an engineer discussing the details of what the team is actually developing. While not always noted for diplomacy, experienced engineers can generally counter virtually any technical challenge from a potential user.

Some AEs hesitate to involve developers directly with prospects, because they cannot control the trajectory of conversation. Engineers are prone to "tell it like it is," without regard for the nuances of prospect relationships. But when trying to build credibility for downstream relationships without a product to sell or deliver, engineering engagement is often needed. Thus, AEs must be comfortable working with engineers and with putting them face-to-face with prospects.

To an AE, success is making a sale. When the product isn't ready yet, success must be measured differently. Prior to FA-320 general availability, Pure Storage sales was in the business of creating enthusiasm for a vision in which flash-based storage arrays would eventually supplant disk-based ones entirely. A successful engagement was one in which the prospect internalized the vision to the extent of showing interest in testing early versions of the technology, the *beta systems*.

Finding Burr

Matt Burr was on an extended vacation from technology in Asia when an email from former colleague Kix suggested that something of possible interest to him was happening in Mountain View. On his return to the United States, Kix introduced him to the Pure Storage vision of leading a transition of enterprise storage from magnetic disks to the flash era and arranged conversations with other former colleagues of his—Coz and Mike.

A veteran of both early-stage startups and established technology companies, Burr knew what to look for and saw it in Pure Storage:

A PLAUSIBLE VISION
Flash was clearly superior to magnetic disks as a storage medium.

A MEANINGFUL ADDRESSABLE MARKET
Every data center has storage; the *total addressable market* (TAM) is in the tens, if not hundreds of billions of dollars annually.

A Realistic Execution Plan

Consumer-grade flash and data reduction would make the technology price-competitive with disk.

A Team That Could Pull it Off

Coz and Hayes supplied architectural expertise; Michael and Ko, hardware expertise and industry contacts; Kix, Mike, and the board of directors expertise in marketing, business, and company-building.

Matt Burr
"I could see that this flash thing was going to be big—maybe as big as the change from bare metal to virtual machines. I wanted in!"

The company knew what to look for as well. From prior acquaintance, several leadership team members knew Burr to be someone who would value the opportunity to be part of a fundamental change in managing and processing digital data.

Technical by nature, Burr saw a strong parallel between computing's transition from "bare metal" to virtual machines and the magnetic-disk-to-flash evolution that Pure Storage predicted. He was excited by the idea of persuading skeptical users that the vision would become a reality and convincing them to prepare for it. As he recalls, "It was a challenge to convince people that with data reduction, storing a terabyte of data would require a lot less than a terabyte of flash."

Burr joined the company nearly a year before the FA-320 came to market. During that time, he evangelized the coming flash revolution, developed leads among early adopters (with considerable support from engineering), made new contacts, and reinforced old ones in anticipation of eventually expanding the company's sales force.

The First Account Executives

To recruit a sales force, Burr had to find individuals who were essentially like himself. Alpha trials were in progress, but the company had yet to ship its first product for revenue. For sales to "hit the ground running" when production arrays *did* ship, AEs and SEs had to be hired and trained in the important geographies. Burr needed individuals who could believe in the flash revolution and evangelize it to potential customers. And he had to team them up with technically savvy and curious SEs who would dig in and figure out how things worked or were eventually going to. At the same time, his recruits had to be motivated by long-term relationship building rather than the "quick win." Such individuals can be difficult to find because sales professionals are essentially motivated by "winning"—usually defined as meeting or exceeding quotas. But with nothing to sell yet, winning meant achieving whatever results the company needed.

The company knew that its technology worked, but prior to product availability there was no assurance that users would accept and adopt it. Moreover, there would inevitably be "rough edges" to smooth. Thus, the most important result that sales could deliver in the near term was convincing users to install and use beta systems in PoCs and provide feedback, good or bad.

**William Danz ("Billy")
and the Danzie**

"Shortly after joining Pure Storage in 2012 from a larger competitor with a reputation for being 'buttoned up,' Billy participated in a web conference with a partner from his home office near Chicago. The day was stiflingly hot, and his air conditioner had malfunctioned, so Billy was shirtless….which was fine until he turned his computer's video camera on by mistake, to the amusement of the partner, who commented on the obvious cultural difference between Pure Storage and his previous employer.

*Following the Dietz dictum of sharing bad news, Billy reported the faux pas to his manager, who contrived to create the **Danzie**—a trophy awarded annually to the account executive reporting the most embarrassing incident."*

—Sot

In 2011, storage companies were enjoying considerable market success with novel technologies like thin provisioning that allowed users to oversubscribe physical storage capacity and deduplication that eliminated redundancy in backup data sets. A few innovative startups were acquired by industry giants, creating a candidate pool for Burr— AEs with experience at selling unfamiliar concepts to skeptical users, but who were happier in the agile small company environment than in the womb of a corporate behemoth. In the early years, some of Pure Storage's most successful AEs and SEs were veterans of acquired startups.

Multiplying the Sales Force with Partners

Some technology vendors sell directly to users; others sell wholly or partly through *channel partners*— resellers, some of whom simply resell the vendor's products, whereas others add value in the form of system integration, application implementation, on-going service, or a combination. Some vendors adopt a dual sales strategy, selling both directly and through partners, but this inevitably put them in competition with their partners, so usually only the largest vendors can sustain that model. Smaller ones typically choose one path or the other.

Burr was well aware of the multiplier effect channel partners could have. If a Pure Storage AE is able to garner half the attention of a partner's 10 sales representatives, there are effectively six people selling the company's products. The sacrifice in *margin points* (the percentage of each sale's revenue paid to the partner) is small compared to the extended sales reach.

To emphasize the importance of partnering, the company designs its sales compensation plans so that there is no incentive for its AEs to sell directly to end users. Instead, the incentive is to identify the most appropriate partner for each situation. Sales opportunities identified and nurtured by Pure Storage are typically fulfilled by a partner introduced by the sales team.[19] This mode of operation invites reciprocity from partners—they will often introduce the company to opportunities that its own sales teams might not have unearthed.

Selling through partners has an ethos all its own. Because most resellers represent

---

[19] Dietz asserts that the company has never done a deal without compensating a partner.

multiple vendors' products, including directly competitive ones, there is a constant struggle for partner attention share. Fundamentally, partners want to make money. Vendors typically compete for attention with higher margins, but there is also a customer satisfaction dimension. A vendor whose products are difficult to sell, complex to install and maintain, or otherwise problematic after deployment, may offer higher margins, but the sales and service costs may cause a partner to prefer others. A Pure Storage account team's role is to ensure that partners propose the correct products and that the customer remains satisfied after deployment. A long-time Pure Storage reseller expresses an ideal relationship thus: "I could get more points elsewhere, but I can rely on Pure Storage and its products, which is better for my business in the long run."

Selling to giant multinationals differs from selling to smaller ones and to governments. Channel partners fall into similar categories that require different treatment. Some operate globally; others cover limited geographic regions. Global resellers tend to concentrate on very large customers; regional ones typically deal with a broader range of smaller ones. Some resellers only offer IT infrastructure products and services; others provide virtualization, security, application implementation, and other services.

In 2011, Pure Storage had no installed base to demonstrate credibility, so while forward-thinking large organizations might experiment with PoCs, they were unlikely to use the company's products for mission-critical applications. Fortunately, there are many more small organizations than large ones, so it made sense to concentrate on what were eventually called *commercial accounts*, and to recruit partners with strong relationships in that space.

Vendors who sell through partners typically employ *channel account managers* (CAMs), each working with one or more partners to maximize the attention devoted to the vendor's products. Some partner agreements go so far as to prohibit dealing with the vendor's competitors. As a new entrant, Pure Storage lacked the market strength to enforce such provisions. More importantly, they run counter to the company's culture with its fundamental "customer first" value. From the beginning, the company treated its channel partners differently in two important respects.

First, it takes skill to persuade long-time customers that what was state-of-the-art several years ago is no longer at the cutting edge, and that they should consider new technologies. Many sales representatives are more comfortable selling the next iteration of what they have sold in the past. Pure Storage CAMs would cultivate close relationships with partner representatives who understood and could articulate the FlashArray value proposition of high performance, low space and power consumption, and above all, ease of use. Such individuals were present in many organizations, large and small. Pure Storage dealt with both, but in the early days, it was primarily representatives from smaller partners who could open customers' eyes to a new way of managing their data and "move the needle" in the storage market.

Once a CAM had established a relationship with a partner representative, each opportunity would be pursued jointly with a Pure Storage account team, to deal with the business and technical aspects of the sale.

Michael Sotnick ("Sot")

"Having sold software for most of my career, I thought the Pure Storage folks were crazy to take on the expense and risk of developing hardware.
I'm glad they made me a believer. It's a privilege to be part of this winning team."

The second respect in which Pure Storage partner relationships are unique is the company's explicit recognition that it is the partner who offers solutions. Pure Storage products are important, but they are only part of an overall solution that delivers a beneficial business outcome to the customer.

The corollary is recognition that Pure Storage products may not be appropriate for every situation. Rather than trying to maximize near-term revenue by aggressively pursuing every potential sale, Pure Storage teams will recommend backing away when the fit isn't right. The goal is a long-term relationship with both partner and customer.

Effective salespeople instinctively want to "own the engagement"—to control how the customer is approached, what products and services are offered, and the terms of delivery, installation, and configuration. Some experienced AEs who join Pure Storage must adjust to the company's *channel-led* (CLED) sales model.

Building Out the Partner Organization

By late 2015, the company had a track record. FlashArray had lived up to promises of performance, reliability, and ease of use. The company had demonstrated consistently outstanding service and a strong commitment to customer satisfaction. It was time to shift sales emphasis toward partners who dealt with larger customers with whom longer-term relationships could be forged. It was time to increase executive attention to the channel.

Michael Sotnick had formerly worked with Coz, Kix, Burr, and Hat. He had stayed in contact with them, so in 2014 he was well aware of the company's rapid rise. But with his background in software sales, he wondered why they had taken on the challenges inherent in designing computing hardware.

The company leaders thought Michael would be an ideal head for the growing partner organization, so they continued to pursue him. Eventually, he became convinced of the market opportunity, and that both the technology and the business approach were special. He joined the Pure Storage in early 2015 as Vice President of Partners and Alliances. He managed the partner organization expansion and recruitment. For the first time in his career, he embraced his lifelong personal nickname *Sot*, by which he is known throughout the company.

In 2017, the company redoubled efforts to increase its presence in the Fortune 1000 by dividing its sales force into "enterprise" and "commercial" segments and by emphasizing partnerships with managed service providers and federal systems integrators. Sales recruiting was specifically focused on enterprise account teams, and SEs and support engineers were dedicated to named enterprise accounts. The company intensified its recruiting of CAMs capable of developing relationships with the largest global resellers and system integrators, many of which have long-standing vendor relationships with its competitors. Global resellers are attractive because large IT users often accord them "approved vendor" status, which makes it easier for them to introduce a new vendor's products.

The philosophy that its products are components of overall solutions delivered by partners gives global integrators confidence that when they propose a solution that includes Pure Storage products, they will be appropriately advised before the sale and competently supported afterward.

Selling Is More than Sales Calls

Selling technology, especially at the high-touch enterprise level, isn't just about "feet on the street." There are leads to track, contacts to manage, pricing and discount schedules to establish, orders to process, customer credit to verify, training courses to create, and a host of other details. And these all have to be updated promptly as products and business practices evolve. A sales department needs a chief of staff to keep the house in order while AEs and SEs are out selling.

A company starting out has no policies or procedures for conducting business; they must be created "from scratch." Tools like salesforce.com help organize a company's sales processes, but tools only make it easier to manage policies once they exist. The department that creates and manages sales processes is usually called *Sales Operations*. A well-organized Sales Operations department is a boon to AEs; a badly designed one can be a barrier to success.

Tyson Gerhold
"In the early days, every new employee was introduced at the Friday all-hands meetings.
After Dietz introduced me, Hayes approached to welcome me and asked, 'What is sales ops anyway?'
It impressed me that our technologist co-founder had no idea what sales ops was but trusted his colleagues to have recognized a need and satisfied it."

"One of our biggest web traffic days in the early years was due to John Hayes' wife posting a blog about him and Pure Storage on her knitting website (which has quite a large following!). We got quite a few hits from really unusual 'prospects' that day, including one from Hayes' mother with whom one of our SDRs actually tried to set up a meeting!"
—**Mollie Golden**

In the summer of 2011, Bill Danz (page 82) and Jeff LaCamera posed a question to former colleague Tyson Gerhold over dinner in Mountain View: "Are you interested in changing the data storage landscape forever?" The three felt that a common former employer had had a similar impact. The prospect of a repeat was enticing to Tyson, so an extended conversation with Burr followed the dinner. Tyson was excited by the prospect of creating a Sales Operations department from the ground up. But with no products yet available, investing in sales operations was premature, so Burr encouraged interest but counseled patience for the moment.

The FA-320 began shipping to customers in May 2012. Tyson joined in August to build Sales Operations, which he describes as, "…supporting AEs with systems and procedures

Mollie Golden

"I remember Dietz telling me that he wanted Inside Sales to get to the point of only dealing with inbound leads. I laughed out loud because I don't know of any storage company that works like that, especially a startup. He said, 'We'll be getting faxed orders for deals we didn't even know about.' While that seemed pretty far-fetched, my response was, 'But until then you're going to need people to make outbound calls. That's what I do, so sign me up!'"

that maximize their time with prospects and minimize the time they spend on admistrivia." The company was already using salesforce.com; Tyson engaged consultants to extend it to track leads and orders, report wins and losses, and manage forecasts and quotas.

As Pure Storage emerged from "stealth mode" with products to sell, its sales department needed more organization. The company needed ways to set sales quotas fairly, determine sales compensation, and track progress against goals. It needed consistent practices for dealing with channel partners. Because it expected to derive significant revenue from ongoing service contracts, it needed a system to encourage customers to renew contracts when they expired. Finally, competition and rapid change often require incentives that encourage the promotion of specific products to customers and prospects. These, plus Inside Sales, became responsibilities of Sales Operations.

Inside Sales

Recommended by a colleague who had previously joined the company, Mollie Golden had come to Pure Storage in mid-2011 as the company's first inside sales representative, charged with hiring and managing an Inside Sales team. The team would ensure that "leads"—advertisement responses, trade show and conference contacts, feedback from "lunch-and-learn" sessions, and so forth—led to conversations with AEs who would assess their validity and interest level and follow up accordingly.

That was the plan. But the FA-320 was delayed, which delayed hiring the inside sales team. In the interim, Mollie herself arranged hundreds of contacts with prospects, most of which required NDAs because although the company had "launched," it had yet to announce a product. She notes that many of those initial meetings with prospects led to them becoming customers and remaining so today.

Shortly after FA-320 general availability, Mollie started hiring and training *Sales Development Representatives* (SDRs) for her team. She recalls proudly that of the first three SDRs hired, two have since become AEs and the third manages the company's Executive Briefing Center (EBC). She managed Inside Sales for about 2½ years, hiring most of the SDRs personally, including the first in EMEA. During her tenure, she also hired the company's first Inside Sales Representative tasked with making sales rather than just arranging contacts between prospects and AEs.

Like all Pure Storage departments, the Inside Sales team made work fun. They ran weekly contests with prizes for SDRs. Once, Mollie persuaded Hat to help the team with outbound calls for an afternoon. She created a "Wall of Wins" to display the logos of customers with whom Inside Sales had initiated contact, explicitly recognizing successes to which her team directly contributed.

In 2016, Hat asked Mollie to capitalize on her experience by transitioning to manage training and enablement for the entire sales force, which she did successfully. She then became Hat's chief of staff, until she took family leave in late 2018.

Keeping Customers in the Fold

Janie O'Toole had worked comfortably with Dietz for several years at a previous startup. When in 2012 he invited her to become Pure Storage's office manager, she accepted enthusiastically. She anticipated that Dietz would recreate the light-hearted atmosphere of their previous startup. The scooters, nerf dart guns, "Wizard of Coz"-themed Halloween parties, and so forth that Dietz encouraged relieved the stress of developing an entirely new product and simultaneously promoting it to early adopters.

When Janie had been with the company for about a year, the first service contracts fell due for renewal. Having had prior experience with that, she volunteered to handle renewals. For nearly two years, she was a "renewals team of one," contacting customers with expiring service contracts and working with AEs to coordinate renewals with pending upgrades and new sales. Making renewals easy for customers was an important goal. Service contracts were often adjusted ("co-termed") to minimize the number of times per year a customer would have to deal with renewals.

With the company's rapid evolution, Sales Operations was a constant whirl. Janie always seemed to be dealing with new programs (*Love Your Storage, Evergreen,* etc.), new service partners, and new types of licenses. The shy [by her own assertion] Janie presented the intricacies of co-terming at SKO events. She has since filled various other roles in the company. Today, she evangelizes The Orange by co-hosting the online series "Outside the Box"[20] with Solutions Architect Cody Hosterman (page 203).

Janie O'Toole
"In 2014 we were still banging the big brass gong to announce every sale. One day I went to the convention center early to hear a SKO keynote. I took my two sons, planning to hear the keynote and then drive them to school. During the keynote, a huge contract renewal closed. Burr heard about it, and at the end of the keynote, brought my boys up on stage and had them bang the gong!
That's the kind of 'family' feeling the culture that Dietz and Coz created encourages."

Paying the Piper

Sales compensation and quotas are tricky subjects. On the one hand, a company has

---

[20] Outside the Box sessions can be found at www.youtube.com.

Mike Chudzik, John Mansperger, Charlie Yu
"The territory Jeff LaCamera and I covered was about 20 states. We traveled a lot, but rarely made overnight trips, except when the prospect was in Texas. Both Jeff and I were based in the Chicago area, but we almost always flew from different airports on different airlines. Amazingly, we never missed a meeting.
All three early teams had big territories to cover, but Jeff and I achieved a couple of unique distinctions. Not only were we responsible for the company's first-ever purchase order, but our first 11 deals were in 11 different states!"—**Mike Chudzik**

financial expectations from sales. On the other hand, territory managers have the best view of what is achievable with the resources they have. Sales Operations is the "honest broker" in quota negotiations, primarily charged with avoiding "feast and famine" conditions in which sales teams that perform equally well are over or under-compensated.

Tracking sales against plans is also dynamic. It fell to Sales Operations to ensure that plans were being met and to keep company leaders aware of exceptional situations that might affect performance. A case in point occurred when a major flood hit a metropolitan area important to Pure Storage revenue. With much of the area shut down for weeks, it was clear that sales quotas could not be met. After first doing what it could to ensure the safety and well-being of affected employees and their families, quotas were adjusted so that affected AEs and SEs would have viable incomes despite the drastic slowdown in business activity.

Sales programs are endemic in technology. Companies create programs to clear inventory at product end-of-life, to launch new products, to counter competitive threats, and so forth. The Sales Operations role is to consolidate field requests and create programs that fulfill overall company needs rather than those of a single geography or market sector. Once a program is justified, Sales Operations works with marketing and sales management to set its parameters and streamlines implementation to minimize the incremental work for sales teams.

Training, Motivating, and Rewarding

Initially, Pure Storage did not offer formal sales training. Tyson started with "open office hours"—group teleconferences in which newly hired AEs and SEs could learn from each other. As the sales organization grew, training was formalized—Mollie moved from

Inside Sales to manage quarterly training in Mountain View, enlisting subject matter experts from around the company to present and discuss their areas of expertise. Today, the company still runs quarterly new hire training sessions, but training now has funding and a dedicated staff.

Finally, Sales Operations managed motivational activities—semi-annual SKO events, and the annual "Club" week-long trip to a resort for the highest-performing individual. Both combine motivation with education. While some "what's new" and refresher information is presented, the events are partly recreational, with opportunities to relax and get to know colleagues from around the world before starting work for the next period. One purpose of these events is to create "lore"—anecdotes that could be retold over time to help bond a geographically dispersed field organization into a cohesive team.

When a company sells internationally, it must deal in multiple currencies. Nearly all buyers prefer to issue purchase orders in local currency. In its early days, Pure Storage was not equipped for that, so international AEs were forced to quote in dollars, forcing the currency fluctuation risk on the customer. Customers

John Mansperger
"In 2014, I went to Asia to help out with a PoC in a VDI application at a casino. The PoC was going fine, but the prospect was hard to convince. I suggested to their IT manager that he migrate a few executives' virtual desktop images back to the older storage.

He did that, and within a few minutes was inundated with phone calls asking why things had suddenly gotten so slow.

When he explained that the PoC was over, the executives' immediate response was, 'Bring it back! Our systems are slowww.'"

understandably disliked that, so as soon it could, Sales Operations created a system to allow international customers to buy in their preferred currencies, effectively assuming any currency fluctuation risk (usually covered by taking positions in other currencies). Today, the company can sell in the currency of any jurisdiction in which it does business.

The Technical Side of Selling

As technically oriented as they may be, AEs in a new company promoting a radical technology to a conservative market need on-the-ground technical support. As the company grows and leads multiply, taking engineers away from their "day jobs" to support sales ceases to be viable. As soon as they have a product to sell, AEs need SEs, whose primary responsibility is supporting sales. SEs need domain expertise, but in addition, must be able to gain the confidence of potential customers' technical staffs, assist with installation and troubleshooting, and maintain long-term customer relationships. Pure Storage paired each AE with a dedicated SE.

The SE candidate pool was obvious. The complexity of incumbent vendors' products had given birth to a sizable cadre of individuals who had installation, administration, and upgrade experience with other storage vendors' products. FlashArray ease of use would make the product easy to sell for individuals experienced in guiding customers

Mike Chudzik
"On a vacation trip in 2012, I stopped in Mountain View so my family could see the office. We dressed my 15-year-old son in Pure regalia, marched into the office unannounced during an all-hands meeting, and banged the gong three times on behalf of the central region.
My AE, Jeff LaCamera, and I had just received THREE purchase orders in one week!"

through complex installations, configurations, "fork lift" upgrades, and data migrations. The challenge was to convince those individuals to join a company whose product, while exciting "on paper," was unproven in the market. Coz suggested that when interviewing candidates, Burr's team look for curiosity about how things work "under the covers" as well as general storage expertise.

Early SE recruits fulfilled an additional purpose. They became a de facto quality assurance and human engineering team. Engineering considered their product reliable, functional, and usable. But to represent it to (sometimes skeptical) prospects, SEs had to *believe* in it. The best way to make them believers was "hands-on" experience, in the lab if possible, but in PoC evaluations with potential customers if necessary.

Experience is not a one-way street. Just as SEs need to understand the product thoroughly, engineering needs to be sensitive and responsive to their technical feedback. SEs spend their working lives in production data centers. They understand users' needs and how well products meet them. They are a valuable source of the sort of feedback that enhances customer satisfaction:

- Is it possible to misconfigure or mis-cable the hardware?
- Is it as easy as it could be to integrate the array into a data center?
- Are administrative commands intuitive and easy to memorize?
- Are utilization and performance reports accurate and timely?
- Are hardware and software upgrades disruptive?

Engineering recognized the importance of SE feedback, so from the beginning, SEs were encouraged to become intimately familiar with the product through headquarters visits during which they would interact with developers and support engineers. Many early sales resulted from PoC trials, some of which were competitive "bake-offs." SEs had had ample opportunity to observe competitors' products in action and were quite vocal in informing engineering about what worked well and what made it difficult for them to sell against competition.

The first three SEs, Mike Chudzik, John Mansperger, and Charlie Yu, supported central, western, and eastern United States respectively. The sizes of the territories and the number of opportunities didn't allow for specialization. They helped their AEs make sales, did installations, supported customers after the sale, and relayed user feedback to engineering.

John Mansperger, a senior SE at a Bay Area storage firm, had been "bitten by the flash bug," which his employer was resisting because it didn't fit their legacy model well. Senior SE talent was difficult to come by, so John was continually fending off recruiters, usually acting on behalf of large storage vendors. But in August 2011 when a friend made him aware of Pure Storage he was intrigued and called Burr to request an interview. The interviewers were so convincing that, as John puts it, "my entire job search took three days."

He was thrown into the proverbial "deep end of the pool." His first assignment was to help staff the company's booth at an Oracle OpenWorld conference. Interest was high, but the company learned from the experience that Database Administrators (DBAs) were usually not involved with storage acquisition; other trade shows yielded more concrete results.

The early AE-SE teams did everything—sales, installations, and service. Surprisingly, most early customers were not technology companies. For example, early orders came from a dairy company, a trucking firm, a brewery, a casino, a university, a municipality, and so forth. The SEs not only learned a lot about FlashArray; they learned about the workings of a wide swath of American business.

Because his "office" was at company headquarters, John became the main conduit through which engineering received beta tester and early customer feedback. He reported the sales teams' experiences in

Chadd Kenney ("DoubleD")
"I picked up the FlashArray for my first installation at the office and delivered it in my car. I installed it in the customer's rack, but initialized both controllers as primary, so of course Purity//FA wouldn't start. I spent about four hours trying to fix it myself before admitting defeat and calling support. Ben Casey walked me through the corrective procedure. Even though the installation took longer than the typical one hour, the customer fell in love with the product from first use. That's when I realized we were onto something big."

the daily "standups" (page 21) throughout the first year of FA-320 shipments. Engineering learned about customers' experiences with their product immediately and unfiltered. As the company grew and product management became more formal, customer feedback grew more organized. The goal was to evolve products gradually by adding relatively small numbers of key features that would be of interest to most of the addressable market.

Mike Chudzik had been working in the Chicago area as an SE for a backup vendor when it was acquired by a larger company. As often happens, the acquisition changed the culture, and by 2011, Mike was considering other opportunities in the storage sector. At the time, there was no shortage of flash-related startups, some enjoying a bit of success in the market. As he looked more closely, however, it appeared that all of them were grafting flash onto storage architectures designed for disks—except Pure Storage, a company that his colleague Jeff LaCamera, had asked him to look into. Pure Storage's stated objective of using a wholly new architecture to deliver the performance, reliability, and environmental advantages of flash at the price of disk interested him so much that he submitted his own resume immediately. He was invited to Mountain View for interviews, which included somewhat daunting sessions with Coz, who asked him to "whiteboard something you're comfortable with," and with Hayes, who asked him to help solve an engineering problem. He passed the test, and joined the company in October, 2011, along with Jeff LaCamera. As is common in technology sales, the two just continued their long-standing sales-SE partnership.

"In the early days, we had virtually no SE documentation or tools.
Once, during a Purity//FA upgrade, which I completed while a passenger in a moving car, I was worried that I might have done something wrong or left out some steps.
I searched our wiki for upgrade instructions—nothing!
At my hotel that evening, I laboriously typed in the sequence of commands I had used and circulated it to my fellow SEs. After quite a bit of refinement, we finally had a Purity//FA upgrade guide.
That's one example of how over time we developed 'tools of the trade' for our SEs."
—**Chadd Kenney**

In 2012, the company made a concerted effort to recruit Chadd Kenney, a field CTO in a large storage vendor's Bay Area office. Chadd agreed to a round of meetings but anticipated more of a learning experience than serious interviews. The round convinced him that (a) he had a lot to learn about flash as an enterprise storage technology, and (b) there might be more to this startup than he had anticipated. Whereas his then-employer's apparent philosophy was "complexity = sophistication," Coz had argued that true sophistication lay in simplicity. He had also slyly suggested that as a Bay Area native, Chadd owed it to himself to have the "startup experience."

Somewhat to his own surprise, he came away from the conversations thinking that he wanted to be part of the company. He was convinced it would have a powerful impact on the storage sector. In the summer of 2012, he joined as a SE,[21] and in his own words, "went from being the smartest guy in the room to being the dumbest." He spent his first few weeks on the job absorbing information—flash memory technology from Michael Cornwell, the Purity//FA architecture and design from the software developers, the practicalities of off-the-shelf hardware from Ko's team.

Early in Chadd's tenure, Burr asked him to prepare a whiteboard talk on Pure Storage's relevance to enterprise storage for delivery to the sales organization and executive team. He had three weeks to prepare. As the "new guy," he was understandably nervous. He rehearsed multiple times in front of his wife and family, asking them after each rehearsal what his three main messages had been, and restructuring the talk if they weren't the three he had intended.

The talk he created became something of a company standard—in one form or another, SEs used it to introduce the company to new prospects, executives used it to explain Pure Storage to the press, and trainers used it as an overview of the company for new AEs and SEs. It started by introducing the growing performance disparity between storage and other parts of IT, and observed that were it not for cost, flash would be a potential solution. Next, it showed that a combination of consumer-grade flash and data reduction could make flash storage affordable. That led up to concluding with the four FlashArray themes: I/O performance, reliability, space and power efficiency, and ease of use.

Due to geographic separation and being extremely busy, Charlie, Mike, John, and Chadd were "independent missionaries" as Chadd puts it. The four met at the company's first SKO event (page 44) and came to the realization that they weren't delivering consistent messages to prospects. They began to develop a consistent line of technical messaging, along with an interviewing process for SE candidates, who by then were being hired at an increasing rate.

---

[21] Later to be known throughout the company as Chief Flash Geek.

In the company's early days, competition was predominantly on product features, and less about customer relationships and long-term *total cost of ownership* (TCO). SEs were key to almost every sale, and they had to be well-grounded in storage fundamentals to deconstruct competitors' arguments and had to function semi-autonomously without a lot of sales support infrastructure. Large competitors typically had thousands of pages of SE documentation. Pure Storage had none.

The company had only a few significant competitors; SEs had to understand their products, be aware of their selling points, and be prepared to rebut their arguments and present FlashArray in a positive light relative to them.

Not every SE hired had knowledge about every competitor, so the "independent missionary" attitude gave way to an informal "everyone helps everyone else" network of email lists and Slack channels, reinforced by an online knowledge base.

Larry Touchette
"Thin provisioning is not a new concept per se, but what's new with FlashArray is that all volumes are always thin provisioned.
Many customers had never used thin provisioning, so few SEs had ever sold the idea.
Similarly, FlashRecover asynchronous replication was unique in preserving data reduction and thin provisioning in replicas, which was another difficult concept to explain simply."

The value of any network increases with the number of nodes. As the number of SEs grew, so did the importance of communication. Messages starting with *"IHAC…"* (I have a customer…) or *"Sorry for the blast,…"* became common as SEs encountered situations new to them and sought advice from any colleague who might have experience.

SEs with prior experience with competitors' products also helped leaven the company's outbound messaging. Described by one observer as "the most cynical people in the company," when exposed to new messaging prior to release, they would often recommend "toning it down" to make it more credible to potential customers.

Taking Technical Sales Up a Level

As the company's installed base grew, the user community gradually gave credibility to the SEs' performance, reliability, and ease of use messages. Selling emphasis shifted from technology to more global value propositions. A favorite tactic was to ask a prospect's CIO or IT manager to (a) list the top initiatives for the coming period, and (b) estimate the percentage of budget devoted to them as compared to the percentage spent on maintaining infrastructure. The SE would follow up by demonstrating how FlashArray ease of use could shift budget allocation from infrastructure toward achieving organizational goals. To reinforce the argument, the SEs developed their own interactive TCO tools that allowed prospects to estimate costs like floor space, power and cooling, and storage administration, and illustrated how FlashArray would reduce them. With the SEs' competitive knowledge, Lou Lydiksen's detailed performance information and benchmarking advice (page 96) to

TechShots Introducer

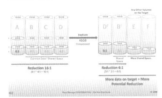

Sample Graphic

Session Trailer

reinforce their veracity, and the quantitative financial advantages provided by TCO tools, technical selling became convincing, and even irresistible.

Keeping the Techies Technical

Each Purity//FA release and each FlashArray product generation introduced new capabilities. Some, like snapshots, were conceptually familiar. Others, like thin provisioning, extended familiar concepts. Still others, like always-on data reduction, were unique to Pure Storage products. FlashArray capabilities were constantly expanding, but in order to present new features and product models to prospects and customers effectively, SEs had to understand them and the technology behind them in depth.

There was also a growing need for product management to regularly share information with the field—to keep SEs up-to-date with upcoming developments (what could be predicted and what to avoid predicting), and to expose them directly to the engineering and support teams.

Larry Touchette joined Pure Storage in the fall of 2014 as the company's first Technical Marketing Manager, assigned to communicate the increasing body of FlashArray technical information to the SE corps concisely, actionably, and in a timely fashion. Documentation in the familiar "whitepaper" format was not a solution—it took too long to produce, was time-consuming to absorb, and most importantly, did not provide for instant feedback and clarification.

He proposed to create a series of ad hoc gatherings of marketing, engineering, and product management, in which a technical marketing host would establish a context, engineers would describe new products or features, and a product manager would provide roadmap details and articulate a value proposition. The information would be conveyed in hour-long webcasts accessible by all company employees and recorded for post-event viewing. The webcast format kept the sessions focused, but also allowed for questions and feedback from the SEs who would be selling the new product or feature.

To establish a common thread for what might otherwise have been viewed as unconnected events at random times, Larry branded the sessions *TechShots*. Each session was a few "shots" of technical information that could be delivered in a short time and absorbed after the event.[22] Each session's content was unique, but the webcasts used a common template with a bottle motif. Sessions were introduced with an image of a full

---

[22] His father's hobby of distilling barrel-aged whiskey had no influence whatsoever on the name.

bottle (Pure Storage branded, naturally) beside a glass. The motif was repeated for each topic with the bottle slightly emptier, until the session ended showing an empty bottle.

The goal of TechShots was field enablement—to give SEs the knowledge and confidence to sell the ever-expanding feature sets of Pure Storage products. They relied heavily on graphical imagery; significant effort was devoted to preparing slides that illustrated sometimes complex technical concepts in ways that could be grasped in an hour or less. After the webcasts, TechShots slide decks were published internally so SEs could adapt the material for use in their own presentations. This had the beneficial side effects of saving SE time and encouraging people to use common imagery to illustrate common concepts. It created an overall impression of well-integrated technology thoroughly understood by the field.

Radha Manga
"We emphasize experience over numbers. Even in 2018, with $1B in annual revenue, Pure Storage had only 11 solution architects."

TechShots often included information about upcoming features and products, typically delivered by product managers, and always accompanied by admonitions not to oversell or sell "futures." Product managers would also articulate the business value of new features and products to help SEs correlate products and features with user requirements and explain them in ways that would be compelling to prospects and customers.

As FlashArray was deployed in more diverse environments, customer success depended increasingly on using features appropriately. Larry often included support and escalations engineers in TechShots to explain best practices—the "do's and don'ts" of using products in various configurations and application contexts.

Building Application Expertise

In the early days of FlashArray availability, the challenge for SEs was to convince potential customers that the technology was real. Prospects tended to be early adopters, accustomed to integrating new technology with their environments. As FlashArray acceptance grew, however, prospects tended to be less concerned about the technology per se; the challenge shifted from "does this thing work?" to "how does it fit into my application environment?"

Most of the company's SEs had had some prior storage experience with one or more major operating system and application platforms, and there was considerable "helping out" across geographic lines. But informal mutual support did not scale well. The company needed "go-to" persons versed in the major FlashArray deployment environments. Kix recognized the need early, and had recruited Ravi Venkat (page 33) in 2012 to provide corporate-level virtualization expertise. Ravi was followed by database expert Charles ("Chas") Dye, who documented techniques for getting the most out of FlashArray with Oracle databases.

Lou Lydiksen

"A Pure Storage FlashArray is not just a storage array. It is a Data-Reducing Storage Array. Thus, when testing its performance, you should use realistic data streams that are simultaneously compressible and dedupable [sic]."

Organizing Solution Architecture

As FlashArray usage expanded into more environments, the company realized that solution architecture needed a formal organization. In 2014, they recruited Radha Manga to expand and manage the solution architecture team. Radha had two immediate questions to answer: (a) which environments needed technical expertise most urgently, and (b) what would be the ideal solution architect profile.

Most arrays were being used for virtual computing, databases, and Microsoft servers, so those were the most urgent needs for application expertise. Kix had recruited Ravi, Chas, and later, Robert Barker (page 215) for expertise in those spaces. Radha's brief was to acquire expertise in additional applications as they became popular with FlashArray users.

Performance Is a Solution, Too

An important part of the FlashArray value proposition is consistently high I/O performance. As market presence increased, competitors began to challenge its performance claims. Prospects would require Pure Storage to participate in competitive "bake-offs," using benchmark software to compare FlashArray to competitors' products. While benchmarks are of dubious value for predicting application performance, many users insist on them, so the company had to participate in order to sell.

Flash device overprovisioning and translation make benchmarking much subtler than it is for magnetic disk-based systems. For example, a "fresh out of box" all-flash array might provide excellent write performance until its SSDs fill, at which point they reclaim space occupied by overwritten data, which typically reduces write performance substantially.

I/O performance has a strong impact on sales and on customer satisfaction after the sale, so marketing asked for a narrative explaining why PoCs with actual applications and data were more predictive than artificial benchmarks and help for SEs in structuring impartial benchmarks for competing all-flash arrays when benchmarking was unavoidable.

In mid-2013, a former colleague made Lou Lydiksen, then a performance specialist for a large storage vendor, aware of Pure Storage. At the time, Lou was comfortable in his position, but upon studying public information about Pure Storage, he was impressed by the technology, the company's leaders, and the market opportunity. He was excited by its promise; in his words, "It was the company I had wanted my previous employer to become."

He joined Pure Storage as its first performance engineer in the fall of 2013. He began by setting up a lab specifically for performance analysis and worked with developers to measure and understand FlashArray performance under a wide variety of I/O loads.

Eventually Lou moved to the Solution Architecture team, where he worked with I/O performance experts throughout the industry to adapt existing public benchmarks and develop load profiles that would treat all-flash arrays impartially, regardless of internal architecture. While doing this, he wrote occasionally for public consumption and extensively for the internal SE audience about the inherent inadequacies of synthetic benchmarks and the rationale for the load profiles he had developed for impartial benchmarking based on Oracle's *vdbench* software for situations in which benchmarking was unavoidable.

The Profile of a Solution Architect

Radha saw solution architecture as having three main components. First, architects are the company's quasi-official technical representatives for their areas of expertise, so strong domain expertise is a must. Second, architects are gatherers of user requirements. To do so, they must interact frequently with customers and prospects, both individually and in groups. Third, they are developers and distributors of demonstrations of effective Pure Storage products use in their domains. To be effective, solution architects must communicate effectively with strategic prospects, the SE community, and the general public.

In This Chapter…

A new company that aspires to be a global leader has to "go global" at some point. There are hosts of challenges—gaining recognition outside one's own country, identifying and hiring a team that can get a business going thousands of miles from headquarters, and not least, cultural differences between US headquarters and other regions of the world, as well as country-to-country differences.

Fairly early, countries in EMEA became aware of Pure Storage and its value proposition. Country-to-country differences existed but were secondary to finding the right team of "prospectors" who could act independently, but in concert with the company's culture, goals, and strategies. Asia was different. Differences in the business culture from country to country are profound. Coupled with the distances involved and the language barriers, a more country-by-country approach was needed.

Finally, there's luck. In the midst of an escalation at a "make or break" customer in Japan, Pure Storage discovered that one of the engineers involved spoke Japanese, despite having not a shred of Japanese background. That went a long way toward overcoming cultural barriers, and was instrumental in an eventual successful resolution.

Going International

Europe, Middle East and Africa (EMEA)

In 2012, with interest in FlashArray growing throughout the world, it was time to establish an international presence. The company started informal recruitment focused on Europe.

At around the same time, Lee Angel, Fred Lherault, and Joao Silva, who had all become believers in flash while at a storage company that had been absorbed by a larger one, were interested in pursuing more entrepreneurial situations, and had reached out to flash-oriented storage companies, including Pure Storage. Dietz had extended an invitation to them to visit its Mountain View headquarters and size up the operation.

On a trip to London, Dietz met with the trio. Lee and Fred were "all-in," but Joao was hesitant, unsure that Pure Storage was his best option. In a marathon pub session, Dietz persuaded him that it was, and in November 2012, the three became the Pure Storage EMEA operation.

They started work before offices had been rented. There were no partners or customers, and the only product was the FA-320.

Their first task was to recruit partners in EMEA. Partner companies tended to be somewhat skeptical; at the time several flash and hybrid array startups were clamoring for attention and it was difficult to differentiate Pure Storage from the herd.

While Joao built relationships with partners who knew and trusted the trio from past experience, Lee and Fred were placing arrays in their labs for testing.

Fred Lherault
1st EMEA Employee (by 2 hours)
"Joao gave early EMEA team members 'Ninja' nicknames reflecting their skills, behaviors or achievements. Some were quite colorful—Ninja Batman, Ninja Machete, and so forth. But he resisted giving himself one, so the team dubbed him Ninja Teflon, 'because nothing sticks!'"

Joao Silva
"My motto is 'sell more faster.' Before we could rent office space, we had to create a UK subsidiary, so our 'office' was my living room. Pretty quickly, we relocated to the kitchen, though, because that's where the coffee machine was."

Lee Angel
2ⁿᵈ EMEA Employee (by 2 hours)
"About a month after we joined, Pure Storage was invited to purchase a seat at a London event where awards for best vendor, product, and so forth were given based on channel partner votes. We accepted, despite having no partners as yet, and despite voting having already closed.
At the event, I encountered another flash-based array vendor with a story similar to ours. They had eight people manning an exhibit table, and I remember wondering whether I had joined the right company.
How wrong I was! That other vendor was soon acquired by an industry behemoth, and its products were at end of life by mid-2015."

A few partners became convinced that FlashArray lived up to its billing and gradually introduced the Pure Storage team to selected customers. The team pursued opportunities, as Fred puts it, "with a maniacal focus," to make sales, but more importantly, to demonstrate the value of working with Pure Storage to the partners.

Data center storage buyers are a skeptical lot. As had been the case in the United States, many EMEA prospects flatly did not believe the company's claims of FlashArray performance, resiliency, and ease of use. The team had to resort to PoC trials in nearly every case. The first success was with a Norwegian energy company, followed by a British user with database performance shortcomings that were about to be compounded by an upcoming *virtual desktop infrastructure* (VDI) project. Joao convinced them to cancel an already-placed order with a competing vendor (That's salesmanship!) and try FlashArray. With classic British reserve, the competitor's representative called the cancellation "highly irregular."

The trial was successful beyond anyone's expectations, and the deal was closed in early 2013, only a few months after the team was formed, with the help of Dietz, who was visiting the UK on other business at the time. The customer went on to become an enthusiastic advocate of FlashArray and Pure Storage, as did the partner, who has since become a presenter at the company's worldwide SKO events.

Momentum built, success followed success, and the EMEA team was off and running. As the business grew, more local representation was needed. 2013 saw the opening of offices in The Netherlands and Germany. France and Italy followed in 2014. Today, the Pure Storage EMEA organization is nearly 400 strong, with offices from Russia to South Africa. In 2018, the region surpassed the milestone goal of a half billion dollars in lifetime sales.

Asia-Pacific and Japan (APJ)

Michael Alp had led channel sales for one of the largest storage companies and successfully created a storage-oriented business in the *Asia-Pacific and Japan* (APJ) region. In 2012, Hat recruited him to create an APJ sales organization for Pure Storage.

When Ko (page 54) joined Pure Storage as its first Director of Hardware, Michael Cornwell shifted his focus to field activities. For a time, he did business development, operating, as he describes it, as "Burr's SE," with most of his attention devoted to nurturing international business. With the arrival of the EMEA team, Michael's concentration shifted entirely to developing a Pure Storage presence in Asia.

Tokyo Electron Device Limited (TED), at the time a subsidiary of a larger company, maintains a presence in Silicon Valley to research new technologies and evaluate them for the Japanese market. When Pure Storage launched, TED immediately expressed interest in its upcoming product, and assigned a representative to build a relationship with the company. The representative wanted to know everything—he met the founders and executives, visited the engineering operation, and toured the early production site. After eight-months of the companies getting to know each other, in early 2013 TED became the company's first Asian distributor. Part of the impetus for Pure Storage to partner with TED was its scope of operation. It not only resold products, it operated a customer call center and was equipped to repair and replace hardware—an important consideration for a small company nearly half a world away.

True to its culture, once Pure Storage engaged with TED, it took an open approach, treating their representative almost as an employee. He participated in company functions, kept aware of company developments related to Asia, and was even asked to interview prospective Japanese employees. This differed from TED's relationships with other US companies, which tended to maintain more conventional vendor-distributor relationships.

"In 2013, I installed FA-320s for a customer in three remote colos where Pure Storage had no partners or local presence. One of them was on Malta! That customer has since expanded into several more colos around the world.
Pure Storage has grown as well—our support now covers all their locations except Malta.
After multiple (non-disruptive) upgrades, today their arrays are //M50R2 models.
That pretty much says it all about FlashArray simplicity and resiliency. By the way, we also have two customers in Iceland, also with no local support or partner presence."
—**Lee Angel**

"Blending into the local business cultures is really important to success in Asia. For example, in the US, our executive closers routinely wore bright orange socks to important customer meetings. In Japan, however, Shima-san explained that orange socks made the wearer look ridiculous, so that bit of Pure Storage pop culture never made it across the Pacific."
—**Michael Cornwell**

The company's original plan for the Asia-Pacific region was to concentrate on Japan and Australia—the former because of the market size, the latter because of its readiness to embrace technology and cultural affinity with the west. When Hat (page 49) arrived on the scene, he advocated a more broad-based approach, but it was difficult to recruit and staff in countries with different cultures, vendor expectations, and business practices. Moreover, in several countries, channel partners capable of promotion and support as well as selling proved difficult to find. In the early years, concentration on Japan and Australia remained heavy.

In the spring of 2014, Michael relocated to Singapore, joining Michael Alp to accelerate development of the Pure Storage Asian business, with his first task being recruiting local teams in the target countries. In doing business in Asia, conforming to local cultural expectations is far more important than it is in EMEA and North America. Michael's recruiting challenge was finding AE and SE teams who could meld their country's culture with the Pure Storage one—who could integrate the company with the local IT business environment while still retaining its identity. As Michael explains, "We had to find in-country leaders with a sense of what about Pure Storage could be adapted to local

Yoshiharu Shima
"In 2013, I was getting bored with the storage company I worked for. I was interested in the Pure Storage technologies, so a colleague and I approached Tyson Gerhold, whom we knew, and asked him to introduce us to the company's executives. The introduction turned into a total of seven interviews, I was most impressed with Coz, because even then he was thinking about how to preserve the company culture as we grew."

cultural norms and what wouldn't work." For example, the branded t-shirts that are almost ubiquitous at US trade shows and conferences are a non-starter in most Asian countries, whereas the [expensive] branded fans that are popular giveaways in Japan or the seasonal moon pies exchanged in China would be lost on most Americans.

A more significant cultural difference in some parts of Asia was the emphasis placed on price as opposed to value. Pure Storage had never positioned itself as low-price leader; it was more committed to delivering the greatest value to its customers. That attitude worked well in some countries—Japan, Australia, Korea, Singapore—and less well in others such as China and India, where low price was typically the most important purchase criterion. Emphasis on value was another reason for choosing the countries in which to lead the company's launch in Asia and the western Pacific.

As Michael's role morphed from business development to helping to manage the company's presence throughout the APJ region, he hired sales and SE teams in the target countries, starting with Yoshiharu Shima and Hideki Yamara in Japan, and Nigel Peach, Boris Jirgens, and Philip Nass in Australia-New Zealand.

There's a difference between being capable of adapting Pure Storage practices to a country and understanding those practices well enough to do so. As APJ's leader, Michael felt that part of his responsibility was to help inculcate both the company's culture and a sense of how to deal with typically more outspoken Americans in the usually more reticent Asians. He would accompany them on visits to headquarters, making introductions, bridging gaps in understanding, and helping make them comfortable in the Silicon Valley environment outside the office.

As in EMEA, selling in APJ was complicated by the need to deal in different currencies. In EMEA, the company initially accepted the conversion risk; later it developed hedge positions in major currencies. That option wasn't practical for Asia. Instead, Asian business was generally developed in two tiers, with Pure Storage selling to a country or area distributor, such as TED in Japan, and the distributor selling to local resellers who dealt with end customers. Each link in the chain is compensated, which puts a company using two-tier distribution at an inherent price disadvantage compared to one that deals directly with resellers, as Pure Storage generally does in the western hemisphere. But for a small company trying to establish a foothold in APJ, it was a necessity.

Several of the company's early field teams elsewhere in the world had gained storage experience working around and with competitors' products. Experience brought relationships with end users and knowledge of competitors strengths and weaknesses, both of which made selling easier. The teams knew where potential customers were found and were familiar with the competition they were up against. But gaining entry based on prior relationships didn't work as well in conservative APJ. Users are generally reluctant to be early adopters and to disclose frustrations with incumbent vendors and products, so it was sometimes difficult to determine what to emphasize during sales calls. Over time, as Pure Storage enlisted partners and became established, relationships developed and, as in other geographies, the company came to be viewed as a technology and business practice leader.

An Incredible Stroke of Luck

In 2013, the Japanese sales team managed to place an array with a major electronics manufacturer as a PoC. The PoC was going well until early 2014, when a failing SSD clashed with a Purity//FA internal feature designed to mitigate the impact of an almost-full array. The combination caused the array to fail with apparent loss of data. As sometimes happens with PoCs, despite agreements to the contrary, the customer had stored valuable and otherwise unrecoverable data on the array. He was understandably upset, the Pure Storage Japanese sales team even more so. A failed installation at this important and highly visible customer would effectively eliminate any chance of a meaningful Pure Storage presence in Japan.

Philip Nass

"One of our first PoC's showed us how good FlashArray really is. A prospect had ruled Pure Storage out as too risky compared to established vendors. But our inside champion managed to get us included with two much larger vendors in a 'bake-off' that tested performance, resiliency, and simplicity, At the end of the test, the FlashArray was the only array still serving data. Overnight, we went from being 'too risky' to being considered the lowest risk option. To this day, the customer considers it one of the best IT decisions they've ever made. Pure Storage really delivers what it claims in PowerPoint."

Putting the customer first, the company swung into action. The nature of the problem was such that it was quickly handed to the escalations team, where Ganesh Ramanarayanan was doing a rotation. Having previously been involved in a successful "data rescue," Ganesh was familiar with the software's internal metadata structures, and incredibly, although he was of Indian heritage and had grown up in New Jersey, *he spoke Japanese.* Speaking Japanese didn't solve the problem, but it did give the partner confidence that the company was doing its utmost to recover the customer's data. Ganesh reported progress to the account team and the partner throughout the month-long recovery. He learned that one person had generated the data in the array, and that he had done virtually no work on it during the holiday season.

The customer gave the escalations team unfettered access to the array, asking only that every effort be made to recover the irreplaceable data. At the time, Purity//FA logged virtually every operation, primarily as a troubleshooting aid. Because there had been no array activity during the holidays, the escalations team was able to devise a way to regenerate metadata from the logs, which allowed them to "rewind the clock" and restore the array to its pre-Christmas state. The team recovered the customer's data except for a

Ganesh Ramanarayanan

"As a teenager I enjoyed video games quite a bit. When the Nintendo 64 came out, there was a game I really wanted to play that was only available in Japanese. So I got myself a dictionary and set out to learn Japanese from the video game subtitles. The very first sentence stymied me for a week, but eventually I picked it up, and continued to study conversational Japanese while I was in college. That's how I was able to correspond and converse with our Japanese team and our partner while we worked to recover the customer's data."

few inconsequential updates made during the holiday season. The customer was impressed by the level of support received and remains one of the company's most important Japanese customers. To be sure, the success of the recovery was due to the escalations team's technical expertise and persistence, but also to Ganesh's ability to reach across the language barrier and give the partner confidence that the problem was being solved and his customer's data would ultimately be recovered.

Ganesh's email announcing that the data had been recovered reached the account team shortly after they had informed the partner that the customer's data was unrecoverable. Needless to say, they were happy to call the partner again to inform them that their earlier communication had been in error.

In This Chapter…

"If you build it, they will come," but first you have to build it. The first generations of Pure Storage products were to be built from off-the-shelf hardware, but even off-the-shelf hardware has to be sourced, and a supply chain established. Contract manufacturers have to be engaged. Components have to be tracked from when they arrive to when they're delivered to customers in products. Starting from nothing, the operations team worked closely with engineering and sales to develop component tracking and inventory control systems, contract with manufacturers, create a supply chain, and develop packaging, shipping, and billing procedures.

Technology products, especially data storage, must work flawlessly. Failures in the field can damage a company's reputation, and for a new entrant in a demanding field, can be fatal. Working with reliable suppliers helps, but exhaustive component testing is the real key to positive customer experiences.

Finally, a company's ability to manufacture and deliver must be as resilient as its products. A flood that inundated the main Pure Storage manufacturing site could have been disastrous. It convinced the company that it must contract with multiple manufacturing sites to guarantee reliable delivery.

Making It

Before You Can Sell Products, You Have to Build 'Em

As the alpha systems were demonstrating that FlashArray was real and was meeting its goals in data centers, the company began to plan to manufacture arrays in volume. Because the primary IP was software, the plan from the beginning had been to build the first generation of products from "off-the-shelf" components—rack-mountable servers, device enclosures, storage network interface cards, and SSDs.

Todd Engle
" 'Live in the present; scale for the future.'
Things we did in the early days ensured that we could grow to the point we're at today."

Michael Cornwell and Ko Yamamoto had dealt with component vendors extensively, but their expertise lay in identifying and qualifying the components that go into products. Once a product is defined, developed, and ready for production, creating a supply chain and a predictable production line is quite a different skill. Pure Storage would need an operations department.

Meanwhile, in far-off Minnesota, Todd Engle, operations vice president for a mid-tier storage company, was ready for a career change. He had begun discreet inquiries into alternatives, but shortly thereafter learned that his company planned to move to Colorado. Faced with relocation whatever he did, he broadened his search to include opportunities in other parts of the country.

During his search, Todd contacted a component supplier, and was introduced to Pure Storage, which at the time was evaluating the supplier for possible use with FlashArray. Like many in the storage industry, Todd knew of and was intrigued by flash, and had been wondering when and how it would move into the mainstream and supplant magnetic disks. Here was a company that claimed to have figured out how to overcome the main obstacles to mass adoption—affordability and endurance. Todd had heard of Coz and was aware of the success of his software, so he had some confidence in the Pure Storage team's credibility.

Pure Storage was in California, some 2,000 miles from Minnesota. But the story was plausible, and the prospect was enticing—if the company could pull it off, they might

Marcus Padro
"Until we were 100 employees, I knew everyone. As we grew larger, we inevitably had to prioritize projects and review decisions more thoroughly."

completely upend the multibillion-dollar enterprise storage sector. Todd visited the Mountain View headquarters and met with the leadership team, who impressed him greatly. (He impressed them as well.) He brought his family out for a visit and learned that they were more adventurous than he'd anticipated—they agreed that relocation to California would be worth a try. The swing factor was a family discussion which concluded that if Pure Storage succeeded, they would rue not having seized the opportunity. So when an offer was extended, Todd accepted. He rented a temporary apartment and started work in early 2011, a bit dismayed to discover on arrival that to access the company's internal information he would have to use a Unix shell script to log into a wiki—the first of many new and mysterious experiences.

What uniquely qualified Todd was breadth of experience. During his career, he'd worked in or managed every facet of technology manufacturing, from component and system testing, to repair, to inventory management, to receiving and shipping, to eventually running the entire operations show. His trajectory had generally been to take over small operations and grow them along with the company's growth. What excited him, however, was the opportunity to create a completely new operations department. That was made to order for Pure Storage, where operations was just starting up, and the company's growth expectations were aggressive.

Getting Manufacturing Off the Ground

Manufacturing hardware is all about predictability. Contract manufacturers must meet their commitments, components have to be ordered and delivered on time, component and system tests have to expose problems, and above all, customers have to receive what they ordered when they expect it. For a company using contract manufacturing, predictability comes in part from engaging contractors that are well-known to be reliable. But even the best contractors can only do what they're told, so the producer must know what to ask for and how to ask for it, down to the last detail. Parts must be precisely specified and tracked, test processes must be developed and rigorously adhered to, detailed foolproof assembly instructions must be created and contractors trained in their use, shipping containers must be designed, and a thousand other details. Pure Storage operations had to build this infrastructure in time for the first arrays to be shipped to customers.

Building an Operations Team

Todd concluded that operations' two most urgent needs were manufacturing tests and a an *enterprise resource planning* (ERP) system, so he created job postings for a test development engineer and a supply chain manager. The first response came from a person known to some of the employees.

In 2011, frustrated by seemingly continuous reorganizations and offshoring, Marcus Padro was receptive to recruiters' overtures, one of which came from Pure Storage. He traveled across town to interview. It went well and he received an offer on the spot. That was pretty typical of Pure Storage. What was unusual was that Marcus *accepted* on the spot... the first time that had happened in the company's short history. The all-flash vision and former colleagues Coz and Mike impressed him.

Grant Perrin
"Operations has many internal and external 'customers' but the most important is the Pure Storage Sales team."

Marcus joined in mid-2011. He spent his first three months with engineering helping expand and move its test infrastructure to a CoLo. He installed, configured, managed, and repaired pre-production arrays and test servers. In retrospect, he believes that was the best possible way to learn the product.

Having previously managed lab equipment for several years, he was well-versed in test procedures for incoming hardware. He started working with Tom Holland, who had been developing component tests for engineering qualification, to create and package test procedures for use by contract manufacturers.

To create the company's parts and inventory management systems, Todd drew on Grant Perrin. Grant had worked with Todd in various capacities for practically his entire career. Like Todd, he had done every job in operations at one time or another.

Minnesotan Grant became a long-distance commuter. His first task was to select and implement an ERP system, which he did so effectively that when the company discovered that a batch of SSDs with an obscure defect had been installed in customers' systems, he was able to track down every defective unit for replacement in a matter of minutes.

In the early days, minimizing the number of product options was key to success—in manufacturing, sales, order fulfillment, inventory, and so forth. Nevertheless, the planning and tracking systems and process automation based on work Grant did prior to the first FlashArray shipments have enabled the company to scale to its present size and range of products without significant change. Pure Storage still uses the sales order flow he designed that starts with salesforce.com's *customer relationship management* (CRM) application and feeds into NetSuite's ERP software. The company still uses the SKU and part number scheme and product lifecycle application that Grant implemented. Organizing for scale a priori has been a key enabler of the company's smooth growth to its current size.

Ko Yamamoto had worked closely with operations in other companies, so he had been filling the vendor negotiation role. But his interests lay primarily in dealing with vendors from an engineering perspective. He was more than happy when Todd took over operations and he could concentrate on hardware engineering, but the two departments remained closely intertwined.

Pure Storage preferred to deal with established hardware vendors. Ko and Michael Cornwell were well-known to major vendors, and were very helpful in establishing the company's credibility, with one exception. The dominant SSD producers normally dealt

Grant and Todd on the First Manufacturing "Floor"

in much larger quantities than Pure Storage could to commit to purchasing and were reluctant to negotiate pricing based on aggressive forecasts from a young company with no track record.

At a meeting with the company's largest SSD provider about two years after the first supply contracts were signed, Todd produced his original forecast and noted that it compared almost exactly with what he had ordered in the interim. Relationships became smoother after that, and in fact, one large SSD manufacturer became an investor during a later round of fund raising.[23] The company's engineers needed to understand SSDs' internal workings, which providers viewed as valuable IP and were unwilling to disclose. Relationships were at arms-length, so to optimize performance, engineering was forced to develop software empirically for each SSD model it qualified by load testing with different conceptual device geometries to determine which delivered the best performance.

All Parts Are Not Necessarily Created Equal

A major challenge for operations in the early days was component sourcing. While multi-sourcing is always desirable, in some cases, such as controller assemblies and device enclosures ("storage shelves") it wasn't practical. For SSDs, however, it was a necessity. As a relatively small purchaser compared to the industry's giants, Pure Storage had little influence with vendors. The company was susceptible to price changes, production shortfalls, and other interruptions in supply.

Each SSD developer has unique firmware and manufacturing processes, so different vendors' devices with similar specifications may perform very differently under load. To compensate for this, engineering developed *flash personality layer* (FPL) software parameters for each device it qualified by testing thousands of I/O patterns to determine which performed best. The FPL used the parameters to remap *logical block addresses* (LBAs) in I/O requests based on device type. [24]

For operations, the SSD problem was different. SSDs would pass incoming component tests, but when installed in an array, would reset themselves at apparently random intervals, events that the team called "blips." After extensive testing, Yi Ding (page 56) determined that different suppliers SSDs behaved differently when connected to the interposers that convert their native SATA to dual-port SAS. Operations introduced a supplier-specific process step to "tune" interposer output based on the type of SSD connected to it. In addition, they began to track the supplier of every SSD installed in every array to expedite diagnosis and correction of intermittent problems in the field. The lesson for nascent manufacturing operations is that while second-sourcing may be a necessity, different vendors' components may behave differently despite similar or even identical specifications.

---

[23] Wall Street Journal, August 23, 2011
[24] This is why FlashArray only recognizes and supports qualified SSD models.

Engaging a Contract Manufacturer

The company assembled alpha and beta arrays and shipped them from its Mountain View headquarters. For production, however, a contract manufacturer would be needed. When Marcus returned to operations from engineering, his first task was to create a relationship with the manufacturer Todd had chosen.

The company contracted with a well-known manufacturer with a Bay Area presence, knowing full well that as it grew, manufacturing would eventually have to scale to support a worldwide customer base, and that a different contractor might ultimately be needed. In fact, in 2015 the company transitioned to a manufacturer with a greater global presence.

Contract manufacturing for technology products can be complicated. Pure Storage had no direct control over contractor's employees, who could not automatically be presumed to understand technology

Avery Pham
"Starting with FlashArray//M, we had to get closer to CPU vendors so we could stay current with their developments."

basics, let alone the product they were to assemble and test. Documentation would be key, both for material handling and assembly, and for what to do when tests failed or things didn't go right. Moreover, at the CoLo, Marcus had learned that the FlashArray tests that engineering had devised for its own use (a) required significant basic technology and product-specific knowledge, and (b) had to be run on demand by human operators. They clearly were not going to be adequate for a production environment. His first task was going to be to create foolproof automated component and system tests and very explicit instructions for running them and actions to be taken when failures occurred.

Managing the Supply Chain

In 2012, Avery Pham was a supply-chain manager with a storage company. He enjoyed the technology, but wasn't entirely satisfied with the company, so he was exploring opportunities when he noticed that Pure Storage was recruiting operations managers. He had been impressed with the company's technology message and attracted by its irreverent marketing. An acquaintance, David Clay, then serving as the company's finance director, introduced him to Todd. The introduction led to interviews, and an offer. Avery joined the company in 2013 as Director of *New Product Introduction* (NPI) Operations at about the same time as Bill Cerreta (page 153), with whom he would work closely during the transition from the FA-400 series to the Platinum (FlashArray//M) generation.

In the company's early days, the supply chain consisted largely of server, enclosure, SSD, and I/O adapter card suppliers who delivered the components to a contract assembly and test house. The contractor shipped completed arrays to customers. While there was some negotiation on prices and priorities, Avery's primary responsibility was to ensure that the contractor's component inventories were adequate to support the company's product build plans. Accurate forecasting was necessary, although as Avery observes, the highest priority of supply-chain management is to ensure that inventory is adequate to deliver orders and support development, even when unforecasted "bluebird" sales or unanticipated internal requirements occur. Inventory carryover is always preferable to delaying customer shipments or delaying development.

Early forecasts were compilations of AEs' projections. As the size of the installed base and number of account teams increased, it became more sophisticated, taking into account delivery history, upcoming sales promotions, and more formalized interaction with the sales force, but it continued to be tempered by the operations team's own intuition.

When the company transitioned from arrays assembled from purchased components to developing its own controllers, NVRAMs, and eventually, Direct Flash Modules, the nature of the supply-chain changed significantly. Whereas the contractor for earlier product generations received components and assembled and tested arrays, FlashArray//M would need a contractor with more comprehensive services, including circuit board design assistance and manufacture. The relationship with the original contractor had been generally satisfactory, so the decision to change was difficult, but as FlashArray matured into a Pure Storage-developed system, it was necessary.

Full-service contract manufacturers typically deal with the industry's largest firms and avoid companies of Pure Storage's 2015 size. Fortunately, both Avery and Bill had prior experience with the leading candidate, which gave the company instant contacts and credibility. Between Bill in engineering and Avery in operations, the favored contractor was persuaded to deal with Pure Storage. The relationship they helped create produced the FlashArray//M and continues today with FlashArray//X.

The original assembly and test house served Pure Storage from one location with relatively fixed employee skills and a single set of procedures. For FlashArray//M, however, both engineering and operations had to deal with the new contractor's operations in different locations with different business cultures. As the company grew, the contractor relationship broadened. Today, it uses the contractor's engineering and manufacturing services at locations in North America, Europe, and Asia.

In principle, supply-chain forecasting remained the same with the new contractor— the company forecasts the number of products and add-ons for each geography, and each contractor location procures the needed components. The contractor can often influence suppliers of high-volume generic components, so it typically leads negotiations with them. For some specialized components, such as SSDs and raw flash, however, Pure Storage has direct relationships with suppliers, so it helps negotiate pricing and priorities. Additionally, the company often pursues relationships with alternate suppliers of key components to hedge against primary vendor supply issues.

The FlashArray//M series resulted in another major change in operations. The controllers in earlier FlashArray generations were servers offered by server vendors. The rate at which Pure Storage could introduce new processors in FlashArray products was constrained by server vendors' support for them. With FlashArray//M, however, Pure

Storage controlled the hardware content, and it strove to introduce new processors and support logic as soon as possible after their introduction. It developed a direct engineering relationship with its processor vendor, and operations. Avery took over a team dedicated to new product introduction and was eventually promoted to Vice President for New Product Introductions.

Shipping Products that Work

As Marcus began to automate engineering tests for manufacturing use and create new ones, he developed a concise set of principles that were eventually codified into four *Manufacturing Test Precepts* that are still the company's manufacturing test "rules to live by," when tens of thousands of incoming components are tested and assembled into FlashArray and FlashBlade systems, which are tested again before being shipped to customers:

SHIP IT ON TIME

This was added to the original three later, when sales volume increased to the point that manufacturing delays could materially impact revenue recognition. Its intent is to remind the manufacturing test team of the importance of continuously striving to streamline testing as much as possible without "cutting corners" on quality.

IT MUST WORK

Products must work when the customer receives and installs them. From a manufacturing test standpoint, this means *precise* tests—a product should pass if and only if it will work correctly in the field, and failed tests should indicate genuine component or software failures. Tests must avoid both "false positives" and "false negatives."

DOCUMENT IT

Documentation means foolproof instructions for assemblers and testers, but also tests that "auto-triage." Tests must indicate which components must be replaced and must track failures to identify faulty batches received from suppliers.

BE EFFICIENT

While "It Must Work" is manufacturing test's "job 1," testing should not impede shipment. As engineers design manufacturing tests, they must be cognizant of their impact on volume production and strive to minimize it.

You Have to Be Ready for Anything

Manufacturing in volume is about predictability. Whether it's consumer products or advanced technology for commercial use, products must roll off the line on schedule to meet customer commitments. This is especially challenging with contract manufacturing, where assemblers and testers are not directly controlled by the developer. Off-the-shelf components add to the challenge because component vendors do not always share relevant information with their customers.

FlashArray Production Floor
April 19, 2016: Four days after the shutdown, the water had receded, building repairs were underway, and production resumed, but things weren't quite back to normal.

View from the Lobby
April 22, 2016: The "lesson learned" was that both our products and our ability to deliver them to customers must be highly available.

Marcus's manufacturing test team created extremely detailed test procedures, implemented "auto-triaging," and made tests self-documenting so that systemic failures could be identified and remediated.

But in addition to the usual manufacturing challenges, there's the unpredictable. For Pure Storage, this ranged from a disgruntled contractor employee who sabotaged components, to an undetected tolerance error in an HBA connector that caused intermittent SSD failures. The latter led the operations team on a root cause hunt that culminated in the discovery that the error was an industry-wide problem that the connector vendor had failed to report.

Another unanticipated event was the purchase of a FlashArray by a third party representing a competitor, presumably to "reverse engineer" it and figure out the magic. The situation was uncovered after delivery and the array was eventually returned. It fell to the operations team to examine the array physically to try to determine whether the company's terms of sale had been violated.

But the proverbial "mother of all unanticipated events" occurred in April 2016. In Houston, Texas, torrential rains over several days resulted in floods throughout the area.

At the time, the main FlashArray manufacturing facility was in a low-lying area of the city that flooded. Water covered the lower part of the building interior. The production floor did not flood, but power was lost and the plant was closed for three days. The operations team worked with contractor representatives to expedite the restart. Shortly after local authorities declared the building safe to occupy, production resumed. The disaster taught the operations team that not only must FlashArray be failure tolerant; the company's ability to produce and ship products must be disaster-proof as well. Today, manufacturing is done in four widely-separated locations, partly because the business now has an international dimension, but also for continuity in case a location is incapacitated. Each location has its own procedures for dealing with its customers, so Pure Storage employs specialists to manage the relationship with each one. It's an inherent cost of doing business in a world of highly available technology.

In This Chapter…

In keeping with the philosophy of measuring what matters, the company uses its audited NPS as a key measure of its success. NPS measures all facets of a company's interactions with its customers, including support after the sale. In anticipation of "going global," the company structured its support organization for eventual world-wide operation, starting with a remote center in Utah—remote, but close enough to headquarters to maintain close relationships with engineering. Support has become global, with operations in Europe and Asia that interact with customers in their own languages and are familiar with their business cultures.

Pure Storage involves customers actively in support; it even allows them to determine case severity. The support organization is backed up by an escalations team staffed by developer rotation. The team improves support's product knowledge, and in addition, developers gain an appreciation for customers' viewpoints.

Hardware breaks, too. The company maintains a worldwide network of logistics centers that stock parts for all products. A network of contractors trained and certified by the company provide "break-fix" support.

On the rare occasions when really tough problems arise, the company demonstrates its values by taking ownership of situations and working through them until the customer is satisfied, as the examples in this chapter attest.

Customer First... *Really*

Pure Storage prides itself on customer satisfaction, which is confirmed quarterly by the highest audited NPS by far of any technology company. NPS scores are based on customer surveys returned to an independent customer experience management firm that audits them and calculates an NPS.

A company's NPS is based on the full range of its customer interactions: product quality, the sales experience, and perhaps most importantly, support after the sale. As information technology becomes increasingly vital to organizations, unrectified problems can have a severe impact, and in extreme cases, put them out of business. Even when everything is working, users often need guidance in effective product use. An IT vendor cannot succeed in this environment without providing robust, effective support. In addition to the company's audited NPS, the Pure Storage support organization uses the NPS process as a separate measure of its effectiveness.

Allen Lu
"Customers' issues must always have highest priority!"

Ben Casey
"Our support team was really tight with engineering and sales. Hayes and Burr were my guys!"

Beginnings

Starting in late 2011, the company started a support organization by recruiting Allen Lu, then with a local clustering software company, and the affable Ben Casey, a longtime customer support veteran of several local technology firms. The headquarters support staff soon grew to eight, one or more of whom was on the overnight shift at all times.

In late 2012, with the growing FlashArray installed base, it was time to create a more robust support organization. The company recruited Christopher Zang to develop and manage the operation. Like Dietz, Christopher describes his pre-Pure Storage self as "not a storage guy," but he had served as VP of support in no fewer than five companies. In the interview round, he discovered that he and Dietz shared a support philosophy: "enterprise

Christopher Zang

"To me, enterprise support has always meant doing whatever it takes to resolve the customer's issue. I was happy to discover that Dietz and I were aligned on that."

"When four of us went to Utah to recruit support engineers, money was still tight. We decided to stay in a suite hotel and use the suites' living rooms for interviewing. For an entire day, we did 'speed dating' with a dozen candidates, about half of whom we hired on the spot. (We hired most of the others later.)"
—**Christopher Zang**

customers deserve 'white glove' treatment." Knowing that made Christopher more interested in Pure Storage and that, plus his background in managing enterprise-level support organizations, made the company more interested in him.

Christopher mapped out the overall form the organization would eventually take and instituted the company's first ticketing system for support case tracking. He believed there should be a core of experienced engineers co-located with developers, but as the company expanded its reach, support centers would eventually have to be distributed. He created a structure that would facilitate the future establishment of remote centers. As a first step, he proposed identifying a location within two flight-hours of headquarters with a population of skilled engineers who would be willing to rotate on night shifts.

A search unearthed a community of experienced support engineers in Utah that had been cast adrift when their employer ceased operation there. Christopher led a group on a fact-finding and interview visit, the upshot of which was the hiring of several engineers and establishment of the company's first remote support center. The decision was fortuitous for several reasons:

- The engineers proved to be skillful, adaptable, and loyal—to this day, the support organization has the company's lowest attrition rate.

- The location was attractive to individuals who fit the support engineer profile, so it was easy to recruit additional staff when needed.

- It gave the company needed experience in remote support center management, but at the same time was a short airplane ride from the Bay Area, so support engineers could easily visit to confer with headquarters colleagues and participate in company events.

By mid-2014, the support organization was up and running, with its core in Mountain View, but most growth occurring in the Utah center. The team had engaged a consultant to integrate the support ticketing system with the sales department's CRM system. A somewhat rocky integration convinced them that in-house resources were needed. Today, developers in the support organization manage the integrated ticketing system.

Going Global

In 2014, Colin Mead was managing global support at a Bay Area networking company, where his team had received J. D. Power and Associates' highest award for IT vendor support practices and customer service experience. He began to notice that many of his customers were migrating to Pure Storage to improve application performance, which piqued his interest. He learned that "Customer First" was a key company value, which resonated with his own "Customer First, Second and Third" attitude.

On closer examination, he found that under Christopher's leadership, Pure Storage had built an outstanding support team, with an attitude towards customers that was second to none. What the company would need in the near future was rapid scaling for global operation without "breaking" anything. Colin describes his first 18 months with Pure Storage as "like changing the wheels on a Formula 1 car racing around the track at 200mph."

Colin Mead
"Attitude is everything.
We can train people with technical aptitude, but attitudes are much harder, and sometimes impossible to change.
As the support organization expanded across the globe, maintaining the 'Customer First' culture continues to be paramount.
It starts with interviews that ensure that the people we hire not only have excellent technical skills but also believe passionately in providing the best possible customer service."

Preparing for Growth

Under Colin's direction, the organization continued integrating support with the CRM system, built a new web site, knowledge base, and phone system, and developed additional tools to prepare for globalization. He oversaw a "hardening" of the escalation process aimed at convincing the world's largest, most demanding IT users that Pure Storage could support them whenever and wherever necessary.

Colin prepared for growth by streamlining support policies, processes, and systems to make it easier for teams to take care of customers. As he did this, he was careful at every step to ensure that customers' interactions with the company were made easier, not more difficult.

Pure Storage constantly strives to make the customer experience easy, starting with easy-to-use products, and extending to everything it does, including support. Delivering a smooth customer experience often entails considerable internal complexity, which the company absorbs. For example, in support:

- The company monitors all arrays with phonehome enabled around the clock so customers don't have to.
- The support organization performs all software upgrades remotely, and without disruption, following customer change control processes.

Customers who contact support never encounter annoying *Interactive Voice Response* (IVR) systems that ask largely pointless questions, delaying the first contact with a live person who can help.

Let the Customer Decide

Colin introduced a customer driven incident severity rating, rather than a system based on vendor definitions as is common among IT vendors, based on a belief that customers

"When users delete files, file systems free the space they occupy for reuse, but arrays aren't aware of that—they retain blocks written by hosts until directed to delete them. In the early days, users were forever calling support to ask why their computers reported 50% available storage while their arrays were reporting that they were nearly full.

Of course, when the host operating systems got around to supporting SCSI UNMAP, the problem disappeared, but until then, Allan and I spent a lot of time handling those calls."
—**Ben Casey**

can better judge importance to their operations than Pure Storage. Customers themselves decide whether incidents deserve "Sev-1" (highest priority) rating.

Most high-priority IT issues involve multiple vendors, partners, and even customer organizations. Pure Storage support is typically first on an escalation conference call and last to leave. The company takes ownership (page 40) regardless of the source of a problem. Coupled with communicating openly with customers, that attitude has helped support develop strong, long-lasting trust relationships with customers.

On a personal level, as a consumer of products and services himself, Colin is a keen observer of both commercial and consumer vendor support practices, good and bad. He will willingly consider adapting exemplary ones, and as for not-so-exemplary ones: "We've all had to deal with 'that' company in which apparently trivial support requests are nearly impossible to fulfill. I don't want Pure Storage to ever be 'that' company."

Implementation

Many Pure Storage support engineers have worked previously for competitors. While they bring valuable experience, cultural adjustment is sometimes needed to change the "Close as many cases per week as possible" attitude to "When a customer reports a problem to us, we own it until it is resolved."

The "customer first" culture has a bearing on support. Engineers frequently encounter issues that require domain expertise outside the Pure Storage product line. Customers may ask for assistance with integrating arrays with virtual environments, optimizing configurations for database use, and so forth. Support engineers call on SEs familiar with specific customer situations, solution architects with deep application domain expertise, and even developers, to assist when their expertise is needed. It is common for people in other departments to drop what they are doing and put the customer first to help resolve an urgent support case.

Colin instituted a system that specifically does *not* measure individuals' case closure rates. Instead, when a case is closed the customer receives a brief survey requesting a 1 to 10 evaluation of satisfaction with its handling and free-form thoughts on how it might have been handled better. The responses are distributed unfiltered to everyone in the support organization, so every closed case becomes a learning opportunity for the entire team.

The support organization uses the case closure surveys to augment the company's externally audited NPS. Based on them, support consistently outperforms the stratospheric company NPS. As Colin puts it, "Our 90+ scores mean that for every negative report on a case there are 11 or 12 positive ones. That's pretty good percentage for inherently high-stress situations."

Survey respondents tend to be specific about why they appreciate the company's approach to support. The three most-frequent comments are:

PRODUCT EASE OF USE

While product ease of use would not seem to be a support issue, respondents observe that to them, the easiest support call is one they don't have to make. Administrators handle many situations that would require support calls with other vendors. From the company's point of view, while support engineers are able and willing to work with customers on minor issues such as creating or resizing volumes or file systems, or changing a replication configuration, most of these calls never happen, so engineers spend more of their time dealing with more complex issues.

FAST RESPONSE

Fast response begins with the support technician who fields the initial contact. Every call is answered by a technician, who in many cases has already identified the caller and is aware of the situation. Routing to the engineer responsible for ongoing cases is fast, and engineers are responsible for cases from start to finish, so customers don't have to start from the beginning on each follow-up call. Issues that persist around the clock rotate to remote centers, but responsibility remains with the center that is geographically and culturally most appropriate.

"We were keeping an eye on the phonehome logs (it wasn't called Pure1 yet) from an array recently installed at a midwestern municipality. The array had been at a comfortable 30% utilization for some time when suddenly it began to rise rapidly and data reduction started to drop. We began to monitor it more closely, and when utilization hit 90%, we were alarmed enough to contact the customer.

After some discussion, we learned that the customer was migrating a large store of (uncompressible) digital video taken by police cruiser cameras from a failing older system to the FlashArray. We gently suggested that uncompressible digital images might not be the best use for FlashArray and persuaded the customer to migrate to a different target.

Disaster was averted and the customer learned something, both about data reduction and about our proactive customer support."

—**John Mansperger**

PREEMPTIVE REMEDIATION

With the logs that Pure1 servers receive from customers' FlashArray and FlashBlade systems, support engineers can identify installations in which known issues *may* occur in the future and initiate preemptive remediation to avoid them.

When support resolves a problem that it suspects may be occurring elsewhere, an engineer creates a *fingerprint* pattern containing relevant configuration and usage information. In one well-known case, a combination of HBA model, Purity//FA version, and volume configuration was found to cause frequent spurious alerts. The fingerprint detected susceptible arrays, and a menu of possible remediations was communicated to users whose arrays had that fingerprint.

AI software constantly compares fingerprints with Pure1 logs and generates support cases when matches are identified. Engineers work with the affected customers to develop resolution plans. Fingerprinting has been so successful that in many reporting periods, more support cases are initiated via fingerprinting than by customers.

Panos Koutsoyannis

"Soon after I started, I was on a call for the company's most critical escalation up to that point (page 127) when a new person joined on the customer side. I asked his role, and he replied authoritatively, 'I am the Master and Commander, charged with getting this resolved as quickly as possible.'

I thought that was a perfect title and job description for escalations, so I immediately adopted it. Today, it's the title used by all of our critical on call managers."

Customers appreciate being warned of potential issues and presented with options before they experience failures or downtime.

Escalations: When the Going Gets *Really* Tough

In a company whose technology is as complex and fast-changing as Pure Storage's, occasional failures in the field are inevitable. Even more occasionally, the nature of a failure is so complex that support must escalate the case to engineering. Escalations are inherently high-pressure situations. Sales wants to preserve the customer relationship while development managers are torn between customer satisfaction and holding to delivery schedules. In this milieu, the natural inclination, especially in a small company, is to immediately enlist the most senior developers to solve the immediate problem.

Most developers aren't accustomed to working with support or interacting with customers. Moreover, solving a problem in a production array without destroying data is quite different from developing software. Escalation engineers are a special breed. They are experienced developers who thrive on the adrenaline rush of the "diving catch" that preserves a customer's data and gets an array back into production. Pure Storage regularly rotates developers through the escalation team to train them to solve problems working with support and to interact directly with customers.

The interplay between development engineering and the support organization needs an experienced manager who can determine and enforce the right course of action for each case and can oversee interactions between support and field organizations and the customer.

In 2013, Palo Alto native Panos Koutsoyannis took a break from technology. He had started his career in the Peace Corps, helped lay the foundations for financial systems throughout eastern Europe and central Asia after the collapse of the Soviet Union, worked in networking during the heyday of dot.com startups, and finally landed at an Internet giant managing an organization charged with keeping dozens of customer applications up and running. While he was vacationing in Indonesia and developing video games on the side, a recruiter contacted him about an opportunity with a small storage company that was "starting to have an impact in the market."

On his return to the United States, although somewhat dubious about "a company that made USB drives and wanted him to carry a pager," he met with Evan. They discovered that they had the same views on escalations, so Panos agreed to a full interview round. The games he had written while in Asia had refreshed his programming skills, so he passed the problem-solving interviews with flying colors.

Pure Storage was a far cry from what he had imagined. The company's technology and people impressed him; the market was large and obviously ripe, so in late summer 2013 he joined as manager of the nascent escalations team.

Despite his varied career, dealing directly with AEs and customers under pressure was new to Panos. He had not previously encountered the expectation level common among enterprise storage users. Worse, he was immediately "thrown into the deep end of the pool." Within a week of starting, he was embroiled in one of the most critical escalations in the company's history (page 127). He (and the company) survived the situation and it helped coalesce his beliefs about high-tech escalation teams.

"Working on escalations in the company's early days was like stabilizing a failed jet engine while the plane is airborne. There is NO alternative to making it work."
—**Panos Koutsoyannis**

Panos believes that an escalations team has three fundamental goals: improve the quality of support, improve the product, and improve pre-shipment testing. The first goal not only enhances the customer experience, it reduces the burden on the escalations team and ultimately on engineering. More capable support means fewer escalations. To make a support organization more capable, "playbooks" (rigidly specified steps to be performed on every call) should be discarded, all possible general product information should be made available, and the team should be empowered to work on a case-by-case basis. This was in total accord with Colin's thinking (page 119).

Improving a product and improving pre-release testing are closely intertwined. An escalations team must ensure that when bona fide product problems are identified, fixes are included in upcoming revisions as soon as practical. Similarly, whether a problem is an actual deficiency or caused by unanticipated usage, escalations must verify that the test regimen is extended to reveal the symptom, so that support and escalations aren't blindsided by recurrences. Ensuring that all of this occurs is the role of the escalations *Master and Commander*. Panos rates his escalations team's performance as adequate in improving products and testing, but outstanding in making the support organization self-sufficient. As he puts it, "If a case gets to us from support, we *know* it's really serious."

An escalations team connects development engineering and the support organization. It must handle all but the most difficult cases itself, so members need excellent technical product knowledge. Pure Storage keeps escalation skill levels high by assigning development engineers to the team for three- to four- month rotations. Developers are both knowledgeable and well-connected to their peers. The experience benefits both the team and developers, who gain broader product experience, awareness of the environments in which they are used, and appreciation for the types of issues support encounters daily.

As his escalations team matured, Panos realized that tools developed specifically for its diagnostic mission would increase its effectiveness. But diagnostic tool development would not fit into engineering schedules. After several tries, he persuaded Bob to fund a few escalations development engineers. Focused directly on diagnosis, escalations development has been outstandingly successful. Its signal accomplishments include

Mike Ahrens
"Ko was a tough interview. In fact, I came away pretty sure I'd blown it, and that that would be the last I heard from Pure Storage. But when I joined, he was among the first to welcome me. I later learned that that's just Ko. He expects people to know what they're talking about."

the fingerprinting framework and automation of the software upgrade process. Both have matured over time and have been handed off to the support organization, increasing its self-sufficiency even further.

Managing Logistics

In 2013, Mike Ahrens was managing logistics for the west coast arm of a storage giant when he noticed a job posting from Pure Storage, just down the road. He decided to respond out of curiosity to see how a much smaller company operated. He had expected to spend a couple hours, but Marcus, Grant, Todd, and Ko grilled him for six long hours. He came away impressed by both the company's customer-centric approach and the caliber and enthusiasm of the people who had interviewed him and shown him around. Ko, though, had been particularly tough, probing him on a spectrum of component reliability issues. He came away believing that he hadn't passed muster and was somewhat surprised to receive an offer.

Mike accepted the offer and became the company's manager of logistics. His first task was to create the logistics function. Coming from a large company environment, with its structured bureaucracy, he was a bit overwhelmed by the culture of individual empowerment at first. There weren't committees to satisfy or approvals to secure. If something had to be done, the stakeholders agreed on approach and did it. In his first week, he received an urgent call from an AE in the Midwest requesting an array for a PoC. A competitor's product had failed. Pure Storage had an opportunity to "show its stuff," *if* the PoC could begin immediately. But at the time the company didn't have inventory waiting to be shipped. Operations worked overtime to locate components, build and test an array, and ship it to the prospect, who ultimately became a customer. Mike was hugely impressed by the "can do" attitude and energy, especially compared to the metric-driven atmosphere at his former employer; he decided that he'd made the right choice.

When Mike joined, Pure Storage had about 200 employees, half of them located at the Mountain View headquarters. He vividly recalls the weekly company meetings at which Hat, Burr, and Coz personally spoke to the entire staff, and where the top sales of the week were celebrated by banging a giant gong suspended on a wooden frame.

You've Come a Long Way, Baby

Mike created the company's logistics team. In fact for the better part of his first year, he *was* the logistics team. The growth since then has been remarkable:

- In 2013, the company was stocking spare parts, including complete arrays, in four domestic locations. Today, 187 depots in 41 countries stock the individual components that make up all Pure Storage products.

- In 2013, Pure Storage was using freelance service contractors to repair customers' systems. Today, there are over 1,500 contract engineers in 69 countries as well as a number of *Authorized Service Partners* (ASPs) certified to provide "break-fix" service for Pure Storage products.

- In 2013, there was no training for field engineers. Today, the company creates mobile training courses as part of every new product introduction. Training includes both repair instructions and advice for what not to do, constantly updated and pushed to all field engineers. Engineers are ranked by training scores and customer feedback. The company regularly reviews field engineers' performance with its contractors.

- In 2013, field engineers would arrive on site with the right parts and a sheet of printed instructions. Today, an automated workflow starts with the call center and tracks the case throughout its life.

- In 2013, root cause analysis was ad hoc at best. Today, every case is analyzed, both technically and in terms of the customer's satisfaction. Every case is followed by a customer survey. Responses that do not enhance the support NPS are followed up directly with the customer.

Today, logistics has a staff of over 20. It reports to Colin Mead's worldwide support organization to consolidate the company's service delivery and sharpen the focus on customer satisfaction. The attitude is "solve the problem," rather than the sometimes-encountered "make sure it's not our problem," even in cases where customer expectations have not been set correctly. The logistics team is a heavy user of and contributor to the company's fingerprinting technology. Often, when it discovers potential issues, the support organization will initiate anticipatory repair tickets.

Planning has become more sophisticated, with machine learning models balancing worldwide logistics requirements against inventory cost. A contractor refurbishes returned components and tests them for possible redeployment. Today, the company supports every product it has ever shipped, although the Evergreen model encourages regular refresh. Evergreen benefits both the service organization and customers—field engineers who focus primarily on newer products enhance their expertise, making service calls smoother.

The company expects its service contractors to meet customers' service level agreements 100% of the time, including on-time arrival, problem resolution, and general satisfaction. Every missed SLA is analyzed, and in many cases results in updates to the service procedure. Field engineers can also annotate their own CBT materials; the mobile device accessible materials become personalized repair instructions. The *Technology Service Industry Association* (TSIA) has designated Pure Storage an industry leader in several dimensions of service technology and execution.

Mike continues to believe that the company's success derives from the culture of its people—customers, employees, and contractors—as well as the quality of its products.

Support Engineers Need Love, Too

Support can be a lonely job. Most interactions are via phone, text, or interactive web chat. As the organization grew, the management team took pains to keep support engineers motivated. For technically oriented people, an important dimension of motivation is recognition—from peers, from other parts of the organization, and from customers. Support engineers who are visibly instrumental in resolving important customer issues are recognized locally and are invited to travel to and participate in company-wide recognition events. Two particularly unique forms of recognition for outstanding support performance have been periodic opportunities to visit customer Mercedes Racing's pit area and to participate in quarterly onsite visits to customer SpaceX's headquarters and launch site. When early investors made Super Bowl tickets available to the company, they would often be awarded to support engineers for outstanding achievements.

Summing Up Support

The overarching philosophy of the Pure Storage support organization is to enable its engineers to make the most appropriate decisions for resolving customer issues and avoid constraining them with procedural "red tape." Engineers are trained and encouraged to regard themselves as participants in critical applications rather than fixers of storage system problems. They are expected to understand customer applications and environments, and to take a larger view, for example thinking of themselves as participating in treatment if the case is with a medical application, in keeping transactions safe if the case is with a financial institution, in improving a retail customer's experience if the case is with a "big box" store, and so forth. They are often reminded to consider personal experiences in a professional context: "How do you react when an IVR system sends you through a series of button pushes before you get to talk to an actual person?"

Based on the company's NPS, this support philosophy has obviously been successful. Under Colin's direction, the support organization has become global, serving customers from centers in Ireland, Japan, Australia, and most recently, Singapore, with technicians and engineers who are geographically and culturally attuned to local needs. The company enlists partners to provide timely support linguistically and geographically remote situations.

There is a strong element of company self-interest in Pure Storage Support's "we own it" attitude. Experienced IT people know that problems requiring vendor support are inevitable in complex data centers, and they expect to have to deal with them. They tend to remember positive support experiences, which predisposes them to continue and expand their dealings with vendors that deliver those experiences.

Not infrequently, customers pay Pure Storage the ultimate compliment of asking how it gets its support organization to function so smoothly to see if they can replicate the techniques in their own environments.

A Data Recovery Team
From top left: Evan, Neil, Rich, Mark, Marco, Feng, Coz, Bob

The Darkest Hours

In 2014, hundreds of arrays were shipping to customers, virtually all with highly positive receptions. The company was eager to land a *marquee* customer—a recognized world leader in its space—to establish credibility with the global 2000. The opportunity came when a major financial institution decided to test the feasibility of VDI for its executives by conducting a PoC using a FlashArray at one of its data centers to store virtual desktop images.

Pure Storage shipped an array to the prospect in the hope that the PoC would result in a highly visible customer. The PoC was under the usual "try then buy" terms: the array was not to be used in production, tests would be monitored by the Pure Storage account team, and the array would be purchased or returned following the test.

The array was installed and the PoC was proceeding extremely well. So well in fact, that the prospect decided to put it into production, virtualizing the desktops of many of its senior executives around the world with the FlashArray holding their disk images, *without informing Pure Storage of what they were doing and with no viable fallback plan.*

As executives began to use their virtual desktops, a storage network glitch tripped a latent Purity//FA bug, and both controllers began to act as primaries, creating two independent update streams. The prospect was understandably upset, and its representatives loudly demanded immediate resolution, pointing out that their senior executives had been doing real work on real data, and losing it was not acceptable. The account team quickly escalated the incident. Engineering formed two dedicated teams to work in parallel, outlined a resolution plan, and set a goal of recovering as much of the customer's data as possible. At first, the teams worked independently to develop separate estimates of recoverable data. Once a solution was devised, they switched to relieving each other every few hours so the solution was worked on continuously.

A telephone conference bridge remained open throughout the incident, manned by incident managers from both Pure Storage and the prospect, as well as representatives of other vendors whose equipment might be involved. Panos (page 122) and Evan (page 65) managed the incident for Pure Storage; both remained on duty for continuous 24-hour stretches. The prospect's incident manager was also on the call almost continuously.

The Pure Storage teams took shifts so that work was continuous and everyone was constantly aware of status. Incident management on the Pure Storage side rotated among Panos, Dan, and Evan, who made sure that the prospect's incident manager was updated at regular intervals. The teams were instructed to be completely frank with the prospect about progress, or lack of it.

The episode lasted nearly three days, including devising and testing a solution, implementing it on the PoC array, and analyzing the incident to discover the root causes (Coz was personally reviewing every root cause analysis at the time), among which was an unreported bug in another vendor's network equipment. Once the solution had been tested locally, engineers patched the PoC array software remotely. None of the prospect's data was lost.

Even by Pure Storage standards, the solution teams were extraordinarily dedicated, returning to the office after brief rest pauses, even when incident managers directed them to stay home. The company's response contrasted with that of another vendor whose equipment was involved. That vendor's representative left the scene *without briefing his replacement*, so time was lost while the replacement was brought up to speed.

From the moment they became aware of the incident, the Pure Storage leadership treated the situation as a point of pride—they harbored no hope of converting the PoC into an order, and little hope of future sales to the prospect. But the prospect is a well-known leader in computing technology, so they believed that the company's response would become common knowledge and that an energetic and persistent reaction might rekindle the possibility of *some* business in the distant future. Moreover, the company's "customer first" ethos meant doing everything possible to recover the prospect's data, including helping another vendor diagnose a problem with his equipment that was eventually shown to have contributed to the incident.

The prospect's representatives noted and appreciated the Pure Storage response. They were sufficiently experienced technology users to realize that problems are inevitable, and that what really matters is a vendor's response when they occur. They decided that Pure Storage was the type of company they wanted as a partner, and about a year after the incident, they placed the first eight-figure FlashArray order ever received by the company.

A similar incident occurred when an east coast hospital put an array acquired for a VDI PoC into production, again without informing Pure Storage. Software in the virtualization server triggered a rare bug in the array, and the entire hospital staff was without computing for a short period. The hospital's IT staff told Pure Storage that it could not accept the lack of reliability and returned the staff's virtual desktops to the original storage infrastructure. The barrage of complaints about poor performance was so intense that the IT staff reinstalled the FlashArray and upgraded its virtualization software to a version that did not trigger the Purity//FA bug until it could be fixed. The hospital remains a satisfied customer at the time of publication.

Learning from Our Users

There's a somewhat disheartening, but true, adage that more is learned from failures than from successes. While it would be gratifying to report that every Pure Storage product ever installed was an unbridled success, there were a few occasions in its early days when the company did not meet customer expectations.

One particularly painful instance occurred during the beta period when a user subjected an FA-320 array to a heavier overwrite load over a longer period than the product had been designed for. The constant barrage of overwrites eventually overwhelmed GC. While the array would degrade gracefully by throttling writes, after a certain time, it would write only about 100 megabytes per second rather than the 300 to 500 the user had been led to expect. Additional arrays were brought in and the application's data was partitioned, but each one would eventually throttle writes. The user decided that FlashArray could not solve his problem, and returned the arrays to Pure Storage, where one was put into a lab for use by SEs.

"Four years, and several releases of Purity//FA software later, an FA-320 that a customer returned was still in use, but the SE lab was growing, and equipment had to be moved and reconfigured periodically. In one instance, five arrays (all newer than the FA-320) hosting virtual machines, had to be evacuated for reconfiguration. The project wasn't time-critical, so I decided to evacuate all five to the old FA-320, however long it took. To my amazement, the old FA-320 sustained between 800 and 900 megabytes per second for more than 12 hours, even when indicating that it was 98% full. This was the very same hardware that a customer had returned years before because it had throttled down to 150 megabytes per second. The difference was in the continuous improvements to Purity//FA over the years."
—**John Mansperger**

Although the array had been subjected to a unique load that had not been encountered previously and was unlikely to be encountered by other customers, engineering considered it a failure to fulfill a promise made to a potential customer. They embarked on a multi-year project to increase sustained write performance under heavy load (page 162). The project went on for over two years and resulted in a six-fold improvement.

In another incident, a FlashArray customer in the business of hosting IT for other organizations experienced periodic array failovers. The failovers would succeed, but they caused momentary latency "spikes" visible to the end users.

FlashArray had been designed for resiliency, emphasizing robust failover over hardening the software to minimize failovers. Users seldom experienced outages, but momentary increases in latency would occur, most of which were either undetectable or ignored. For the hosting company, however, latency spikes were significant, because they represented failure to meet its service level agreements.

The hosting customer insisted that the number of failovers be reduced, and visited Pure Storage headquarters to inspect the company's testing processes and gain a close understanding of FlashArray resiliency mechanisms. Engineering undertook a concerted effort to understand and eliminate root causes of failovers. Simultaneously, it began to track outages per array-day, regardless of duration, as a reliability metric.

At about the same time as the hosting company events were occurring, a second customer was experiencing outages, the majority of which were attributable to the data center environment—power outages, over temperature shutdowns, human errors, host and network infrastructure failures, and so forth—rather than to the arrays. This customer emphatically pointed out that while a FlashArray outage might last a minute or less, recovering and restarting hosts might take hours, and therefore Pure Storage should strive to minimize FlashArray restarts.

The high percentage of this customer's array outages caused by the environment convinced the company to track outages more granularly to distinguish between those caused by hardware, software, and environmental faults. The goal was to identify root causes so that customers could be informed of and forestall potential outages before they occurred. Today, the company's goal is no more than one severity level 1 ("Sev-1") outage per day, regardless of the number of arrays in the field. To meet this goal, not only must product quality improve as customers deploy more products, but the products must become more resistant to data center environmental faults and human errors. Today, most Sev-1s result from the latter factors.

In both these situations, as in other lesser ones over the years, Pure Storage has consistently shown its desire to listen to and learn from its customers, both when they request new product features, and when they discuss issues fundamental to them, such as product quality metrics and their impact.

In This Chapter…

Pure Storage aimed not only to disrupt storage technology, but the entire customer experience. The company created Evergreen Storage to make enterprise data storage ownership as close to a consumer experience as possible. Evergreen contrasts sharply with storage industry business practices that preceded it.

Evergreen Storage starts with all-inclusive pricing. Product purchase prices include all applicable software features, present and future.

Storage technology constantly evolves, and it is to both the customer's and the company's advantage to employ the latest available. Evergreen includes regular equipment refresh and "trade-in" policies that make it easy for customers to increase capacity while reducing "footprint" in the data center.

To a customer, a Pure Storage product is a decade-long investment. At the end of a decade, an array may contain few or none of the original parts, but there will have been no planned service outages and no bulk data migrations.

Evergreen: Rethinking the Storage Business

This chapter is largely the work of Jason Nadeau, who is justifiably proud of his contribution to Evergreen Storage.

Disrupting the storage user experience started with technology and products, but that was just the beginning. From the outset, the Pure Storage founders intended to deliver a more customer-friendly business model as well. The technology enabled a different way of doing business which over time became today's Evergreen Storage.

Evergreen Storage has redirected customer conversations from speeds and feeds to business values and outcomes. Today, senior executives, CIOs, and CFOs are regular participants in conversations with the company.

It's Not Just About the Technology

Prior to Evergreen, the prevailing enterprise storage business model was "tech refresh." Customers would purchase storage, license associated software and contract for support. After three to five years, equipment would be due for "refreshing"—in a word, replacement. Customers either had to purchase extended support contracts, usually at much higher prices, or purchase new equipment and migrate data from old storage to new, accepting intervals of degraded service in the form of availability and performance impacts, and worst of all, risk. Storage vendors encouraged refreshing, effectively requiring customers to purchase the same storage over and over again. Tech refresh was expensive, time consuming, and risky, but as the only practical option, it was the norm.

Evergreen Storage changes all that. Pure Storage customers can expect FlashArray and FlashBlade system lifetimes of a decade or more without planned downtime, and most importantly, without the impact and risk of data migration. Years after deployment, most or all of a system's parts may have been replaced, but in almost all cases, the system will have been operating continuously.

The fundamental technology that makes Evergreen possible is NDU. Every FRU in a Pure Storage product—cables, midplanes controllers, media, and software—is just that—replaceable in the field without affecting availability or performance. The concept is simple, but profound. For the first time ever, data can remain in place and in use while the storage that contains it is upgraded. With Pure Storage, so-called "forklift upgrades"

Jason Nadeau

"Building the Evergreen model to be so customer-friendly took teamwork by Product Management, Product Marketing, Legal, Finance, and Sales. Together we broke a lot of new ground and had a ton of fun doing it."

and disruptive data migrations are things of the past. Moreover, storage functionality, performance, and reliability improve with every NDU. NDU enables a new business model that takes advantage of it.

Enter Evergreen Storage

For Pure Storage, a business model defines what customers purchase from the company and when they purchase it. In 2014, Coz, Kix, and others defined the first Evergreen Storage business model. Their goals were to radically simplify storage ownership and substantially lower customers' TCO. They felt this would help users justify buying from a relatively unknown company with a short track record. They added new provisions to purchase agreements, to show that the model was real and not "just good marketing" as competitors often claimed.

Kix recruited veteran enterprise software product manager and product marketer Jason Nadeau, with whom he had worked previously, to lead the growing product marketing team, whose responsibilities had expanded to oversee the new business model. Under Jason's leadership the team introduced Evergreen Storage, refined and extended the model over time, setting a new bar that competitors are still struggling to meet.

The Evergreen Storage model had five powerful features that together comprised an alternative to tech refresh and also made it easier for prospects to try Pure Storage products:

The Love Your Storage (LYS) Guarantee

LYS is a 30-day "no-questions-asked" return policy. An alternative to PoCs, LYS allowed prospects to purchase a product with the right to return it within 30 days for any reason at all. This consumer-like approach was unheard of among enterprise storage vendors.

All Array Software Included

FlashArray and FlashBlade support contracts included all applicable software features, current and future, for as long as support contracts were in force. Customers who purchased a product and a corresponding support contract would receive all applicable software, both current at time of purchase and in the future.

Including both present and future software simplified customer procurement processes compared to competitors' typical multi-page purchase orders. Much like *Software as a Service* (SaaS), a Pure Storage service contract includes a subscription to new software features as they are introduced. It helped keep ongoing costs predictable and relieved anxieties about future increases. Moreover, with NDU, deploying new software features did not impact operations.

Free Every Three

Free Every Three included a controller hardware refresh with each three-year support contract renewal. Pure Storage exchanged customers' controllers for the then-current equivalents (non-disruptively). Customers enjoyed the benefits of newer hardware; the company benefitted from having a higher percentage of up-to-date hardware in its installed base.

Flat and Fair

Flat and Fair guaranteed that customers' three-year support contract renewal price would remain flat (not exceed that of their original contract). Contracts would be fair—renewal price would go down if the company had reduced the support price for the installed hardware. This simplified purchasing and provided buyers with budget predictability. Again, it was in stark contrast to competitors' typical practice of substantial price increases when support contracts were renewed.

Evergreen Maintenance

In 2014, most users were concerned about SSD endurance. Evergreen Maintenance guaranteed that Pure Storage would replace failed components, including SSDs, with similar or superior ones for customers with active support contracts. This alleviated concerns about flash endurance. Coupled with Free Every Three, this ensured that over time an array's hardware would modernize without disruption or the need for data migration.

Even this initial Evergreen Storage offering gave customers a simpler, more cost-effective lifetime ownership model that resembled SaaS much more closely than conventional tech refresh. In fact, the six-year FlashArray TCO was typically half that of its competitors! But the team kept learning from customers and innovating to make it even better.

Evergreen Storage Arrives in Full

The team soon realized that many customers were filling their arrays to capacity much faster than industry norms, and would need more powerful controllers earlier than the Free Every Three renewal interval. To accommodate these customers, they created an additional Evergreen Storage program:

Upgrade Flex Bundles

Upgrade Flex Bundles allowed customers to purchase qualifying capacity expansion packs bundled with upgraded controllers and receive trade-in credit for their older controllers, up to their full list price. This allowed customers to grow their arrays apace with their storage requirements without forcing them to buy new controllers as they grew. Upgrade Flex Bundles delivered incremental growth and cost benefits similar to those of scale out architectures, as well as NDU.

The introduction of FlashArray//X with DirectFlash™ Modules (DFMs) offered a dramatic performance density boost, and further reduced the power, cooling, and rack space requirements of the already efficient arrays. To enable customers to take advantage of DirectFlash as quickly as possible, the team added a new feature to Evergreen Storage:

Capacity Consolidation

Capacity Consolidation allows customers to trade-in a portion of their media whenever they purchase additional capacity. As with other Evergreen programs, customers replace (non-disruptively) their older media and return it to Pure Storage. Customers could modernize their media, transitioning from SSDs to DFMs, without repurchasing capacity or suffering performance or availability impact.

In general, data reduction is enormously beneficial, but it is data-specific. Some data sets reduce well—by factors of five or more, while others reduce much less. Both prospects and existing customers who wish to add workloads to their arrays consider under-sizing a risk. If their data reduction is less than expected, they are faced with an additional purchasing cycle for additional capacity. Many chose PoCs with samples of their data to ensure proper sizing. This slows things down for customers, and for us. Jason proposed a *Right-Size Guarantee* (RSG) for Evergreen to completely eliminate purchasers' data reduction risk:

The Right-Size Guarantee (RSG)

The RSG guarantees that an array configuration or capacity expansion proposed by Pure Storage for data of a size and type specified by the customer will be adequate. The guarantee is valid for six months from purchase. If additional capacity is required to contain the specified data, the company provides it at no additional cost to the customer. With RSG, Pure Storage becomes responsible for configurations it proposes, simplifying evaluation, purchase, and ongoing operations for customers.

RSG is made possible by the constant stream of metadata sent to Pure1 by thousands of installed arrays. Machine learning algorithms constantly analyze installed base utilization data to refine estimates of typical data reduction for a wide variety of data types and workloads. When proposing an array or capacity expansion, Pure Storage uses these estimates conservatively. Most customers who use an RSG realize better data reduction than the installed base average. After data reduction, customers are likely to get more effective storage than guaranteed, but they never get less.

While the Evergreen Storage model was developed primarily for FlashArray, many of its provisions apply to FlashBlade as well. Controller-oriented programs like Free Every Three controller upgrades and Upgrade Flex bundles are obviously not relevant, but over time, the company expects to introduce Evergreen concepts in its entire product line, and even work with server and network partners to develop complete Evergreen-style solutions.

How Can the Company Afford Evergreen?

There is no magic in Evergreen. The business model is feasible because unlike other storage vendors, Pure Storage designs its products from the ground up for SaaS-like deployment and support. Unlike legacy storage vendors, the company has never earned revenue from tech refresh. This makes it difficult for competitors to adopt Evergreen-like business practices.

The company's products and Evergreen Storage help customers succeed and over time entrust more of their critical information to Pure Storage. They eliminate tech refresh and periodic repurchase of the same storage.

Evergreen increases both the company's and its customers' overall efficiency. Sales can focus on expanding the business rather than promoting tech refresh to the same customers every few years. Support cost is reduced because customers regularly upgrade their deployments with the newest technology, which invariably outperforms and is more reliable and functional than what it replaces. Customers gain access to new innovations smoothly, without disrupting their operations.

Satisfied customers increase their investments in Pure Storage, which funds innovation that is delivered back to them, creating a virtuous cycle of information technology progress.

PART II

Building a Product

The FlashArray Story

In This Chapter...

The Pure Storage founders' "big idea" was to revolutionize data storage by making flash affordable and by simplifying the user experience. Affordability came in part from employing so-called "consumer-grade" flash devices and using advanced software techniques to bring their performance and endurance up to data center standards. Simplicity came from making the arrays nearly autonomous by performing most routine storage administration tasks without administrator involvement.

The highest responsibility of enterprise storage is *correctness*—data should never be lost or corrupted. The affordability, performance, and administrative simplicity of Pure Storage products is underpinned by architectures that deliver the best data integrity available today, and deliver it without administrator involvement.

First Principles

Discarding Legacy Storage System Concepts

Coz and Hayes had started Pure Storage with the proverbial "blank sheet of paper." Their goal was to build an all-flash storage array that would outperform disk-based arrays, be more reliable, be affordable, and establish a new norm for ease of use. In 2009, most flash-based computer storage devices were in disk drive form factors with disk I/O interfaces. This was understandable, because from laptops to supercomputers, disks are the universal medium for data storage, software loading and swapping, and backup. SSDs that "look like" disks fit into virtually any computing scenario.

Making a group of flash dies emulate a disk drive isn't easy. Flash cells are organized as *erase blocks* consisting of *pages* whose capacity is several times larger than the 512-byte sectors common to disks. Flash pages can only be written when their erase block has been initialized to a common state, and they must be written sequentially. Worse yet, once a page has been overwritten a relatively modest number of times, it is unable to retain data reliably.

SSD developers mitigate these problems with elaborate FTL firmware. FTLs receive I/O commands and translate them into operations on flash. They continually remap the sector addresses recognized externally to different flash locations to minimize erase block reinitializations (called *program/erase*, or P/E, cycles in flash jargon) and to balance the P/E cycles that can't be avoided across all erase blocks.

SSDs can replace magnetic disk drives in laptop and desktop computers, improving I/O performance and power consumptoin. For data centers, however, the fit is not quite as good. P/E cycles and continual sector address remapping make write performance wildly unpredictable—the time to write the same block of data can vary by more than three orders of magnitude depending on what an SSD is doing internally. Far more problematic, however, is the Achilles heel of flash memory—limited *endurance*. Most software assumes that disk blocks can be overwritten an unlimited number of times. But the number of overwrites a block of flash can sustain is limited—about 100,000 for the most expensive devices; 10,000 or fewer for the "consumer grade" SSDs that Coz and Hayes proposed to use.

Software wasn't about to change to accommodate the vagaries of flash, so the challenge was to develop reliable arrays that were functionally identical to their disk-based competitors but ten times as fast and cost about the same.

Coz and Hayes articulated six principles on which to base their design:

PRINCIPLE 1: OPTIMIZE PERFORMANCE FOR ALL TYPES OF SSDS

All SSDs have FTLs, but each model is unique. A given I/O load typically performs quite differently on two vendors' devices, or even on two models from the same vendor. The design must optimize SSD performance without committing to a single device model or vendor.

SSD vendors are loath to expose the inner workings of their devices. To determine the optimal performance for each type of SSD, the engineers developed parameter-driven FPL controller software. They test each SSD model by executing millions of I/O operations on tens of thousands of LBA patterns to determine the optimal mapping parameters and I/O sizes for it.[25]

PRINCIPLE 2: WRITE SPARINGLY TO MAXIMIZE SSD ENDURANCE

In 2009, a gigabyte of consumer-grade flash cost about five times as much as a gigabyte of high-performance disk and about 30 times as much as a gigabyte of high-capacity disk. To be price-competitive, the company would have to use flash ultra-efficiently. This led to some fundamental concepts that lie at the core of Purity//FA:

- Eliminate redundancy from stored data. Purity//FA *reduces* (removes redundancy from) data received from hosts before storing, so it writes less data to flash than hosts send to it.
- Write incoming data in a time-ordered log of large, densely packed blocks aligned with SSD erase blocks.
- Support any conventional SSD with the FPL but plan for eventual evolution to in-house flash device designs (DFMs).

PRINCIPLE 3: EXPLOIT FLASH STRENGTHS; AVOID ITS WEAKNESSES

Differences in read and write performance had limited flash adoption by storage system developers. Whereas magnetic disks read and write data at about the same speed, reading from flash is extremely fast (tens to hundreds of microseconds), while writing even a relatively small block can take tens to hundreds of milliseconds. To deliver consistent write performance, *stage* writes redundantly in NVRAM, and store them persistently on flash only after informing the host that they are complete. NVRAMs retain their contents when powered off, so with staging, a host that receives a write completion notice from an array can assume that its data is intact, even if power fails or a controller resets.

Lightning-fast reading and slow writing suggested another concept that can be summarized as "spend reads to save writes." For example:

---

[25] The inability to gain detailed knowledge of SSDs' internal workings was one of several factors that ultimately led to the decision to develop Direct Flash Modules (DFMs) which could be more closely aligned with FlashArray needs.

- Approximate space consumption reporting by scanning metadata periodically and recalculating rather than updating persistent counts on every host write.
- Use tables to avoid "reference counts" for deduplicated data.
- Use RAID reconstruction to satisfy reads from devices busy executing lengthy writes.

PRINCIPLE 4: NO "KNOBS"

The founders believed that storage administration was far too complicated, and in its corollary, "options are the enemy of ease of use." In 2009, servers and network switches were nearly self-managing; administrators could concentrate on their overall missions rather than on the workings of individual boxes. But storage administrators were still micromanaging—defining RAID groups, allocating "spare" capacity, masking LUNs from hosts, and so forth. As they developed the architecture, Coz and Hayes continually asked themselves what could be done by the array itself and what was absolutely necessary to expose to administrators. Their decisions have been trend-setting for the entire storage sector:

- Volume properties. A FlashArray *volume* (virtual disk or LUN) has a name and a size—period. Arrays treat all volumes equally.[26] They are completely virtual—the LBAs by which hosts address stored data have no fixed relationship to locations on flash; indeed, the location of the data in an LBA typically changes many times during its lifetime. Administrators cannot specify physical location or any other volume properties.
- No redundancy options. An adaptation of RAID, called RAID-HA, provides optimal data protection. Historically, disk array developers had resisted dual checksums because of the performance impact. But with flash performance and NVRAM staging, arrays could protect against double device failures and still deliver high performance. All data and metadata are always protected; no exceptions, no options.
- Always-on encryption. By 2009, digital data security had become a headline issue for enterprises. Data security is a broad topic, but for Pure Storage it meant protecting data "at rest" in the company's arrays. Two techniques were common at the time: encryption by hosts prior to writing, and encryption in SSD firmware (encryption by magnetic disks impacted performance too much to be practical). With both, managing encryption keys was complicated and breach-prone.

  Initially, FlashArray used SSD encryption for all data stored on devices that supported it. When it was shown to be of variable quality, however, the design changed to all-software encryption. Engineering devised a mechanism for autonomous secure key management to prevent data on misappropriated SSDs from being deciphered.
- Reduce all data all the time. As with encryption, FlashArray "just does it." Administrators cannot tune or bypass data reduction.

---

[26] Later, a user-selectable quality of service (QoS) feature was implemented to prevent "noisy neighbor" volumes from monopolizing array resources. QoS did not change the original name-and-size model, however.

"We were demonstrating a FlashArray at a trade show where our electricity came from power strips connected in series. An exhibitor a few booths away accidentally tripped a switch, which abruptly shut off everything below, including our array. People crowded around, expecting to watch us fumble through recovering from the data corruption they were sure would occur. As soon as power came back, our array rebooted. I pulled up the command history, restarted the demo script, and within three minutes the array was doing 100,000 IOPS. The astonished crowd applauded. Incidents like this made us trust engineering and be comfortable 'operating without a safety net' under pressure."
—**Chadd Kenney**

• Use networks for zoning. Storage networks are usually configured to restrict inter-device communication for security. Many arrays support an overlay on this called LUN masking. FlashArray does not mask LUNs per se; arrays expose each volume on all ports but only respond to commands from host network addresses that administrators have explicitly connected to volumes. Host-volume connections are equivalent to LUN masking but are one less thing to manage.

PRINCIPLE 5: DON'T LOSE OR CORRUPT DATA... EVER!

RAID-HA makes the probability of data loss due to read failures extremely low, but errors of other types are more insidious. For example, storage devices can signal that data was written correctly when in fact it was not. Similarly, they can report read success, and return incorrect data, or data from the wrong media location. So-called *silent corruption*[27] is rare, but the chances increase as array capacities grow to hundreds of terabytes. FlashArray guards against it with interlocking checksums that reveal when incorrect data is returned for any reason.

PRINCIPLE 6: PROTECT USERS FROM THEMSELVES

Coz's insistence on ease of use eliminated many opportunities for administrative errors that plagued other storage arrays at the time. One common source of catastrophic error was erroneous deletion of a volume.

The conventional countermeasure was the archetypal "Are you sure?" message prior to executing the command. Such messages are so commonplace, however, that administrators' responses often become automatic. FlashArray takes a different approach: Destroying[28] a volume triggers an internal snapshot of its contents with a lifetime of 24 hours. At any time during the 24 hours, a single command can restore the volume in its entirety. Thus, there is a 24-hour grace period during which to correct errors. In the spirit of "no knobs," the grace period is not adjustable. If space reclamation is urgent, an administrator can terminate the grace period and **eradicate** the volume to start reclaiming its space immediately.

---

[27] https://www.perform.illinois.edu/Papers/USAN_papers/09ROZ01.pdf
[28] The Purity//FA CLI command **destroy** emphasizes that data is obliterated as well as the volume object. The command for removing objects that do not contain data is **delete**.

Coz constantly strove to make the storage user experience easier. He insisted that nothing an array could optimize for itself should require administrative action, or even be exposed to administrators. With FlashArray, there is no RAID group or spare configuration, no volume placement, no balancing of data sets across volumes, and so forth, because an array can optimize these better and faster than a human. Perhaps the most visible example of this is the absence of a FlashArray shutdown procedure. Since an array must be able to recover from crashes, why shouldn't every shutdown be a crash?

In This Chapter…

Conventional startup wisdom holds that to disrupt a technology, the disruptor must be markedly superior to the incumbents in one metric that a few adventurous users value highly. For Pure Storage, that metric was an order of magnitude increase in I/O performance at an affordable price. Engineering concentrated on that first, and released three waves of pre-production alpha arrays to non-paying "customers" for testing under realistic conditions. The alpha arrays were not suitable for production, but they demonstrated that data reduction in real time was possible, making consumer-grade flash a viable storage option.

Alpha arrays were replaced by beta arrays built from hardware components that would eventually see production, but with somewhat limited software functionality. When the beta arrays proved themselves in the field, the company completed the software by adding high availability and delivered the first production FlashArray, the FA-320.

When the FA-320 became generally available, engineering was already looking forward to the next generation, the FA-420. FA-420 arrays became generally available about 18 months after the FA-320. Realizing that there was demand for FlashArray performance and simplicity at both higher capacity points and lower price points than the FA-420 offered, in mid-2014, the company introduced the FA-450 and FA-405, larger and smaller variants of the FA-420 respectively.

Building FlashArray

Getting Started

When Pure Storage was founded in 2009, Clayton M. Christensen's model for disruptive innovation was well-established. First articulated in 1997 in "The Innovator's Dilemma,"[29] Professor Christensen's advice to innovators was to focus on the one metric in which their product outdid all incumbents by a wide margin. The product might be inferior in all other dimensions, but if the metric is important to even a few users, it can help the innovator gain a market foothold and can eventually become a, if not *the*, main purchase criterion.

With market presence, the new product improves in other dimensions until it eventually supplants previous incumbents. Christensen's favorite example was magnetic disks. Smaller form factor disks have repeatedly replaced larger ones. When introduced, each generation of smaller disks was slower and less reliable than the incumbent, but smaller disks enabled more flexible system designs—rack-mounting, deskside towers, and laptops. Over time, performance and reliability improvements in smaller disks gradually eliminated the market for larger ones, over and over again.

For Pure Storage, the metric of focus was performance: improve it by an order of magnitude at the same price. Given the per-byte cost difference between high-performance disk drives and flash, the only way to make an all-flash array affordable was to *reduce* the data stored in it. But data reduction is compute-intensive. Could an all-flash array reduce data inline and still deliver the performance increase on which the company was predicated?

In 2009, customer expectations for enterprise storage systems were pretty high. High availability, flexible configurations, snapshots, data replication, and similar advanced features were generally considered essential. Even if Pure Storage delivered an order of magnitude better cost:performance, would that be enough to establish a foothold?

Where Will The Customers Come From?

Another guru of the technology business, Geoffrey A. Moore, had described a model for companies entering technology markets in his "Crossing the Chasm," first published in 1991.[30]

---

[29] https://www.amazon.com/Innovators-Dilemma-Technologies-Management-Innovation/dp/1633691780
[30] https://www.amazon.com/Crossing-Chasm-3rd-Disruptive-Mainstream/dp/0062292986

Moore postulated that customers for technology appear in distinct waves during different product lifecycle stages. While Moore's main focus was on how companies could cross the "chasm" that separates the small number of early adopters and the much larger but more conservative mainstream, he suggested that the very first adopters of a new technology were actually a third class that he called *technology enthusiasts*, and defined as:

They are the ones who first appreciate the architecture of your product and why it therefore has a competitive advantage over the current crop of products established in the marketplace. They are the ones who will spend hours trying to get products to work that, in all conscience, never should have been shipped in the first place. They will forgive ghastly documentation, horrendously slow performance, ludicrous omissions in functionality, and bizarrely obtuse methods of invoking some needed function—all in the name of moving technology forward. They make great critics because they truly care.[31]

From Technology Enthusiasts to Early Adopters

The optimal path to success would be for engineering to focus on high-speed data reduction, while the go-to-market arm (Kix and Burr) identified technology enthusiasts whose primary interest was affordable storage with much higher performance than anything then available. Affordability was key—there were high-performing alternatives, including flash-based ones, but for most users, their cost precluded broad deployment.

The company had to use its working capital wisely to demonstrate that its technology was viable in production in order to address the next wave of prospects: the early adopters. Moore defines these as "…*that rare breed of people who have the insight to match an emerging technology to a strategic opportunity, the temperament to translate that insight into a high-visibility, high-risk project, and the charisma to get the rest of their organizations to buy into that project.*"[32]

Early adopters don't value technology for its own sake. Instead, they recognize opportunities to use it to realize their own goals. Thus, while they may not demand the same maturity as the mainstream, they require more complete products than technology enthusiasts because they regard them as tools to better achieve their own ends. Pure Storage would have to deliver a product with sufficient features to attract these early adopters.

They started by implementing the most important features in stages and delivering each stage to technology enthusiast organizations in "alpha" arrays for *proof-of-concept* (PoC) trials. No revenue was accepted, and the PoC contract terms prohibited using the arrays for production.

The most important feature to deliver was the predicted order of magnitude cost:performance improvement over disk-based systems. The main contributor to affordability was data reduction. The alpha arrays utilized hardware that was admittedly not suitable for production products. They were not highly available and there was no

---

[31] "Crossing the Chasm, Revised Edition," Adobe Acrobat E-Book Reader edition, October 2001, page 23
[32] Ibid, page 25

user configurability, nor any administrative interface. Maximizing endurance of the consumer-grade SSDs (the second contributor to affordability) was not robustly addressed, but the performance goal was to sustain 100,000 IOPS while reducing incoming data prior to storing and expanding it upon retrieval.

Michael Cornwell and Joe Hasbani "shipping" an alpha array

Mike and Kix identified a local organization willing to exercise an alpha array with data compression (only) in a test environment. An array was delivered to them in the fall of 2010. It had limited functionality and was clearly suitable only for lab use. But it met the all-important goal of 100,000 IOPS while compressing data for storage and decompressing it on retrieval.

Within three months, engineering had added deduplication and rudimentary *garbage collection* (GC, reclamation of space occupied by overwritten data) to the software. Arrays with these capabilities, called "alpha-2," were delivered to six local users that had been identified by Kix and Burr in the interim. Alpha arrays used Fibre Channel (8Gb/s) connections with fixed WWNs (storage network addresses) assigned by engineering. They presented ten pre-configured *volumes* (LUNs), all with the same capacity.

In August 2011, ten "alpha-3" arrays were delivered to users spread over a larger geographic area. These supported volumes of different sizes and included a speedup of GC and a steady stream of 100,000 *writes* per second.

One alpha-3 user gave Pure Storage quite a surprise by attempting to purchase its alpha array, which unbeknownst to the company they had put into production processing medical records. Aware that alpha arrays differed in several important ways from what would eventually be released, the company rebuffed the attempt. When the FA-320 shipped, the user became a customer for the more mature, highly-available product.

From Beta to Release

Even as the software team was adding functionality, they and the hardware team were preparing significant changes for the released product:

HARDWARE PLATFORM

Ko's hardware team believed that neither the alpha array hardware nor its supplier were suitable for volume production, in part because the hardware could not be configured for high availability. They selected an alternate vendor and a configuration with separate controller and storage device chassis. Separate device enclosures made stateless controllers possible, which was key to fast, reliable failover and NDU.

SOFTWARE UNDERPINNINGS

Alpha software ran on OpenSolaris, selected for its maturity and stability. It became apparent, however, that the OpenSolaris developer community was largely inactive. Linux, the other viable alternative, was less mature but broadly accepted, had a large community of active developers, and received prompt attention from hardware vendors. That made it a better choice for production arrays, so engineering ported the software to it for production and further development.

NVRAM ARCHITECTURE

To provide low latency to a constant stream of host writes without risking data loss, the software *staged* them in high-speed NVRAM before persisting them on flash. But for high availability, arrays would need a way for a controller taking over from a failed partner to flush the partner's staged writes from NVRAM to flash. Mounting NVRAMs in device enclosures accessible to both controllers solved that problem.

STORAGE LAYOUT

FlashArray virtualizes the volumes presented to hosts. This allows flexibility in mapping LBAs used by hosts to the locations of stored data. The arrays' storage layout continued to evolve during alpha system deployment but stabilized by the time of production.

With these changes, and with tuning the software to deliver 300,000 IOPS, the company felt that the product was releasable. They verified that with two "beta" releases. Users who deployed beta arrays, called FA-310, received production hardware and software, "feature complete" except for high availability, which was delivered in the first half of 2012.

FA-320 with Two Shelves

FA-420 with Four Shelves

General Availability: The FA-320

In the spring of 2012, the high availability software was ready. Arrays were delivered to carefully vetted beta users. The company had received its first revenue purchase order in November 2011, but not until about six months later were engineering, sales, support, and operations ready for FA-320 general availability.

The FA-320 offered either 5.5 or 11 terabytes of physical flash in one or two *storage shelves* (SSD enclosures). Hosts connected to each controller via four 8Gb/s Fibre Channel ports. Users could configure as many as 500 volumes per array. Administrators managed arrays using a command line interface connected to a terminal emulator, or later, through a browser-based GUI connected to Ethernet management ports.

Even as the FA-320 gained market traction, the hardware team was working to broaden the product line's appeal. In rapid succession came:

SUPPORT FOR ISCSI

As 10 Gb/s Ethernet became readily available and affordable, a number of data centers sought to simplify their networks by "going all Ethernet." FlashArray support for iSCSI over 10GbE HBAs broadened the addressable market to include those data centers.

Capacity Increases

As SSD vendors delivered higher-capacity devices during 2012 and 2013, the company qualified and supported selected models. Mid-2013 saw 11-terabyte storage shelves, increasing maximum physical capacity to 23 terabytes. In 2013, support for four storage shelves, two with 5.5 terabytes and two with 12 terabytes, increased maximum physical capacity to 35 terabytes.

FlashArray: The Next Generation

Customers rapidly and enthusiastically accepted the FA-320 and were soon asking for more—more capacity, more connectivity, more features.

As FlashArray popularity grew, sales uncovered opportunities for larger capacity arrays. But more capacity implied more IOPS, which would in turn require more powerful controllers with more DRAM. Already in 2012, Ko's team had been searching for a platform for next-generation controllers. They qualified a candidate and started work on what would become the FA-400 series. In late 2013, the FA-420 was released, supported by Purity//FA Version 4. FA-420 arrays outperformed their FA320 predecessors but remained at the 35-terabyte maximum physical flash capacity for the moment.

"After a long sales campaign, we finally placed an 11 terabyte FA-420 at a semiconductor process control manufacturer. We mounted our array in 8U of rack space beside their main storage system that occupied a row of 7 floor tiles and needed 28 30-amp circuits.

When the customer received a quote for renewing the service contract on their older system, they chose to upgrade their FlashArray instead. After a capacity and model upgrade, their array became FlashArray//M70 with four storage shelves. It included every model of flash device we were selling—256, 512, and 1024 gigabyte SSDs and two terabyte flash modules in the chassis. Mixed configurations don't faze FlashArray.

The customer migrated all the data from their older system to the FlashArray, and powered the older system off permanently. 12U of FlashArray replaced a 14 foot row of cabinets with no sacrifice in performance! For a while, this was one of our five busiest arrays. To this day there has never been a hiccup."

—John Mansperger

In mid-2014, the FA-400 became a family with the addition of two new members:

FA-450

With higher-performing processors, larger DRAM, and two additional back-end SAS ports, the FA-450 supported six storage shelves, for a maximum physical flash capacity of 70 terabytes.

FA-405

A compact entry-level array made FlashArray technology available to users with modest storage and I/O needs that did not require the larger models.

Purity//FA Version 4 supported the FA-400 series, and in addition, included important functional enhancements, including *FlashRecover* asynchronous data replication, SSL certificates that enabled arrays to identify themselves securely on TCP/IP networks, and FIPS 140-2 validation. The latter made it easier to sell to the United States Federal Government, most of whose departments require FIPS 140-2 compliance.

In This Chapter...

A company that aspires to leadership in any type of computer system must ultimately develop and build hardware. To minimize time to market, the first arrays were built from off-the-shelf hardware components, but it was generally acknowledged that some upcoming generation of products would have to be based on hardware of the company's own design.

Designing complex computer hardware is a lengthy and expensive proposition. There were questions about whether the company was ready. Fortunately, experienced hardware designers became available, and were recruited as the core of an in-house hardware design team.

The team created a multi-generational architecture in which underlying components could be updated as more capable ones came to market. To date, four FlashArray generations have been delivered using the same basic architecture—FlashArray//M, FlashArray//MR2, FlashArray//X, and FlashArray//XR2. All are non disruptively upgradable in the field.

A key feature of the architecture was an NVRAM that used NVMe to communicate with controllers. Not only was the NVRAM faster and more reliable than the products it replaced, it gave the team valuable experience with the NVMe technology, which eventually became the interface to Pure Storage-designed Direct Flash Modules and for connecting arrays to hosts.

Taking A Giant Step

In 2013, the FA-320 was shipping, and the FA-420 was slated for release late in the year. To keep pace with the constant evolution of technology, however, the company was also exploring options for its next product generation. Experience had made it clear that it would need more control over hardware, but there were three options for achieving that—another generation based on "off-the-shelf" components, a joint development with an OEM hardware vendor, and an in-house hardware design.

Earlier, Roland Dreier had introduced Pure Storage to Bill Cerreta, then a hardware engineering director with a local tech company. Bill considered joining, but concluded that Pure Storage wasn't ready to develop hardware and elected to go elsewhere. "Elsewhere" didn't quite work out as planned, so in mid-2013, he re-engaged with Bob Wood and soon joined the company along with Pete Kirkpatrick to develop the next FlashArray generation.

To define and develop the next generation of arrays, Bill sought experienced engineers who would be able to design for the long term, and in his words, "make decisions even when information was incomplete." Soon after he and Pete joined, he recruited Alex Gregory, a long-time veteran of hardware design with whom he had previously worked.

Bill Cerreta
"Initially, the company focused on software, which was the right call, but by 2013 it was clear the hardware platform needed attention. Bob and Coz had decided that the next big investment would be hardware, which meant expanding the team.

I was super-excited to join, because I saw the opportunity. For the company to take off, it had to unlock the potential of hardware. I accepted in mid-summer, and Platinum was off to the races by the fall. The new design was awesome. It not only solved the immediate product concern, it set us up for future FlashArray generations."

Pete had been happy to consider moving to Pure Storage. During his interviews, he had been impressed by the company's values and the culture that made them a reality. Living as he did within easy walking distance of the Castro Street headquarters didn't hurt.

Alex had been satisfied with his situation leading a major blade server project. He happened to notice Bill's move to Pure Storage on social media and sent a "what's up?" note. Bill's response led to an interview round in which the interviewers impressed him.

Pete Kirkpatrick

"Most companies talk about their values and culture—for example putting the customer first, and having a creative, collaborative atmosphere. But not every company lives them like Pure Storage, even as the company has grown."

Alex Gregory

"When Bob Wood interviewed me, he described Platinum in general terms. My reaction was, 'I've done that before—it'll be a piece of cake.' He was a bit taken aback, but we did deliver Platinum within a month of our original estimate."

That, plus having previously worked with Bill, and some introspection about "wanting the Silicon Valley startup experience before he was too old," helped him decide to join.

So, What Exactly Do We Build?

Bill had joined the company with an open brief to create the next generation of FlashArray hardware. Off-the-shelf hardware might have a time-to-market advantage but would expose the company to pricing, support, and ongoing supply risks. Having worked with hardware OEMs in the past, he felt that joint development would have similar exposure. Moreover, either approach would inevitably compromise functionality in small ways. Within three months, he and Pete had concluded that a Pure Storage design was the optimal approach and had mapped out steps to achieve it.

By the time Alex joined, the company had decided on in-house development rather than another generation of arrays based on externally sourced components. The project was called Platinum in keeping with the tradition of naming major projects after dense natural elements. The team committed to deliver in-house controller, NVRAM, and chassis designs supported by Purity//FA within 18 months (actual development time was 19 months). To minimize risk, the new product would initially use the same SSDs and storage shelves as the FA-400 series.

Alex, Bill, and Pete were the core of the team that defined and developed Platinum, announced in mid-2015 as the FlashArray//M series. They had streamlined the design to the extent possible. While the limitations of SSDs were recognized, and even though Pete had proposed what would ultimately become the DirectFlash Module (DFM), the idea of a custom device was shelved until FlashArray//M development was complete and the products shipped.

In the early stages of the project, Bill was very much a working manager. Because of his contacts and credibility with major contract manufacturers, the team was very quickly able to engage a contractor with a competent design arm. Supplied with specifications and schematics developed by Pete and Alex, the contractor was able to accelerate development by assisting with many low-level design details. By early 2014, the team had working "first pass" hardware which they used for ongoing development—hardware's version of the "dogfood" concept (page 66).

Over time, the company's relationship with its manufacturing contractor has matured and deepened. Today, the contractor's design department is a gateway to its entire range of services—electrical, printed circuit board, packaging, and more. Because it is essentially a volume manufacturer, it is sensitive to "design for manufacturability and serviceability," which goes a long way toward easing new product introductions.

The Stealth Feature

In 2013, the standards-based NVMe I/O interface for intelligent devices was on the horizon. It grew out of industry-wide realization that SCSI in all its forms had become a performance constraint and I/O bottleneck, and that storage device processing power, then used largely to emulate disk drives, could interact more intelligently with hosts. SSDs with NVMe weren't generally available, but it was clear that the new interface would ultimately revolutionize the way computers interacted with storage.

"Pete and I made a week-long visit to our contractor's design department armed with a sheaf of specs and schematics. The first day, we entered the room expecting to meet with two or three counterparts, but there were about 50 people around a huge conference table. We both had a cultural adjustment to make, but once we understood each others' working styles, it became a very productive partnership."
—**Alex Gregory**

"The original Platinum lab was a conference room next to the kitchen. If systems were running during lunch, the extra load from the ovens would trip a breaker and ruin lunch for everyone, so we learned to tone it down at that time. That was just the first of many adventures in developing a hardware platform in an office building."
—**Pete Kirkpatrick**

Using NVMe, Pure Storage could develop its own flash devices, eliminating the FPL (page 110) and enabling controllers to optimize flash performance and endurance across an entire array. Eventually, arrays could use it to communicate with hosts.

More Reasons for NVMe

NVMe connects intelligent storage devices directly to computers' PCIe buses. It improves I/O performance, by increasing the data transfer rate and by simplifying the transformations on the path between computer DRAM and storage. Including it in the Platinum design would develop experience for eventual Pure Storage-designed flash devices and would firmly establish the company as a storage technology leader.

Although NVMe was unproven as a storage interface, the Platinum team mapped out a multi-generation architecture that would eventually evolve to all-NVMe arrays. The first step was the FlashArray//M series with NVMe-based NVRAMs (mid-2015). The progression continued with FlashArray//MR2 (2016), FlashArray//X (2017), and FlashArray//XR2 (2018). FlashArray//XR2 supports NVMe-connected NVRAMs, storage devices, and Ethernet-connected storage shelves of Direct Flash Modules (DFMs) that use NVMe to communicate.

Platinum hardware is more reliable and compact than its predecessor. It packs two controllers, two or four NVRAMs, and 20 flash modules into a single 3RU (5.25 inch)-high rack-mountable chassis. The chassis midplane carries both SAS and NVMe to all components, as well as non-transparent PCIe bridges (NTBs) that connect the controllers, replacing the Infiniband links used on earlier models.

NVRAMs: The Tip of the NVMe Iceberg

The NVRAMs used in earlier arrays had been somewhat problematic. While their performance was adequate, but their failure rate was high and they were expensive. No viable alternative was available, so the Platinum team added a custom NVRAM to its list of hardware to design.

Because FlashArray NVRAMs are in the path of write response to hosts, they must be the highest-performing FlashArray storage devices. NVMe's speed and intelligent interface contributed significantly to the remarkable performance increases of FlashArray//M series arrays compared to their predecessors. SSDs with NVMe interfaces were not expected in time for Platinum's planned ship date but the NVMe NVRAMs gave the team hands-on experience with the technology much earlier than the company's competitors, experience that was exploited during development of the DFMs.

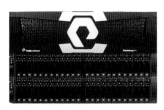

FlashArray//M

With the contract manufacturer producing in volume, the company shipped its first FlashArray//M series arrays in mid-2015, about 19 months after the project began. The achievement was remarkable considering that chassis, controller mainboards, midplane, NVRAM, and adaptation of the SSD carrier were all completely new designs, and that Purity//FA was adapted to support the new hardware as it was being developed.

The FlashArray//M series was followed in late 2016 by FlashArray//MR2. In 2017, the FlashArray//X series added support for NVMe-based DFMs in the array chassis. In 2018, FlashArray//XR2 added NVMe over Fabric (NVMe-oF) support for high-speed Ethernet-connected external storage shelves of DFMs. Each generation featured higher performance, larger maximum capacity, and additional software features compared to its predecessor.

With the delivery of FlashArray//XR2 and NVMe-oF storage shelves of DFMs, FlashArray was completely-NVMe-based internally. In early 2019, support for NVMe-oF host interface cards was delivered, finally completing the evolution to an all-NVMe FlashArray generation.

The Platinum and FlashBlade hardware teams have merged to form the Platform Business Unit. Under Bill's leadership, the unit is responsible for designing hardware for future generations of both families.

The Problem with SSDs

Like FlashArray, SSDs organize data as a log, selecting the location for each block received to optimize longevity and performance. They maintain maps that relate the LBAs they present externally to the flash locations of the data most recently written to them. Occasionally, they must pre-erase an entire erase block before storing incoming data in it.

Like any log-structured storage, SSDs periodically to reclaim space occupied by obsolete data. This makes SSD write performance highly variable. A host writing an LBA might see sub-millisecond response one time, and tens or hundreds of milliseconds at others.

For personal computers and small servers, SSD write variability is hardly noticeable, but in the data center it's a serious drawback. To overcome SSD write performance variability, the Pure Storage founders included redundant NVRAMs in the arrays and staged every host write in them before reducing the data and packing it into buffers for writing to flash.

Direct Flash Module

Optimizing SSD performance was also important. Coz spent many hours experimenting with each model considered for qualification to create an abstract LBA space and set of I/O parameters that the Purity//FA FPL would use to remap internal writes. The FPL allowed the software to treat all SSDs of a given capacity alike, while optimizing write performance for each device type. In effect, the FPL homogenizes SSDs, minimizing

FlashArray//X90

the differences in how devices optimize flash longevity and performance.

A key aspect of the Purity//FA architecture is that like SSDs, it attempts to optimize flash longevity and I/O performance, but it does so for the entire array. In essence, the Purity//FA FPL and SSDs' FTL firmware do the same work. It had been a long-term goal of the founders to find a way for Purity//FA FPL to read and write flash blocks directly, without either its own FPL or devices' FTLs getting in the way.

The Direct Flash Module (DFM): Less Really is More

As the FlashBlade team began to gain experience with "raw" flash, the Platinum team embarked on the design of a flash device to eventually supersede conventional SSDs in FlashArray. The two key properties of the new device were an NVMe interface for transferring data significantly faster than the SAS network used to connect SSDs, and direct addressability of the device's flash blocks. Direct addressability would shorten the I/O path and enable an array-wide locus for flash optimization. The new devices were called *DirectFlash Modules* (DFMs) and had physical capacities of 9.1 and 18.3 terabytes. Like SSD-based flash modules, DFMs are sold in datapacks of 10 (for chassis installation) and 14 (for installation in DirectFlash shelves). In 2019, the maximum physical capacity of a single-chassis (3RU-high) FlashArray//XR2 is 366 terabytes. A DirectFlash shelf can accommodate two datapacks, for a total of 512 terabytes of physical capacity.

In This Chapter...

The first FlashArray models included high performance, efficient data reduction, high-availability, and administrative simplicity. To be an industry leader, however, Pure Storage would also have to deliver addtional features that were equal or superior to those of its competition. The first such feature delivered was snapshots. The Purity//FA metadata structures enabled a highly-functional, efficient snapshot implementation. Snapshot creation is near-instantaneous, volumes cloned from snapshots offer performance equal to their parents, and any arbitrary snapshot can be deleted with no impact on others.

Snapshots formed the basis for the next advanced feature introduced: FlashRecover periodic replication of data to remote arrays. FlashRecover was followed by the industry's most advanced implementation of synchronous replication, in which two arrays maintain identical images of sets of volumes that can be updated by hosts connected to either array.

While this and other functionality was being added to Purity//FA, the software was also tracking hardware developments, supporting each new FlashArray generation as it was introduced, and continuing to provide non-disruptive upgrade to newer software releases and hardware generations.

Not By Hardware Alone

A s FlashArray hardware evolved, Purity//FA was not only keeping pace but was steadily becoming more feature-rich.

When the FA-320 was launched in mid-2012, its maximum physical storage capacity was a relatively modest 11 terabytes in two shelves, each populated with 22 256-gigabyte SSDs. Four 8Gb/s Fibre Channel ports in each controller connected an array to the storage network for host access. The arrays were highly available, able to sustain SSD, SAS path, and even controller failures without loss of data or service. By connecting both hosts and array controllers to two independent Fibre Channel fabrics, the complete path between host and data could be made highly available.

The arrays' main attraction, though, was the data reduction that lowered the effective cost of flash storage to that of high-performance disk arrays. Users reported reduction ratios as high as five and six for certain types of data while they enjoyed the "three tens" (10X the performance, 10X reduction in power and cooling cost, 10X reduction in data center footprint) of FlashArray storage. Uptake was rapid and enthusiastic.

But users are never satisfied. In 2012, 10Gb/s Ethernet was becoming mainstream and some data centers were moving to a single network technology strategy. The company recognized this, and within six months of FA-320 introduction, released Purity//FA version 2.5, whose most significant feature was support for 10Gb/s Ethernet HBAs for iSCSI host connection.

Toward more Flexible Administration

In response to customer requests, a mid-2013 Purity//FA release introduced role-based administration. Three administrative roles are defined: array administrator, encompassing all operations, storage administrator, for managing volumes, snapshots, and host connections, and reader, for displaying array properties and conditions, but not allowing any action. In addition, an audit trail facility allowed administrators to review all actions taken on an array. Finally, a *Representational State Transformation* (REST) API introduced late in the year made it possible for data centers to manage their arrays from user-developed programs and scripts and data-center management frameworks.

Snapshots

2013 was an especially eventful year for Purity//FA. With the introduction of snapshots, users could capture immutable images of groups of volumes *atomically* (as of a single point in time). This enabled them to recover from data corruption by overwriting corrupted volumes with an earlier snapshot, and to *clone* (create) new volumes from snapshots to use for backup, analytics, software testing and other purposes. Cloned volumes provide the same performance as the originals.

Purity//FA snapshot creation is nearly instantaneous; it makes a copy of each snapped volume's metadata that occupies almost no space until parent volume data is overwritten, and then only in proportion to the overwritten data. The structure is extremely flexible. Any snapshot can overwrite its parent volume, for example to recover from data corruption by restoring volumes to a known valid time. Individual snapshots can be deleted from anywhere in a time-ordered chain.

Another technology maturing at the time was VDI, the use of one powerful storage system to host virtual system disks for the desktop computers of hundreds of knowledge workers. VDI reduces per-seat computing cost, but perhaps more importantly, it centralizes configuration control—hundreds of operating systems and their applications can be kept consistent at a substantial reduction in IT support cost. A script could create hundreds of virtual system disk volumes from a single FlashArray snapshot in minutes. VDI and FlashArray seemed to be made for each other.

With Replication, Snapshots Took Off...

Initially, customer adoption of FlashArray snapshots was quite low (page 64). It increased significantly in 2014, however, when *FlashRecover* asynchronous replication, based on snapshots was delivered. By 2014, it was apparent that the lack of a way to protect data against a data center disaster was inhibiting sales. The architects realized that sending FlashArray snapshots to remote arrays could provide protection. Dan created a team to develop the idea, but quickly realized that with his larger responsibilities, he could not manage the project directly. He asked Shiva Ankam, with whom he had worked in the past, if she would be interested in leading a team that was developing an interesting new storage technology.

At the time, Shiva was a technical director with a large Bay Area storage company. A fan of the small company atmosphere that "makes it easy to get things done," she was interested in what Pure Storage might have to offer. So, when Dan called, she came for a round of interviews, including some with engineers who were already on the replication project. She was impressed by the people and interested in the project. The interviewers were favorably impressed by her, so an offer was extended and accepted, and in early-2014 she joined Pure Storage engineering.

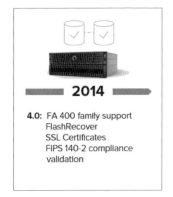

2014

4.0: FA 400 family support
FlashRecover
SSL Certificates
FIPS 140-2 compliance
validation

Initially, Shiva worked closely with the replication team, and soon became engineering manager for the project. While still learning about the company and the products, she had become responsible for delivering an important new Purity//FA feature in about six months.

Assessing where the project stood and what it would take to complete it, Shiva quickly realized that replication touched most of Purity//FA. Her replication team had to align with the GC team, the space reporting team, the user interface team, and others to deliver a functionally complete release. Things were further complicated by the introduction of 512 gigabyte SSDs and the extension of maximum array capacity to 70 terabytes with the FA-450. In addition to everything else, replication would test the scalability of Purity//FA data structures and algorithms.

Shiva Ankam

"Pure Storage expects new engineers to 'hit the ground running,' regardless of experience, and to ask for help when they need it.

Within two weeks of my joining, Dan handed off the replication team to me. It was like drinking from a fire hose. Our team represented four countries, none of them the U.S. We quickly became a 'work family'—we worked very hard, but the collaborative no-nonsense attitude in engineering made it fun. That aspect of the culture is something I love about the company."

…But Didn't Quite Get Airborne

Purity//FA version 4, including FlashRecover asynchronous replication, shipped in late 2014. FlashRecover uptake, especially among larger customers, was greater than expected. Unfortunately, so were the customers' expectations. Many users created schedules that replicated groups of volumes every few minutes, which overwhelmed the metadata structures. Performance and space utilization reporting both suffered. Replicating daily, or even hourly, was manageable in most cases, but more frequent replication caused unanticipated surges in memory usage and GC slowdowns, resulting in fluctuating space utilization reports, especially on target arrays. It turned out that snapshots weren't "free"—at least when they were replicated. There were highly-visible escalations—support cases filed by customers reporting that replication backlogs were affecting their operations.

The engineering teams collaborated to resolve the issues quickly. Shiva's view of the company's culture was reinforced by the way in which the teams came together to improve the product, insisting on "solving problems right," rather than circumventing them, and in how openly the support organization communicated progress to customers. She observes that to this day, the "get it done" culture, common in small startups but difficult to maintain in large organizations, continues to be the norm, even as Pure Storage has grown to over 3,000 employees and thousands of customers.

But resolution of the escalations notwithstanding, there was broad realization within the company that with even larger arrays on the near horizon and with customers demonstrating needs for up-to-the-minute disaster protection for critical data, scalable long-term solutions were needed.

From Lemons, Lemonade

Once the escalations were resolved, engineering started two new projects, one to scale array metadata to support more local and replicated snapshots, and one to replicate data between two arrays *synchronously*.

Improving metadata structures to accommodate more frequent replication was doubly fortuitous. Not only did it greatly improve arrays' ability to cope with frequent replications, it also facilitated XCOPY support at a time when users were starting to adopt VDI in large numbers. Purity//FA was able to create thousands of virtual machine disk images in minutes. The new structures eventually made possible the 2016 increase in the maximum number of supported objects to 5,000 volumes, 50,000 snapshots, and 500 hosts.

After managing the replication team for just over two years, Shiva relocated to the company's recently-opened office in Bellevue Washington for personal reasons. In the Bellevue office, which had been established to develop tools for integrating FlashArray with Microsoft products, she first managed a small team working on replication monitoring for Pure1. Her experience and Mountain View engineering connections made her the obvious choice to lead development of the *Purity//FA VASA Provider* for VMware's *vStorage APIs for Storage Awareness* (VASA) storage management paradigm. The team produced the provider in record time, but even so, the insistence on "doing it right" created a release hailed by the field as one of the industry's best implementations of VVol support.[33]

Recognizing that greater Seattle has a rich pool of potential employees with cloud-related development experience, the company expanded the Pure1 engineering presence there. Today, Shiva manages a significant part of the Pure1 Manage team, which collaborates closely with Ben Borowiec's (page 187) data science team in Mountain View. Together they are redefining the user storage management experience by continuing to extend Pure1's management capabilities for entire Pure Storage product "fleets." Like all engineering locations, as the Bellevue team expands by hiring from outside, managers follow the company's time-honored interview practices (page 54).

In Search of The Right Write

In 2012 Constantine Sapuntzakis ("Costa") realized that the market for his startup company's product wasn't developing as expected. He began to consider alternatives, both with established companies and with other startups, one of which was Pure Storage, suggested to him by Doug Mohr. The company's technology interested him; the market for its product was huge, so after a rigorous interview round followed by a talk with Mike Speiser, he joined in the fall of 2012. His start was delayed for a day because the company was on a celebratory boat ride in San Francisco Bay.

Costa joined the team focused on improving FlashArray write performance. He was a bit intimidated at first, because it seemed that everyone but him had been with the company for a long time and knew a lot about the software. It took him a while to realize that for some of his colleagues, "a long time" was a few weeks.

Subsequently, he worked on a variety of Purity//FA 'infrastructure' projects whose overall

---

[33] Responsibility for VMware integration has since moved to an engineering site in Vancouver, British Columbia.

intent was to improve reliability and performance. He found himself spending considerable time analyzing the root causes of obscure bugs uncovered during testing and fixing them. In the process, he wrote a lot of code, which he enjoyed, having done progressively less coding in his previous job. His infrastructure projects were hardly glamorous, but quite visible and important to his fellow engineers.

In 2013 he gave a talk about FlashArray hardware and software architecture to a Stanford University (his graduate school alma mater) computer science forum. The talk was extremely well-received; it became a recruiting tool and a staple of the company's "on-boarding" process for new engineers.

Prototyping Purity//FA support for VMware VVols, eliminating test failures caused by "race conditions" in library functions, developing an asynchronous procedure call mechanism that Hayes had prototyped, and similar infrastructure projects gradually made Costa one of a small cadre of "go to" people for Purity//FA knowledge.

Constantine Sapuntzakis ("Costa")

"I had been working in a startup that was trying to create a new market and a product to enter it simultaneously. What impressed me about Pure Storage, aside from the rigorous interviews and Mike Speiser's awesome sales pitch, was that the company was attacking a well-established market. The challenge was going to be execution, not execution plus market creation."

In 2015, with FlashArray//M nearing release, maximum write throughput was about 1.2 gigabytes per second, although the new hardware was clearly capable of much more. Costa dug into the problem and discovered that the speed of the new NVMe-based NVRAMs exposed the fact that the software was waiting far too long for SSD write completions as it "flushed" data to them. He made improvements to the flush path that doubled write performance. Other engineers joined in, and a two-year project increased FlashArray maximum write throughput by a factor of six.

Because of his broad and deep knowledge of FlashArray, today Costa works as a Purity//FA *area lead*, responsible for reviewing and vetting other engineers' proposals, designs, and code. His personal contributions are in end-to-end data security, for which he collaborates with host-based encryption vendors to ensure that data can be secured throughout the processing, storage, and retrieval cycle, and yet still reap the space efficiency benefits of FlashArray data reduction.

Space Cadets

In any log-structured storage system, determining how much space is in use and how much is available at any point in time is difficult. The difficulty arises because GC occurs in the background. When a host overwrites a block of data, there is a period during which both new and overwritten data occupy space. Not until GC reclaims the space occupied by the overwritten data does it become available for reuse. If the incoming data rate exceeds

Ganesh Ramanarayanan
"Leading the escalations team for a year made me aware of the complexity of the data centers that use our products. There's no way someone could appreciate that without experience."

GC's reclamation rate, the system will eventually fill, although from the user's point of view, there is plenty of free space.

To forestall filling, FlashArray *throttles* (slows down) host writes when GC falls behind the incoming data stream. The team further mitigated the effect by reserving a category of *system space* that would ordinarily be used to store data but could be preempted by GC when it fell behind.

Mitigations notwithstanding, FlashArray space management and reporting resulted in enough escalations of issues reported by users that a team was formed specifically to improve GC's space utilization and the accuracy of CLI and GUI space reports.

Neil (page 58) and childhood friend Ganesh Ramanarayanan had moved to the Bay Area upon university graduation. Both had become disillusioned with large, bureaucratic companies and joined startups, in Neil's case, Pure Storage. After multiple recruitment attempts by Neil and some hesitation, Ganesh joined the company in 2012, abetted by the collapse of his startup.

Initially, Ganesh joined a team that included Costa (page 163) and Rich (page 60), working to improve FlashArray write performance. Following that, he rotated into escalations (page 123), where he soon became a leader, serving for about a year. His tenure in escalations coincided with a large number of space-related escalations, which gave him an appreciation for the technical side of space management and reporting that suited him perfectly for leading a newly-formed team charged with alleviating space-related problems.

Bringing Order from Chaos

As more capabilities were added to Purity//FA and existing ones were improved, software engineering divided into quasi-independent teams. Teams would test their work in isolation, and when they were satisfied with it, "check it in" to a central code base. Difficulties often arose when a team's updates interfered with those of others. The working code base would become unstable, and development would stop until the base had been rolled back and bugs in the destructive updates remedied.

With even more complex code in sight, this was clearly an unsatisfactory way to operate. Ganesh helped institute a scheme to improve the then-current situation and moreover, to scale as the number of development teams increased. As before, each team worked on a private code branch. At designated times only, "pools" of teams would check their work in to the main code base and collaborate to resolve any issues that arose. The process nearly eliminated development stoppages but required constant coordination to ensure that all issues in the main code base were resolved before it was opened to the next pool of teams. In addition to leading the space team, Ganesh organized and coordinated the merge pool, both full-time jobs, for about six months before he was asked to manage the ActiveCluster project (page 167) in 2016.

Supporting Our Own Hardware

2014 also saw the introduction of the FA-400 family, starting with the FA-420. For the Purity//FA team, this meant simultaneously supporting new FA-400 series hardware and the FlashArray//M series with its NVMe-connected NVRAMs and PCIe bridging for controller intercommunication.

SMI-S

2015

4.1: 24 terabyte shelves
4.5: FlashArray//M
4.6: 44 terabyte shelves
VLAN tagging
Throttling
Over-wire deduplication
SMI-S support
Volume group copy

The FA-450, with six SAS ports per controller supported six storage shelves for a total physical flash capacity of 70 terabytes. For Purity//FA, this meant extensive stress testing of metadata structures and algorithms, first to ensure that they worked at the new maximum capacity, and then to verify that I/O and load balancing algorithms delivered performance and resiliency that scaled with capacity.

In mid-2015, the FlashArray//M series was introduced along with the first 1-terabyte SSDs. The work that had gone into extending Purity//FA's metadata structures and algorithms continued to pay off as maximum capacity increased to 136 terabytes with the new devices. A little over a year later, in the fall of 2016, the FlashArray//MR2 series, with faster processors and additional DRAM for buffers and metadata cache, along with new SSD carriers able to accommodate two 1-terabyte SSDs, increased the arrays' maximum capacity to 256 terabytes.

Sweating the Details

Along with supporting a steady stream of new hardware, Purity//FA was continually being enhanced with features that users took for granted in enterprise-class storage. Already in 2013, a REST API had been added to the software to enable users to manage arrays from management frameworks, programs, and scripts. In 2014, support for managing SSL certificates for remote authentication had been added.

In addition, Purity//FA security measures enabled FlashArray to receive FIPS-140-2[34] certification (validated by an independent testing organization), a necessity for purchase by most U.S. Federal government operations. In mid-2016, NIAP/Common Criteria validation made Pure Storage the first storage vendor with products certified to meet the stringent security requirements for U.S. National Security Systems.

As 10 Gb/s Ethernet entered the mainstream, many users chose to simplify their data center networks by adopting it to connect servers to storage. They secured access with *virtual local area networks* (VLANs). To enable seamless failover between separate network fabrics configured for redundancy, Purity//FA introduced VLAN tagging to allow controller

---

[34] Federal Information Processing Standard Publication 140-2, "Security Requirements for Crypto-graphic Modules," a U.S. government computer security standard used to evaluate cryptographic modules.

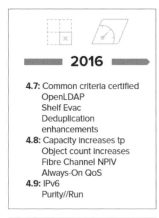

2016

4.7: Common criteria certified
OpenLDAP
Shelf Evac
Deduplication
enhancements
4.8: Capacity increases tp
Object count increases
Fibre Channel NPIV
Always-On QoS
4.9: IPv6
Purity//Run

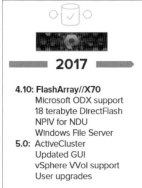

2017

4.10: FlashArray//X70
Microsoft ODX support
18 terabyte DirectFlash
NPIV for NDU
Windows File Server
5.0: ActiveCluster
Updated GUI
vSphere VVol support
User upgrades

ports to connect to multiple VLANs. FlashRecover was enhanced to preserve deduplication during replication, reducing network traffic and bandwidth requirements. In late 2016, support for IPv6 was implemented to support the increasing use of the newer Internet Protocol, especially in larger *hyperscale* environments.

In 2015 and 2016, FlashArray was further integrated into enterprise data center administrative infrastructures with support for the SNIA's *Storage Management Initiative Specification* (SMI-S) and the OpenLDAP (*Lightweight Directory Access Protocol*) for centralized administrator authentication. Deduplication algorithms were enhanced, and support for *N_Port ID Virtualization* (NPIV) was added to enable arrays' Fibre Channel ports to respond to multiple storage network addresses.

From the beginning, a fundamental principle of Purity//FA had been to treat all I/O commands equally, starting execution immediately upon receipt. While this eliminated administrators' need to prioritize volumes, it was possible for heavily loaded volumes ("noisy neighbors") to affect other volumes' responsiveness. Purity//FA combatted this with "*always-on*" *Quality of Service* (QoS) which detected gross load imbalances, and when heavily loaded volumes started to monopolize resources, gave preference to others.

As larger SSDs made it possible for users to increase array capacities while reducing "footprint," migration of data from older shelves to new ones became increasingly important. Starting in 2016, Purity//FA supported "evacuating" data from older shelves to new ones during operation, thus extending the NDU promise to encompass software, controllers, and entire shelves of flash devices.

The majority of arrays in the field have significant processing power and I/O "headroom." 2016 saw Purity//Run introduced, enabling users to to run certain containerized applications in their "extra" array capacity without deploying dedicated servers.

Expanding Capability and Capacity

2017 was primarily a year of Purity//FA internal enhancement. The team delivered support for *Offloaded Data Transfer* (ODX), a facility similar to XCOPY used by Microsoft operating systems. With it, large blocks of data, including entire volumes, could be "copied" from one server to another almost instantly.

Significant effort went to supporting the FlashArray//X series, particularly DFMs. Because Purity//FA addresses DFM flash blocks directly, there is no FPL as with SSDs, but controller software must manage flash longevity, schedule block erasures, and strategize writes to optimize performance.

N-Port ID Virtualization (NPIV) support was extended for use during Fibre Channel array upgrade, enabling new controllers to take over from the ones being replaced without disrupting host I/O.

Purity//Run was enhanced by the addition of a *Windows File Server* (WFS). WFS delivers Windows Server file services to clients from a virtual server cluster running in controllers in the array that contains the shared files.

And one other project…

> *"During my first meeting with Coz, before I was even an employee, I asked when synchronous replication would be available.*
>
> *His answer was, 'Never. The performance hit wouldn't make sense with FlashArray.'*
>
> *The way things eventually turned out taught me two things:*
>
> *1. Coz can be wrong.*
>
> *2. He can change his mind, but it takes pretty convincing evidence."*
>
> —**Fred Lherault**

ActiveCluster: The Replication Tour de Force

Computer users that deal in high-value transactions, such as financial institutions, have long insisted on protecting their critical data against disasters by replicating it to remote locations *transaction by transaction*. From a storage perspective, this means replicating data updates *synchronously*—ensuring that every write to a critical data set is persistent at both the primary data center and a remote location before it is considered complete.

Storage and software vendors have responded with *synchronous replication*. A variety of products replicate every update to managed data objects (disk sectors, logical volume blocks, database updates), but all have one thing in common: they replicate data updated at a *leader* or *primary* location to a passive *follower* one. If the leader is incapacitated, the follower *activates* (becomes the leader), and processing restarts using the data and computing resources at the replication location.

Pure Storage recognized that to become true top-tier storage, FlashArray would need synchronous replication. For users who needed write-by-write replication, FlashRecover was only a stopgap. Deploying FlashArray meant accepting a worst-case *recovery point objective* (RPO) equal to the five minute or greater interval between replicated snapshots. To succeed in markets where any data loss was unacceptable, synchronous replication was a must.

In late 2014, FlashArray engineering started projects to implement synchronous replication and *federated scale-out*. The goal of the latter, for which Naveen Neelakantam was a key engineer, was clustering arrays to create very high capacity arrays that presented a *single system image* to hosts. Several important software components would be needed by both projects, so concurrent implementation was synergistic.

The federated scale-out project initially concentrated on robust *distributed database*[35] designs, which synchronous replication would also need, for example to enable arrays to replicate different groups of volumes ("pods") to different partners. The distributed database design was extremely robust and performed well. Today, it is the basis for

---

[35] In cluster computing parlance, a distributed database is a body of metadata that describes an object. It is synchronized (kept identical) on all active nodes and resynchronized when failed nodes return to service.

Naveen Neelakantam
*"The ActiveCluster team's mantra
was 'correctness first.' We did three
complete designs before anyone
started coding. That turned out to
be very beneficial—our third design
survived implementation pretty much
intact."*

David Grunwald ("dag")
*"Active-active was an easy sell to the
company's technology strategists,
but we had to lobby pretty hard for
tight integration of our synchronous
replication with Purity//FA's powerful
metadata engine. That integration
turned out to be the key to the
easiest to deploy, yet most functional,
synchronous replication capability
ever delivered by anyone."*

distributed databases that identify replicated volume groups and other ActiveCluster state.

Federated scale-out was obviously going to be a lengthy, expensive project. As field demand for synchronous replication intensified, scale-out began to look like the proverbial "bridge too far." More powerful controllers and higher-density flash devices on the near horizon would eliminate much of the need for federating arrays to increase capacity and performance. Engineering decided to postpone federation and redirect its resources to the more immediate need. The synchronous replication team was beefed up and began to develop design proposals.

In 2010, David Grunwald ("dag") had left an enterprise storage company to join a consumer-oriented firm. He soon discovered that his preference was developing for the enterprise rather than developing for the consumer market. Recruiting efforts by prior acquaintances Chris Golden, Bob Wood, and Joe Hasbani helped persuade him to join Pure Storage in late 2013.

David's first assignment was with the team enhancing Purity//FA's metadata engine to more effectively support snapshots and the larger array capacities due soon. An escalations rotation followed but ended early when he was asked to join the team implementing the synchronous replication that the field had been urgently requesting.

The team felt they should "solve the problem right" and deliver *symmetric* (also called *active-active*) synchronous replication that would allow applications accessing two arrays full read-write access to a set of volumes replicated at both. From a host standpoint, writes would appear at the same instant on both arrays and reads would return the same content whichever array received them. The team devised a design that would deliver the same I/O response regardless of which array received a write to a replicated volume.

If successful, active-active synchronous replication would be enormously beneficial to IT's most demanding users. In addition to FlashArray performance, reliability, and ease of use, users would be able to treat cluster applications running in groups of hosts at separate locations as though they were in the same room.[36] Gone would be primary-secondary relationships between storage and hosts. Gone would be the need to start up applications at a secondary location and connect them to replicated storage when the primary location failed. Gone would be the steep software licensing costs that many vendors charged for long-distance replication.

> *"ActiveCluster taught me a valuable management lesson. When I inherited the project after more than a year, several people were driving critical efforts solo, and they were getting burned out. We had to scramble to add people to these areas. I learned that we need redundancy in our development teams as well as in our products."*
>
> —**Ganesh Ramanarayanan**

Active-active synchronous replication would be enormously important to users, as well as to Pure Storage. Managed by Ganesh, the team kicked off what would become one of the company's most audacious and complex development projects.[37] Because the avowed goal was for both arrays to execute reads and writes to replicated volumes actively, marketing called the feature *ActiveCluster*.

A FlashArray *Is* a Cluster. What's the Big Deal?

Synchronous replication is a form of the more general *clustering problem*. Two "nodes" (arrays) linked by an unreliable connection guarantee to maintain identical state (stored data) despite the possibility that either of them or the connection between them may fail. If the two cannot communicate, because one or both has failed, or because the connection has been severed, both must always reach the same conclusion about which should continue to operate ("survive") and which should shut down.

The clustering problem has been studied for decades. Known solutions generally involve a set of "voters" who establish a quorum of active nodes when a failure occurs. The ActiveCluster team implemented a basic form of that principle: if replicating arrays cannot communicate, they "race" to ask a remote *mediator* which of them should survive. If a node has failed, the other becomes the survivor. If the link is broken, the winner of the "race" survives. That's the easy part. The more difficult part is for the arrays to *resynchronize* (reconstruct the common state) when they resume full operation after a failure, regardless of what each was doing when the failure occurred.

FlashArray's controllers had always been a two-node cluster, connected by Infiniband (FA-320 and FA-400 series) or PCIe bridging (FlashArray//M and FlashArray//X). The storage devices connected to both controllers serve as mediator. FlashArray controllers are stateless, but an array's state is inherently common to both, because it is contained in the storage devices and NVRAMs.

Clustering arrays in separate locations is more complicated. To begin with, there isn't an obvious mediator. Worse, state must be maintained in two locations rather than in common devices as with FlashArray. Finally, state is more complex than that in a single array, where acknowledged host writes are preserved and commands in flight at the instant of failure are discarded. For example, a write received by one replicating array

---

[36] Unfortunately, the speed of light in fiber is the ultimate barrier. To avoid I/O timeouts, the round-trip transmission time between synchronously replicating arrays should be less than 11 milliseconds, implying in most cases a separation of 25 kilometers or less,

[37] The size of the team increased five-fold between the project's start and delivery of the feature.

Tabriz Holtz
"I had pretty much decided to join another small storage company, but when I interviewed at Pure Storage I was so impressed with the experience and the people I met that I knew I had to be part of that team."

might have been staged locally but not by its remote partner—without communication between them, there is no way to tell. Similarly, two arrays might have received overlapping writes that were in transit between them when a failure occurred. There are literally thousands of situations that the team had to handle so that when things returned to normal, the two arrays could resynchronize to common data and resume active-active replication.

Several pieces of ActiveCluster software were implemented by individual engineers. This caused delays when people left the company or transferred to other teams. The failure and recovery logic, for example, resulted in the project's only schedule slip, but the delay was worth the cost—new logic was implemented and integrated without a hitch a mere two months prior to shipment.

Simplicity Rules

While seemingly trivial in principle, mediation usually entails significant cost and effort on the user's part. Clusters typically use an additional node to establish quorum—a reliable system, ideally in a separate location ("failure domain"), that the user must supply, configure, and manage. From a user standpoint, it is nearly always idle, but it must be present when it's needed. It's one more element in the data center that can fail or be mishandled.

With his usual emphasis on ease of use, Coz insisted that ActiveCluster not require "extra" mediation hardware or software. The team conceived the idea of using Pure1 cloud servers to mediate ActiveCluster. The Pure1 cloud is always available, and is accessible by any array with an Internet connection.

Compared to most mediators, the ActiveCluster one is extremely passive. Its only role is to respond to arrays' requests for a "token" when they cannot communicate with each other. It takes no other part in failover or recovery.

With the Pure1 cloud mediator, which is pre-configured by default, ActiveCluster users need only the two arrays—there is no separate hardware to configure,[38] nor is there additional software configuration or cost. With Pure Storage all-inclusive pricing, ActiveCluster is a Purity//FA feature available to every FlashArray whose hardware can support it.

---

[38] For arrays that cannot be connected to the Internet, the company supplies a virtual machine im-age containing mediation software that can run within the user's intranet.

Active-Active—*Really*!

Even though it is symmetric from a host standpoint, for ActiveCluster's two nodes to guarantee data consistency, one must be the leader, directing the other (the follower) regardless of which one receives a command that changes state (for example, a host's write command, a volume resizing, etc.). In a simplistic implementation, this can lead to asymmetric performance—updates may complete noticeably faster when received by the leader than when received by the follower. This would not fulfill the team's goal of delivering the same performance regardless which array received a host's write command.

By overlapping internal operations and conveying multiple pieces of information in messages between the arrays, the team was able to devise an algorithm that required at most a single message exchange between arrays for each replicated write. Implementation of the algorithm fell largely to Tabriz Holtz. Tabriz had joined Pure Storage in 2014 from another Bay Area storage vendor. She had worked on several projects of increasing complexity prior to joining the ActiveCluster team where she developed much of the *data path*—the software that executed host commands to replicated volumes and ensured that updates were persisted on both arrays.

"Pure Storage engineering management is very mobility-focused. They provide engineers with ample opportunity to move among projects based on their interests and the projects' requirements. This culture of mobility helped the ActiveCluster team scale as demand for the feature and pressure on the resources increased."
—**Tabriz Holtz**

"During the 'crunch' in late 2017, we needed 'all hands on deck'—weekdays weren't going to be enough to finish the project. One engineer declared a willingness to work weekends and holidays in exchange for free food, so I arranged team outings and food in-house for about six weeks. To relax the pressure and strengthen team cohesion, I tried to make it fun, for example by visiting places with similar cuisines and rating them.
We also organized occasional offsite activities for team-bonding and stress relief. The most successful was a 'reward' excursion to the Tahoe region right after ActiveCluster was delivered. We invited families, which was kind of unique for tech company offsites, but hugely popular with the team."
—**Ganesh Ramanarayanan**

…You Know It Ain't Easy…

While from a user perspective, ActiveCluster is a breakthrough in ease of deployment and functionality, internally it is extremely complex. But customer demand, expressed frequently and loudly by AEs and SEs, was urgent, especially in enterprises perceived as IT leaders, where the company wished to gain a foothold. These two factors put tremendous pressure on the team to deliver a very complex feature in an impossibly short time. Morale was a constant concern—sustaining enthusiasm over two years of constant high pressure is tough; doubly so for a team creating something for which there is no precedent. Hours were long and stress was high—the work-life balance so key to the company culture was upset. Ganesh sought ways to alleviate the pressure on the team, partly with offsite meetings and team outings, but it was a difficult period.

"Hat told the team (in jest) that if ActiveCluster were delivered by the end of 2017, he would wear Coz's shorts to work for an entire month. Well, the team delivered two weeks early, and Hat made good on his promise. Even today, there's a 3-foot high photo of him wearing Coz's shorts hanging in the ActiveCluster team's area.
—**David Grunwald**

...But We Did It!

The team delivered ActiveCluster slightly over two years from project inception. By and large, the rollout was smooth, although as uptake increased over the months, there were a few highly visible escalations, most involving heavily loaded arrays that uncovered "corner cases" of obscure combinations of events and interactions between hosts, network connections, and arrays. But the great majority of deployments were smooth.

What was surprising to the team, although perhaps less so to the field organization, was the adoption rate. Within a year of shipment, fully 20% of installed arrays running current Purity//FA releases were using ActiveCluster. When one considers the expense and effort that users undergo to implement distributed disaster tolerance (with FlashArray, storage is a small part), it's obvious that only the highest-value, most critical data and applications justify it. It is equally clear that the clamor that the field organization had been raising since 2012 was justified—the demand was there.

Historically, the cost and complexity of distributed applications with synchronously replicated data has limited their deployment to sophisticated users with high-value critical data sets. The ease with which ActiveCluster can be deployed, however, has "democratized" the technology, making synchronous data replication feasible for a wider range of users, some of whom are not fully aware that for disaster tolerance, not only storage, but also networks, host multipathing, operating systems, and applications must be configured for robust distributed operation. In many deployments, the "ecosystem" surrounding ActiveCluster has proven to be a more frequent source of user issues than the feature itself.

2018

5.1: FlashArray//XR2
Snap-to-NFS
Local User Accounts
SMTP Authorization
QoS Limits
REST API v1.14
Deep compression
5.2 CloudSnap
NVMe-oF DirectFlash shelf
Asynchronous ActiveCluster

More, More, More

The 2018 releases extended Purity//FA with support for FlashArray//XR2 and DirectFlash shelves that use the NVMe-oF protocol for controller-shelf communication via Ethernet using the *RDMA over Converged Ethernet* (RoCE) protocol mapping.

Also in 2018, the company took a step toward embracing "the cloud" with the release of the *Snap-to-NFS* capability for transferring Purity//FA snapshots to *Network File System* (NFS) servers for long-term retention. Snap-to-NFS was later extended with Snap-to-Cloud which made it possible for users to send Purity//FA snapshots directly to public cloud provider facilities.

ActiveCluster was extended with an asynchronous option that optimized bandwidth by allowing replication of volume updates to lag by a specified amount.

Automatic quality of service (page 166) was extended by the addition of explicit data transfer rate ("bandwidth") limits for specified volumes. The REST API was updated to the newest version of the standard protocol, and background deep compression was improved by the addition of data and workload-sensitive adaptive algorithms.

In This Chapter...

"Job 1" for an enterprise storage system is correctness. Data that hosts write must be retrievable exactly as written, and from the logical location to which it was written. In parallel with developing Purity//FA software, engineering created an exhaustive regime of tests that run constantly during development to verify that software upgrades do not affect data integrity adversely.

FlashArray claims to tolerate component failures and keep running. The claim is validated by an equally exhaustive battery of torture tests in which components are deliberately failed or failures are simulated to ensure that arrays continue to perform correctly and can recover full performance and capacity without administrative intervention when failed components are replaced.

As an overlay on these, long-running tests run continuously to ensure that arrays continue to function correctly and perform well for months on end. Long-running tests continue to run through non-disruptive upgrades throughout the development process.

All of these tests are highly automated; tests are initiated on every software check-in to the code base, and results are auto-triaged and routed to engineering teams for remediation. But one type of test cannot readily be automated: system tests that evaluate how well the company's products fit into the most important data center and application environments. System tests are conducted by engineers with a wide breadth of data center experience. The results are fed back to developers, resulting in products that are not only reliable and high-performing, but also fit seamlessly into data center environments.

Relentless Testing

It's About Customers' Data. It *Has* to Be Right!

A highly-available storage system must be able to survive failure of any *field replaceable unit* (FRU) and be repairable without service outage. At a more basic level, however, it *cannot* lose or corrupt the data entrusted to it.

Internally, Purity//FA is extremely complex. Mapping blocks of data from hosts and reduced by the software to flash locations, making GC release precisely the space occupied by obsolete data, computing and validating the overlapping checksums that verify stored data, and so forth, all must work flawlessly all the time. The company recruited Patrick Lee, already familiar to several members from prior association, to help organize its engineering test program.

First, Get it Right!

The testing mantra was, and is, correctness. Performance improvements are good; recovering from faults is important, but it's absolutely imperative that data be stored and delivered correctly. The first tests developed were aimed at ensuring that no matter what data pattern a host wrote, no matter what LBAs it was written to, no matter how soon it was retrieved by the same or another host, what was delivered was exactly what had been written. By and large, the early tests used tools that Coz and Hayes had developed to exercise array I/O paths.

Initially, tests used actual arrays and servers (called "initiators"), but scarce hardware resources and the

Patrick Lee

"One evening Steve and I were trying to figure out where our code was spending most of its time. Coz happened by and suggested something we could try. Steve modified the kernel to capture more statistics, and I ran a test.

It went on like that for several hours. Coz would suggest something, Steve would modify the code, and I'd test it. We didn't notice how late it was getting.

At around 2AM, a test crashed hard. Steve realized it was due to a bug in his latest kernel change and announced he was too tired to be doing this. Only then did we quit for the night."

"I remember when Bob Wood first started, we were discussing the automated testing environment. Bob said something like, 'This is better than anything we had at my previous company.' That's when we had a single project display board with five test stages. Now there are easily hundreds of times more tests and dozens of project boards throughout the company."
—**John Mansperger**

inconvenience of manually restarting arrays when tests failed soon led the team to conclude that much of its testing could be performed equally well on virtual machines emulating FlashArray controllers.

Then, Get Tough

As Purity//FA functionality increased, correctness tests were augmented by *torture tests* in which component failures were deliberately caused or simulated. Torture tests ensured that arrays remained resilient to failures as Purity//FA functionality increased. The tests verified that arrays survived component failures and replacements and continued to perform correctly before, during, and after failures. and replacements, and that they continued to perform correctly before, during, and after failures. To make torture testing as realistic as possible, the team inserted defective components received from operations in arrays to cause genuine, rather than simulated, failures.

The correctness and torture tests were especially important during the alpha to beta transition, when the software was also converted from OpenSolaris to Linux. The change to Linux was motivated by a more enthusiastic embrace by component vendors and the user community, but at the time, Linux was less mature than OpenSolaris, especially with respect to vendor-provided I/O drivers, on which FlashArray depended completely.

Third in the engineering test hierarchy were performance tests. In the alpha timeframe, the threshold for success was a modest 40,000 32 kilobyte IOPS, but from day one, there was a continuous effort to improve upon that. The philosophy was to make capabilities work first, then analyze their effect on performance and figure out how to improve it.

Then, See How Long It Lasts

Before the FA-320 shipped, the team added a fourth category of tests—*long-running tests* (LRTs). LRTs subjected arrays to saturation-level workloads for as long as they continued to run without corrupting data or returning I/O errors—the correctness mantra again. At first, LRTs would run for a few hours before failing. As time passed and the software matured, they ran longer and longer. Today, LRT arrays run continuously. As new software releases become available, test engineers upgrade the LRT arrays while they continue to operate. The arrays routinely run Purity//FA releases at saturation level for months.

Escape Velocity

The team referred to software bugs that eluded pre-shipment testing and found their way into releases as "escapes." Escapes, typically became visible when escalations (page 122) were analyzed. They often resulted in the creation of additional tests to ensure that bugs had been fixed and did not reappear in later software versions.

Over time, as the software becomes more complex, the number and rigor of tests also increases. Tests may be updated or modified to better match the properties of re-engineered software components, but they are almost never completely retired.

You Can't Automate Everything

The regimen of correctness, torture, performance, and endurance testing creates a high level of confidence in FlashArray software reliability, borne out by the company's consistently high NPS. But there is another

Michelle Barreda
"You can't automate everything."

dimension to customer satisfaction with high-tech products—usability. Advanced product features are all well and good, but if they don't integrate easily into data center environments, they are likely to be ignored at best, and to cause complaints at worst. Before a product ships, it should also be tested from an overall system point of view:

- Does it integrate naturally into typical data center environments?
- Does it present its features in a way that conforms to typical workflows?
- Do user interactions produce the type of results that would normally be expected?

Given its ease of use mantra, the company recognized the need for this type of testing, albeit belatedly. The FA-320 shipped before formal system testing was initiated.

Quality assurance (QA) from a user perspective requires different skills than from a developer's perspective. Scott Sewall of the FlashArray QA team contacted former colleague Michelle Barreda to ask if she would join the Pure Storage engineering test team to add a user dimension to product testing. Michelle interviewed successfully, and in mid-2013 joined Scott and Howard Lin as a release testing engineer.

Because the FA-320 had shipped without formal system testing, developers were skeptical about whether it was actually necessary. Functional and performance testing could be, and to a large extent, had been automated, whereas testing the product in an overall system context would require humans acting as administrators. Initially, Michelle felt that in some instances, she had to persuade developers that not only must their products work correctly, they must also fit seamlessly into common data center workflows and make things easier rather than more difficult for administrators. Former roles as an SE, a QA manager, and a technical trainer lent her credibility in negotiations with developers.

In the early days, system testing was constrained by a limited engineering budget. There was a pool of arrays and servers from which QA engineers could "check out" equipment for 24-hour periods. But system test setup is typically more complicated than tests of array back end functionality—they verify configurability, integration, and operation with applications. They require realistic host environments—operating systems, applications, and network connections—that can be difficult to set up within 24 hours. Michelle argued vigorously for dedicated usability testing equipment, and eventually an array and host were allocated. With dedicated equipment, the team was able to work with engineering to test new features in a complete system context while they were still in development.

In 2015, the company split hardware and system testing into separate teams. Michelle built the system test team, recruiting people with SE, technical support, and QA backgrounds. In addition to pre-release system testing, her team performed another extremely valuable function: with dedicated resources and equipment, it could often reproduce complex problems reported by customers. This helped support remediate them and in addition, provided product improvement input to engineering. As the installed base grew in size and complexity, there were naturally more escalations, requiring more elaborate test equipment. At one early point, the team acquired server racks for 60 blades to successfully reproduce a particularly critical customer scenario (page 127). Today, its equipment and expertise enable it to reproduce virtually any application environment.

In 2016, prior to FlashBlade shipment, Evan established a QA function and asked Michelle's assistance in interviewing prospective recruits. After over a year of managing the FlashArray QA team, she followed fellow-engineer Rukhsana Ali, whom she had originally recruited, to FlashBlade. The pair established a QA function well before the product shipped. They found QA more readily accepted by the FlashBlade developers than had been the case with FlashArray. Michelle speculates that this may have been partly due to having established it prior to product shipment.

In This Chapter…

It would be comforting to report that the Pure Storage founders had worked out every detail to make the product and the company successful a priori, and that there was a uniformly smooth progression from opening for business to today's data-centric IT powerhouse. But the plain fact is that there were a number of key decisions, architectural and otherwise, that had fortuitous consequences that helped make the company successful. This chapter recounts decisions that range from adoption of consumer-grade flash to the "active-active-front-end-active-passive-back-end" model to the phonehome capability that was originally created as a convenience to engineering and beyond. This chapter surveys a number of the key decisions that in slightly unintended ways helped the company deliver a consumer-like experience for enterprise data storage.

Sometimes You Get Lucky

I t would be reassuring to believe that Coz and Hayes thought of everything, and that from the very first deliveries, FlashArray was fully formed and mature. But as with most new technologies, there was adaptation as development progressed—some changes to the original plan were motivated by discoveries during development; others resulted from exposing early prototypes to outsiders:

"Always-on" Data Reduction

While data reduction was necessary for affordability, there was an additional motivation for reducing *all* data *all* the time that may have been even more important. Minimizing the decisions left to an administrator (Principle 4—page 143) was a design goal, but minimizing pre-shipment testing was an imperative for a startup with limited working capital.

Wherever possible, developers eliminated code paths to minimize testing needs. An option to reduce only specified data would increase the numbers of code paths and test combinations exponentially. Once it was clear that reducing everything was viable, alternatives were no longer considered.

RAID-HA

Disk I/O performance depends on rotation speed, linear bit density, and average seek time. The ideal RAID scheme for each workload depends on disk type, workload properties, and the criticality of the data.

SSD I/O performance is different. Read performance is uniformly high; write performance depends on devices' internal activity (GC, block erasure, etc.). The FPL optimized performance for each type of SSD. NVRAM staging and writing in large, well-aligned blocks made write performance variations transparent to hosts. Performance was therefore independent of RAID layout, so the architects designed a single RAID scheme that made data loss extremely improbable and applied it to all data and metadata on flash.

From an engineering and test standpoint, a single array-wide RAID scheme minimized software paths. From a user standpoint, it eliminated the need for administrators to specify RAID protection, define RAID groups, allocate spare devices, and control data set placement, all of which helped realize Coz's goal of simplifying the storage user experience.

PHONEHOME

Other storage products were reporting faults directly to their vendors when FlashArray alpha systems were delivered. The developers initially regarded it as a feature that would eventually be needed but was not a MVP requirement.

It quickly became apparent, however, that monitoring arrays without intruding on each customer's operations would be necessary, so a rudimentary "phonehome" capability was introduced in the second alpha wave. In addition to reporting component failures, temperature changes, and so forth, FlashArray phonehome sent frequent reports of space utilization and I/O performance. Developers monitored array performance to evaluate internal algorithms; support engineers used failure reports to diagnose and repair problems, in some cases even before array owners were aware they existed.

"The acid test of NDU was the transition from the FA-320 to the FA-400 series. One of our biggest customers at the time was skeptical, but willing to try it if I, who had been their SE since the beginning, would personally upgrade the key production system.
I did two practice upgrades in our lab before I went to the customer's site.
The customer was so critical to us, and the FA-420 was so new, that the executive team was as nervous as I was. They stayed in constant contact throughout.
We upgraded the secondary controller first, and then the customer decided **we should go out to lunch**! *I was thinking, 'This is like doing brain surgery on a marathon runner.'*
But I wanted to show confidence, so I agreed, and we went. After lunch, I completed the upgrade without a hitch. We and the customer breathed enormous sighs of relief.
This was the moment when I really began to believe that Pure Storage would change computing in fundamental ways."
—**Chadd Kenney**

Phonehome has evolved into the popular Pure1 Manage, used by customers to monitor their arrays and estimate future requirements, and by the company to gather statistics and to detect potential customer problems and initiate proactive remedial action.

"ACTIVE-ACTIVE FRONT END, ACTIVE-PASSIVE BACK END"

From the outset, the company planned to ship only highly-available arrays, with controllers that were "just another FRU" that could be replaced without disrupting operation. That essentially required stateless array controllers. If a controller failed, the state of everything it was doing had to be available to the other controller.

The plan was for "active-active" production arrays, with both controllers receiving and executing I/O commands, but beta users received arrays with a single controller. During the beta phase, it became apparent that a single controller was more than capable of delivering the required performance, so the active-active plan was replaced by the "active-active front end, active-passive back end" architecture that FlashArray still uses today. Both controllers receive and respond to host I/O commands, but one primary controller executes them. The other (secondary) controller relays commands and responses between hosts and the primary.

The design had an important side benefit: when a controller fails or is removed from service, there is virtually no decrease in array performance, as there would be with active-active arrays. This is an extraordinarily useful property both when a controller fails or is upgraded. Customers experience no outage during controller replacement, but also no performance degradation.

Non-disruptive Upgrade

The concept of upgrading an array while it was operating was instigated by an SE who asserted that it was a competitive product feature. This turned out to be inaccurate, but by then it had become part of the development plan.

As storage system capacities increase, data migration during upgrade consumes more and more time and effort. Being able to upgrade an operating array and add capacity by plugging in devices without changing data layout are important competitive advantages for Pure Storage.

FlashRecover Replication

It was clear from the outset that FlashArray would need snapshot capability, because all competitors offered it in some form. The first arrays shipped did not support snapshots, but the Purity//FA metadata structure made it possible to deliver the capability by mid-2013. The data structures that supported snapshots made it easy to clone volumes from them. If, for example, backup and development testing both needed production data from a certain time, an array administrator could clone volumes from the same snapshot for each usage. The snapshot itself never changed until it was destroyed. Snapshots also made it easy to implement the 24-hour "eradication delay" for destroyed volumes by automatically creating snapshots and retaining them for 24 hours.

What the company perhaps underappreciated, however, was the urgency with which customers would require replication of data from one array to another at a remote location. As FlashArray gained the trust of users, arrays were deployed in increasingly critical applications, where loss of data would be catastrophic. Replicating key data sets to a remote location was, and is, a common means of protecting against such loss. Thus, the lack of a replication capability was a roadblock to deploying FlashArray in mission-critical applications.

Snapshot technology became the basis for a rapid implementation of periodic replication from a source array to one or more targets. Because FlashArray snapshots track changes to volumes, it was possible to bundle the changes and transmit them to remote arrays, where they were used to create new snapshots based on preceding ones. Because replicated snapshots are identical to the originals, they can be used to create clone volumes at remote locations.

Software Choices

The first Purity//FA prototypes used the OpenSolaris operating system. Several early engineers had done much of their past work on Solaris, so they were familiar with it and believed that prompt, high-quality support would be forthcoming. Moreover, support for Fibre Channel target mode was markedly superior to that of Linux, the other potential platform. It quickly became apparent, however, that the owner was less than enthusiastic about support and that the developer community was tiny and inactive compared to that of Linux. Candidates were far more likely to have Linux experience than OpenSolaris. It was also obvious that hardware vendors were supporting their products more quickly and reliably for the much larger Linux market. Dietz argued that OpenSolaris would be clinging to the past, whereas Linux was embracing the future. He also argued against optimizing time to market by shipping an OpenSolaris-based product and retrofitting Linux-based software later, due to the risk of disrupting customers' operations. The team accepted a ship date delay and ported the software to Linux, which remains the Purity//FA platform.

Coz and Hayes engaged in a spirited debate over whether their software should run in kernel or user space. FlashArray software would be extremely asynchronous, continually responding to I/O interrupts. Running in the kernel would eliminate the overhead of constant context switching, but many more tools were available for user space development, so debugging would be much easier. Coz settled the argument by developing a "driver" that shared buffers between kernel and user spaces and used a set of interrupt assignments to eliminate nearly all context switching overhead. With that concern eliminated, the software that eventually became Purity//FA was developed for user space.

A third software discussion concerned programming languages. Coz favored the C programming language because of its maturity and ubiquity, and because with it, engineers could "program closer to the hardware." Hayes favored C++ because its structured nature inherently imposes discipline. He believed that the right set of objects and methods would eliminate much of the coding flexibility that leads to obscure bugs. Both founders were concerned, however, about the quality of C++ compilers and the efficiency of the code they generated. Hayes prevailed through force of will, and Purity//FA was developed in C++. As it happened, by 2010, C++ compiler quality and efficiency were on a par with those of C. Moreover, most engineering candidates either already had C++ experience, or were able to acquire it relatively quickly.

Thus, Purity//FA is based on a periodically upgraded Linux distribution, runs almost entirely in user mode, uses a shared buffer and interrupt assignment mechanism to minimize I/O interrupts, and is written in the C++ language. Whenever those subjects come up, Coz is sure to remark, "I'm glad Hayes won those arguments."

THE IMPORTANCE OF VOLUME

There were concerns about the reliability of the "consumer-grade" SSDs used in FlashArray which heightened as vendors published lower endurance specifications for higher-capacity devices. To minimize the risk, engineering only qualified SSDs from leading vendors, and designed Purity//FA to both minimize and optimize writes to flash.

But vendors ship millions of consumer-grade SSDs annually. As with most consumer products, margins are low, so profitability hinges on trouble-free user experiences. Service calls can very quickly eliminate profits. Thus, paradoxically vendors tend to expend much more effort on making consumer devices reliable than they do on commercial ones. The latter are shipped in much lower volumes and "high-touch" service is the norm. Pure Storage's experience was that the reliability of SSDs used in FlashArray far exceeded vendors' published specifications, and moreover, it increased over time, so the company eventually felt comfortable offering lifetime guarantees on

FlashArray SSDs. This contrasted sharply with the NVRAMs in pre-FlashArray//M generations, which were based on SSD technology. They were produced in much lower volumes for a higher market tier than consumer-grade SSDs, and perhaps partly for that reason were found to be more problematic. Relatively low NVRAM reliability was a motivating factor in the company's decision to develop its own NVRAMs for newer product generations.

THE PLATINUM DECISION

The key decision for the Platinum program was whether to base another generation of arrays on off-the-shelf hardware. FA-400 controllers were commodity servers; moving to the supplier's next server generation was expected to be straightforward. While there were cost and vendor dependability risks, off-the-shelf hardware was likely to mean shorter time-to-market. But given the success of the FA-420 and the introduction of the FA-405 and FA-450 the following year, the company did not expect to need a new generation until 2015, so Bill's team chose the long-term approach of in-house hardware development.

In 2015, shortly after FlashArray//M was delivered, the vendor whose servers were used as FA-400 series controllers acquired one of the main Pure Storage competitors. Had off-the-shelf hardware been chosen for Platinum, the company would have been in the awkward position of buying hardware from the parent of a competitor, so the decision to design Platinum hardware in-house was doubly fortuitous.

> *"I've attended quite a few trade shows over the years but since joining Pure Storage, two attendees have told me things that stick in my mind because I'd never before heard people say anything remotely similar about storage vendors:*
>
> *A back-handed compliment:*
> *'You annoy me less than my other IT vendors.'*
>
> *…and unalloyed enthusiasm:*
> *'Pure Storage is the only storage vendor with fanboys.'"*
> —**Tom Kozlowski**

Toward a Consumer-like Customer Experience

In consumer products, "low touch" is both an important success factor and an economic necessity. Consumers don't want to be visiting the smartphone store every time something unexpected happens, and for vendors operating on thin margins, a single service call can erase the profit on a unit.

The enterprise data center market is different. Customers expect, even if they do not appreciate, periodic "preventive maintenance" with associated downtime. Regular interaction with vendor support is the norm.

The Pure Storage founders set out to change this—to make enterprise storage systems that were much closer to the consumer product model in ease of use, maintainability, and evolution. They succeeded, partly because of a priori design decisions, but also due to discoveries during early deployments.

The Pure Storage model of making storage ownership and operation easy has been so successful that competitors are forced to emulate it as best they can in products constrained by legacy designs and business practices.

In This Chapter...

Initially, engineering developed the phonehome capability as a convenience for itself—having arrays report status and issues directly to Pure Storage in real time meant that there was no need to poll early adopters and customers periodically to see how they were doing. Augmented with logs of performance and utilization, however, phonehome became an indispensable tool for the support organization, improving diagnostic accuracy and in many cases, enabling support engineers to anticipate problems before they occurred, a capability that became known as "fingerprinting."

As the company's installed base grew, the volume of data collected became too great to host in-house, and the database was moved to a public cloud. This set the stage for Pure1 Manage, which provided customers with direct access to their arrays' histories and alert status, and soon thereafter, status of their outstanding support cases.

As the company's database of historical information grew, engineering applied machine learning techniques to develop predictive tools that customers could use to estimate the impact of additional workloads on their arrays and to help size new arrays for given workloads.

Machine learning is extremely computation and I/O intensive. To control public cloud data access charges, they developed a system that constantly imported data from the user-accessible public cloud to in-house FlashBlade systems, where it could be analyzed without incurring public cloud charges.

Managing Pure Storage

In mid-2011, a recruiter[39] suggested that software engineer Benjamin Borowiec look into an opportunity with a relatively young, but thriving startup called Pure Storage. At the time, Ben was comfortable with his situation, but like many Bay Area engineers, had a touch of the "Silicon Valley startup bug," so he scheduled an interview with Hayes, telling himself it was to test his interviewing skill. The vision Hayes described sounded plausible, and the well-funded company run by people with prior successful startups to their credit made it seem like a safe bet even though it had yet to ship its first product. As Ben met with more people, he became more impressed with the engineering team.

Benjamin Borowiec
"Shortly after we shipped the first production arrays, I remember Kix telling the company that the storage market was now a 'two horse race' between us and the number one vendor. It seemed pretty optimistic at the time but it quickly started to become true!"

The company knew that to be competitive, FlashArray would need a GUI for management. Although Ben had little prior GUI experience, interviewers were impressed by his intelligence, overall knowledge, and especially his enthusiasm, so an offer was extended, and he became a key member of the three-person FlashArray GUI team. Under the guidance of Chuck Clanton, an experienced GUI designer whom Kix had engaged as a consultant, Ben, Manny Noik, and Dave Keehn developed a GUI for FlashArray management in time for general availability.

After the FlashArray GUI was delivered, Ben spent several months developing a FlashArray plugin for the VMware vSphere management console. The plugin, which is still in use today, enables VMware administrators to manage their arrays using the vSphere framework familiar to them.

As the number of arrays in the field increased, the support organization's need for timely information about array health and performance grew as well. The phonehome capability that Chris Golden had devised for the alpha arrays was being overwhelmed by the volume of incoming data.

---

[39] Surprisingly, not Doug Mohr—a rarity for engineering recruits at the time.

Terry Noonan
*"As we develop management tools
for our products, we try to adopt the
personas of the people who will use
them. It's quite different from the
developer's perspective."*

In late 2012, Ben and Joe Hasbani created *CloudAssist*—a reporting tool that extended phonehome with hourly status reports and I/O performance and utilization logs every few seconds. To maximize availability and user convenience and cope with the high volume of data, arrays sent reports to virtual machine applications running in a public cloud, where they were stored for viewing by support engineers when issues arose. Reliable records of historical behavior made support engineers much more efficient at diagnosing and remediating customer issues. Eventually the team extended monitoring to include *fingerprinting*, identifying arrays that *might* be susceptible to known issues and proactively initiating remedial action. Fingerprinting has been so successful that today, more service tickets for customers' arrays are created by the company than by customers. Pure Storage absorbs the cost of storing data in the cloud and makes CloudAssist data collection available without charge for all customers whose arrays can be connected to the Internet.

Customers could Use All This Data, Too!

In 2013, with the company's technology base expanding, Coz recruited former colleague Terry Noonan, then serving as CTO of another small company, to share development of the company's future technology strategy with him. The two split responsibilities according to their primary interests, with Coz overseeing the base "engine" technology and Terry developing a strategy for users to manage the company's growing product portfolio. Terry decided to "do something about multi-array management" to improve the experience of the growing number of customers with multiple arrays.

It didn't take long for him to realize that the CloudAssist data used by support and engineering contained a wealth of historical and current information that customers might find extraordinarily useful for administration and planning. He proposed a service that would permit FlashArray owners to view current status and performance and utilization history of their arrays by extracting and presenting information from the CloudAssist database. Terry felt it was important to give the growing number of customers with multiple products an "at a glance" view of their Pure Storage "fleets" that would let them quickly assess the state of their storage and react as necessary.

He started by engaging a human interface design firm with which he had had prior experience to develop visual concepts showing how customers could view information about their Pure Storage products in real time. He asked the firm to adopt a storage administration rather than a developer "persona" and to adhere to two principles:

• Avoid a "management server" approach that would require customers to install and maintain yet another tool for managing the storage part of their infrastructures.

- Avoid a design that assumed that administrators would spend their days at consoles flipping between infrastructure management tools.

The firm came up with the idea of "cards"—rectangular display objects that showed the current utilization, performance, and alert status of each of a customer's arrays. Logging in via a browser would display a dashboard containing a rectangular array of cards. Terry proposed that cards be reversible with a mouse click to show more detailed information about pending alerts.

Initially, there was some uncertainty about whether customers would accept the idea of putting information about their storage infrastructures on the Internet, even if it was protected by credentialed login. Once assured that all information came from servers controlled by Pure Storage and not directly from their arrays, and reassured that the displayed information was read-only, they readily accepted the concept.

From Concept to Realization

With a design concept in hand, Terry engaged Ben's CloudAssist team to develop tools for "back end" data retrieval and analysis, and GUI engineers Manny Noik and Samridh Srinath to create a browser interface to display information to users. They produced a browser-based monitoring and management service based on CloudAssist data. The company made the service available to all customers whose arrays sent phonehome data to the CloudAssist servers. The model was software as a service (SaaS)—customers were not required to install or manage anything. All they needed was login credentials to view the status and history of their Pure Storage products. Kix adapted a naming scheme from a then-popular SaaS offering and called the service *Pure1 Manage*.

In its first release, Pure1 Manage (soon shortened to *Pure1*) was an array monitoring service. It presented customers with graphical histories of their arrays' performance and utilization as well as up-to-date status and information about any outstanding service tickets. It was especially useful for the growing number of customers with multiple arrays, because its dashboard presented a concise summary of a customer's entire "fleet" of arrays on one browser page, a so-called *single pane of glass* (SPOG). Users could instantly observe the status of dozens of arrays. Web statistics indicated that the tool quickly became extremely popular with the company's customers.

Going Mobile

As Pure1 utilization grew, Terry drew on a previous experience, and proposed that the company create a mobile version. The goal, as he describes it, was that "an administrator who had left the office not to have to return to deal with issues that arose in his or her absence." He engaged the outside design firm again, and the company's Seattle-based engineering team implemented Pure1 Mobile, using a portable development platform so it could support both iPhones and Android-based smartphones. Uptake was rapid. The most important Pure1 Mobile feature was "push" notification of alerts, which instantly informed administrators of conditions that might need attention rather than waiting for notification from a data center employee, or worse, an IT executive. Today, indications are that upwards of 30% of Pure Storage product owners make regular use of Pure1 Mobile.

Meanwhile, the engineering team continued to evolve Pure1, continuously refining the user interface, providing utilization and performance visibility at the volume level, and making it possible for customers to initiate and manage service tickets directly. The latter feature rounded out Pure1 Mobile by allowing storage administrators to react to issues instantly from any location with mobile phone data service.

Getting Smarter

The team continued to extend Pure1. A plug-in module made it possible to supply data to vSphere so that VMware administrators could use familiar tools to view information about their Pure Storage products. They added predictive tools to help customers plan future storage capacity and performance needs. Initially, the tools were self-referencing; they predicted each array's future needs based on its own history. As the importance of predictive analysis to customers became clear, data scientists were hired, starting with Sergey Zhuravlev, who transferred from Panos' escalation team, where he had developed a keen appreciation of what FlashArray users needed and wanted. Sergey added machine learning to Pure1's capabilities, so that capacity and performance predictions could be based on models that took into account the historical behavior of the entire installed base.

Today, Pure1 is a sophisticated predictor of capacity and performance needs that assists customers in choosing the optimal product for their future requirements based on knowledge of the entire installed base and on the current and projected uses to which they put their arrays. Pure1 can estimate the consequences of adding an application workload to an array and allow users to test current and projected load scenarios with various array models.

Hey, We Can Use All This Data, Too

In its initial release, Pure1 was a kind of administrative gateway—it offered customers single-click access to the GUI of any of their own arrays. Over time, the team has enhanced it with a single sign-on (SSO) capability that allows a user to directly manage arrays for which he or she is authorized. This creates additional possibilities, for example, an administrator can observe the performance and utilization impact of FlashRecover replication by looking at both source and targets directly.

In 2016, FlashBlade systems shipped, with an interface to Pure1 consistent with that of FlashArray, so the team extended Pure1 services to support their users. FlashBlade gave the company a foothold in "big data" applications which analyzed largely unstructured data from a variety of sources to correlate events, identify trends, and perhaps most importantly, make more accurate predictions about everything from market fluctuations to health and safety trends than had hitherto been possible.

The original CloudAssist team proudly observes that the data collection, cloud storage, and extraction infrastructure they created is still used by Pure1 today, even with FlashBlade data added to the mix. The total amount of data collected has multiplied over a thousand-fold and is being used in far more ways than were anticipated when they started the project.

While big data analytics and machine learning are gaining importance in many industry and service sectors, they are also important to Pure Storage itself. With an installed base in excess of fifteen thousand FlashArray and FlashBlade systems, the volume of phonehome data is formidable—in 2018, more than 20 terabytes were collected every day.

By analyzing Pure1 data against fingerprints of known issues, the support organization has been able to identify susceptible arrays before issues occur. It is not uncommon for customers to receive notification from Pure Storage Support that one or more of their arrays have configurations or workloads similar to others that have been problematic and recommending preventive measures. Fingerprints have increased Pure1 utilization significantly.

As the importance of big data to the company's business grew, the need for expertise in the form of *data scientists*—individuals skilled in analyzing large amounts of unstructured data from multiple sources with non-obvious relationships to extract valuable knowledge— became clear. The company's first data scientists were *solution architects* (page 94), but engineering soon realized that Pure1 data was a trove of information that could be used both to enhance the customer experience and to streamline its own engineering processes. In addition, there was a sizable body of data gathered during internal testing of new software and hardware.

Among the first uses to which the data scientists put Pure1 data was enhancing the quality of predictive analysis. Pure1 prediction was originally based on extrapolating an array's own history. The data scientists used a combination of installed base history and data gathered during new product development to support "what if" scenarios that allow users to predict both the impact of adding workloads to their arrays and the performance of alternate array models with their workloads. The models are updated continuously, so as new products are introduced, the basis for predictions gradually shifts from internal test data to actual behavior of arrays in the installed base.

As the company's product line expanded with the addition of new hardware and software features, the complexity of engineering testing increased exponentially. The sheer number of tests implied by the CI/CD development methodology (page 21) made it imperative to automate testing, but there remained the need to *triage*—to correlate and sift through millions of logs produced by the infrastructure and by the tests themselves to determine where to best concentrate bug fixing efforts. Triage is complicated by the fact that while many test failures are the result of bugs in new hardware or software, others occur because of failures in the infrastructure—the servers that create the I/O loads, the network that interconnects the systems, and so forth. And while it sounds trivial, the numbers are daunting—in 2018, FlashBlade development testing alone utilized over 200 systems driven by 700 load generating servers to run over 70,000 separate tests every day. The vast majority succeed; the problem is to isolate log data that pertains to the failures and rank them for handling by engineering.

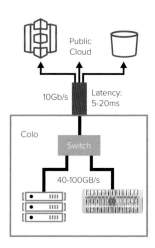

"Hybrid Cloud" with FlashBlade

The data scientists devised a scheme for automating test triage using an *analytics pipeline*[40] to identify the less than one percent of failed tests in the mass of data. Of that percentage, most result from previously identified causes that had not yet been remedied. The remainder, amounting to a few dozen on a typical day, require developer attention. Every day, the analytics pipeline extracts the tiny number of test failures that require attention from the forest of log data. The pipeline provides side benefits as well—as the analytics applications run, they inject raw performance information into a structured database that developers use to analyze the performance impact of each hardware and software change. Needless to mention, the storage that supports the pipeline is the company's own FlashBlade product.

Pure1 modeling creates opportunities for further enhancing the customer experience. For example, when a customer has determined from a model that a particular configuration would satisfy future needs, it is entirely conceivable for the tool to generate requests for quotes and route them directly to the fulfillment partner. Similarly, once an order has been placed, its status could be tracked within Pure1 without recourse to separate mechanisms.

The Cloud Costs Money

Even before Pure Storage made the commitment to keep Pure1 data online and available to customers through Pure1 Manage, the company realized that the cost of storing logs and frequent diagnostics indefinitely would be unbounded and took steps to minimize as the installed base grew. Recognizing from the outset that the most recent historical data is of greatest interest, the engineers adopted a technique for "thinning" CloudAssist data as it aged. For example, the tool might store every received log for a few hours, logs at five minute intervals for a few days, hourly logs for a month, and so forth. The idea of thinning preceded CloudAssist; it was first adopted to limit the amount of historical data that an array would have to store locally to create historical graphs, and later incorporated into the cloud database on which Pure1 is based.

As CloudAssist evolved into Pure1 and the number of arrays contributing to its database grew, the cost of cloud storage, which Pure Storage bears entirely, grew as well. Ageing mitigates the cost of cloud storage somewhat—data moves to a less expensive, lower-performing tier as it ages, but cloud provider charges levied for every retrieval mean that analysis becomes costly, especially with machine learning algorithms that are constantly updated as new data arrives. Logs newly arrived in the Pure1 database may be retrieved dozens or hundreds of times by machine learning algorithms updating the parameters of their models.

---

[40] The FlashBlade test triage pipeline is described in TB-180501, available from Pure Storage.

To control costs as the volume of data stored in the cloud continues to grow, the company adopted a hybrid cloud approach for some of the analyses on Pure1 data. FlashArray and FlashBlade systems send logs directly to cloud storage, which incurs no charge. They must be retrieved for analysis, whether the servers that analyze them are located in the cloud or are located on premises. With the hybrid approach, new logs are retrieved from the cloud (once), incurring a charge, and written to on-premises storage (the graphic shows a FlashBlade system used for this purpose). Servers running machine learning algorithms can then iterate, retrieving logs an arbitrary number of times without incurring cloud provider retrieval charges, whether in the cloud or on premises. (On-premises servers incur capital cost but offer advantages in performance and can utilize advanced capabilities such as snapshots to make processing more flexible.

The hybrid cloud technique has proven effective to the point that customers who use FlashBlade systems for analytics are beginning to adopt similar techniques. Rather than making hard choices between cloud and on-premises for each application, they are adapting applications to make use the best use of both on-premises and cloud processing and storage resources.

In This Part...

Today, tens of thousands of arrays store data for applications as diverse as securities trading, *computer assisted design* (CAD), medical imaging, and many others. While the applications are myriad, they fall into a few broad categories:

STRUCTURED DATABASES

Structured databases, implemented by mature software suites such as Oracle and SQL server, hold personal information about much of the world's population and record billions of transactions every day. They rely on the availability and data integrity of storage systems.

VIRTUAL MACHINES AND VIRTUAL DESKTOP INFRASTRUCTURES (VDI)

The power of today's servers is too much for many applications. Virtual machine technology divides super-powerful servers into multiple virtual machines, each with a share of the physical resources.

Organizations with hundreds of knowledge workers use VDI to reduce computing and storage costs and to keep the software on thousands of individuals' computers consistent. Deduplication is especially important for VDI.

WINDOWS SERVERS

Today, a substantial percentage of servers run the Windows Server operating system. Windows Server performs some functions usually performed by storage systems and supports others. While the advanced storage functionality is comprehensive, it has inherent limitations.

ANALYTICS AND ARTIFICIAL INTELLIGENCE (AI)

Many organizations analyze millions of data items using AI techniques to discover relationships that they use to improve their operation. AI is used to predict everything from weather to inventories to markets. AI relies on big data—billions of items that must be readily accessible.

FlashArray provides unique advantages for all these applications, in some cases altering data center workflows quite dramatically. The chapters in Part III describe the storage challenges in each of these areas and explain how FlashArray streamlines workflows and improves the quality of service delivered to users.

PART III

Where's FlashArray?

In This Chapter...

In most large IT organizations, database management and storage administration are separate functions, whose knowledge of each other's needs and techniques may not be broadly known. For example, database administrators must negotiate with storage administrators to acquire storage for new and expanding databases—storage whose capacity, performance, and availability are consistent with the value of the databases. Often, they must create copies of live databases for development testing, backup, analytics, and other purposes.

FlashArray's ease of use simplifies database administrators' storage-related responsibilities in multiple ways. With inherent thin provisioning, storage for new databases can be sized for expected needs without consuming storage until data is actually written. There is no need to create multiple volumes due to size restrictions or performance considerations. Purity//FA can clone snapshots of databases in an instant for ancillary uses, on or off-host. Always-on encryption of all stored data means that database contents are secure against misappropriation. And storage can be expanded or upgraded without database migration.

FlashArray and Databases

A Day in the Life of a DBA

DBAs are concerned with storage from the day a database is created. They work with business users to estimate overall requirements, from which they develop requirements for each database component (tables, logs, configuration files, etc.). They then negotiate with storage administration (a different department in most organizations) which provisions (allocates) suitable (e.g., RAID or mirrored) capacity for each component. DBAs generally try to acquire sufficient storage to meet both initial and future needs, but storage that goes unused is a cost without an immediate payback.

Another important aspect of the negotiations is separating certain database components from each other by locating them on separate devices to promote I/O concurrency.

The long-term capacity and performance needs of new databases are often unknown, so initial allocations are only estimates. If data growth or I/O activity exceeds initial estimates, more storage must be provisioned. Because databases are so highly structured, storage configuration changes often disrupt operations and require bulk data movement. DBAs try to minimize disruption by closely tracking component-by-component data growth so additional storage can be provisioned everywhere it's needed in one disruptive operation.

Because storage has historically been disk-based, common DBA practice tries to optimize database performance by configuring multiple storage devices, each of which is a separate object for both DBA and storage administrator to manage. Some database software goes so far as to allocate performance-critical components at the outer periphery of disks. Such micromanagement is both tedious and a distraction from the DBA's primary mission.

Somu Rajarathinam
Database Solution Architect
"The brain power, products, and culture at Pure Storage were what convinced me to switch careers after 20 years.
It has been extremely satisfying to be able to answer questions like, 'Are you seriously going to upgrade my storage in the middle of the day?' with a simple, 'Sure. Why not?' "

Managing Production Database Performance

Once a database is up and running, DBA storage responsibilities shift to maintaining and improving performance. The biggest risk to increasing storage capacity is the potential performance impact. It doesn't even take a configuration change to impact performance. With disk-based storage, performance can also vary as data access patterns change. DBAs typically spend considerable time and energy trying various tools and techniques to improve database performance. This again is managing the storage rather than performing their primary database management mission.

Send in the Clones

A third storage-related DBA responsibility is provisioning and management of so-called *accessory databases*. Backup administrators, application developers, QA teams, and business analysts all need real data to work with. DBAs are often asked to make copies ("clones") of production databases for them.

Most storage systems can clone sets of volumes, but with disk-based storage, cloning is time-consuming, and can result in poor performance for both clone and production database. Moreover, most disk-based database clones occupy as much storage as the original databases, so clones quickly become expensive. Clones based on so-called *space-saving snapshots* require less incremental storage, but they can impact production database performance severely, and dismantling them can be awkward and time-consuming.

Cost and disruption make DBAs and storage managers hesitant to clone database volumes. Quarterly or semiannual cloning of production databases is usually scheduled long in advance, even though more frequent access to up-to-date production data would better suit development and business purposes.

To Transform or Not to Transform

For many organizations, structured databases are their most valuable digital assets. They protect them with RAID, mirroring, frequent backup, and replication to offsite locations. Production servers also compress data to conserve storage and encrypt it prior to storing to protect it against theft. In the financial arena, laws mandate encryption of stored data ("data at rest").

Compression and encryption are vital, but they take a toll. Both are compute-intensive, so they reduce the processing power available to execute applications. Moreover, some database vendors increase customer cost by exacting license fees for compression and encryption software.

Nothing Is Forever

Data center equipment typically has a three-to-five-year lifetime, because the rapid pace of progress means that more capable and cost-effective servers, networks, and storage become available. Equipment vendors often use service pricing to encourage customers to upgrade regularly by pricing contract renewals high to make replacing products with new ones attractive. Superficially it's all good. The old equipment is removed and the new is installed ("forklift upgrade"). The customer gets better equipment and the vendor's revenue stream continues.

But forklift upgrades are traumatic for DBAs. They must be planned months in advance to minimize the inevitable disruption to users, equipment must be allocated for testing, and when the time to upgrade comes, the database must be copied from old storage system to new. Upgrades must include fallback strategies at every stage so that if something goes wrong, applications can resume operating until the failure is remedied.

It's a lot of work for DBAs (and for their server, network, storage, and application administration counterparts), especially considering that a typical DBA manages multiple databases, hosted on the same or different equipment, some destined for upgrade and some not. DBAs can become consumed with storage-related tasks rather than performing their primary functions.

FlashArray to the Rescue

With FlashArray as database storage, all storage-related DBA tasks—initial provisioning, ongoing management, and hardware and software upgrades—change significantly.

Provisioning

To provision FlashArray storage for new databases, a DBA can create volumes as dictated by the database architecture. Purity//FA completely decouples volumes from their physical storage locations and prioritizes all I/O commands equally so there is no need to "stripe" data to distribute I/O load.

All FlashArray volumes are inherently thin-provisioned. They occupy no space until data is written to them, and when hosts do write data, it is reduced before storing, so it occupies only the space needed to represent it. There is no "rounding up" to sector multiples. Thus, a DBA can request volumes sized for anticipated long-term needs, but they consume physical storage only when data is written to them.

As database sizes grow, FlashArray data reduction minimizes physical storage consumption. Many database management systems store data in fixed-length records. When they store items smaller than the record size, they fill with zeros or other byte patterns. FlashArray pattern removal and compression eliminate or reduce fill to a bare minimum. Deduplication detects multiple copies of identical data and stores only a single instance. Arrays search for duplicate data sector by sector; thus, identical data runs can be deduplicated even when they are at different block offsets.

Planned and ad hoc requirements for additional storage can be negotiated by DBAs, and most important of all, when database storage is increased, there is no need to rearrange data. Storage administrators increase volume sizes, and Purity//FA automatically uses the additional storage. At worst, a DBA may have to cause the database software to recognize the additional storage.

Performance

The most significant FlashArray performance boost comes from flash itself. There is no physical positioning so I/O is extremely fast. Purity//FA stages writes in NVRAM and persists data in large blocks, so latency is consistently low and flash is written efficiently. Average I/O latency in typical database applications is less than a half millisecond for blocks of 32 kilobytes or less.

With FlashArray, placing parts of a database on different devices to enable parallel I/O is irrelevant. Arrays store data in a log structure, and with flash, retrieval time is the same for any block of a given size, regardless of volume.

FlashArray eliminates the need for host data compression. Arrays compress all incoming data. Additional compression by database software would serve no purpose, so the compute power it would consume can be devoted to database processing. In addition, FlashArray encrypts all data (and metadata) before storing it, thus satisfying regulatory and organizational requirements for protecting data at rest from misappropriation. Arrays manage keys autonomously, refreshing them at regular intervals, eliminating another storage management task that often falls to the DBA.

DBAs and storage administrators can track I/O performance directly. Using Pure1 Manage they can observe long-term trends and use built-in artificial intelligence algorithms to forecast future performance and capacity requirements.

Accessorize for Success

Databases on FlashArray volumes can be cloned in minutes. A database on multiple volumes can be cloned as of a single logical instant by taking a snapshot of its volumes and using it to clone them.

Clone volumes are *allocate-on-write*. They consume no storage until an application writes data to them. Even then, only the (reduced) data written occupies space. This is important for development testing. If, for example, a test modifies one percent of a database clone, the incremental storage required is only about one percent of the database size.

When clone volumes have served their purpose and are deleted, deletion is instantaneous;[41] there is no impact on the original volumes or on other clones that may still be in use.

Because the impact of database cloning is so small, there is less impetus to plan far in advance. Moreover, the minimal storage requirements minimize the cost of clones. DBAs can clone databases more frequently to accelerate development and meet other business needs more expeditiously.

Continuous Operation

FlashArray is designed to operate continuously throughout arrays' service lives. There is no scheduled downtime. They consist entirely of redundant FRUs. Arrays function with failed power supplies, fans, flash devices, NVRAMs, network and internal I/O interfaces,

---

[41] Deletion (destruction in FlashArray argot) creates a snapshot from which the volumes can be restored if necessary. Arrays automatically remove the snapshots after 24 hours.

and even controllers. They automatically phonehome to notify Pure Storage Support of failures, so remediation begins immediately, in some cases even before the owner is aware of the failure. FRU replacement does not disrupt operation. FlashArray component failures should essentially be transparent to DBAs.

More significant for the DBA is that both software and hardware upgrades are non-disruptive. With the FlashArray "active-active front end/active-passive back end" architecture (page 182), the *primary* controller executes all host I/O commands. The *secondary* controller forwards commands and incoming data to it. It executes them and returns status messages and outgoing data to the secondary for forwarding to hosts.

With this architecture, new Purity//FA releases can be installed on a secondary controller while the primary one is servicing hosts. If hosts have paths to both (a system design best practice), there is no service interruption. When secondary controller software installation is complete, the installer makes it the primary, and installs the new software on the other one. Throughout the process, the array remains in service. Impact on DBAs is negligible.

Non-disruptive upgrade includes hardware. If an upgrade to a more powerful array model is needed, or additional storage is required, the upgrade can be performed using the same procedure while the array is operating. From the DBA standpoint, not only is there no downtime, but the database remains in place, and there is no interruption or slowdown to copy data from old storage to new—a huge benefit for applications and users, and a huge reduction in DBA effort.

In summary, FlashArray storage greatly reduces the need for DBAs to act as de facto storage administrators; it frees them to concentrate on administering databases rather than on the storage they occupy. FlashArray delivers DBA benefits in three principal areas:

ADMINISTRATION

FlashArray eliminates or greatly simplifies many operations in which DBAs typically have a hand. Capacity planning, accommodating growth, and software and hardware upgrades all reduce to negotiations with storage administrators.

PERFORMANCE

Moving from legacy disk-based storage to FlashArray can improve performance by an order of magnitude or more. Data reduction, encryption, and the "active-active front end/active-passive back end" design enhance performance further.

DATA SERVICES

Instant snapshots and clones can dramatically improve business and development workflows. Data reduction and encryption reduce application and database server load, free the DBA from managing those functions, and may also provide license cost relief.

In This Chapter…

As data centers "go virtual," adapting storage to virtual machine environments becomes important, especially true with virtual desktop infrastructures (VDIs). VDI reduces "per-seat" cost for knowledge workers, but more importantly, it simplifies the problem of keeping large numbers of personal computing environments consistent and error-free. FlashArray cloning makes it an attractive platform for VDI.

VMware, a leading provider of virtualization software, has created management paradigms for virtual environments that storage vendors can "plug into." Pure Storage offers a plugin for VMware's vSphere and fully supports the virtual volume (VVOL) construct by mapping its requirements to FlashArray services. Both are available to FlashArray users without incremental charge.

Virtualization is an excellent example of complementary vendors cooperating to the benefit of their mutual customers. Pure Storage developed support for the VMware paradigms within the context of an active partnership between the two companies. The company consults with virtualization vendors on storage issues, and in turn receives advice from them on virtualization issues.

FlashArray and Virtualization

One consequence of the recent dramatic increases in processor performance has been that most servers are too powerful for most applications. There are, and probably always will be, compute-intensive applications—weather forecasting, physical and chemical modeling, simulation, and so forth—that can use all the compute power they can get, but for the vast majority of applications, today's multi-core servers are overpowered.

The Virtualization Phenomenon

The supply-demand mismatch in compute power revived an old concept that had become moribund—*virtualization*. With virtualization, a software kernel, or *hypervisor*, uses a computer's physical resources to simulate multiple *virtual machines*, each appearing as an entire computer to applications running on it. Virtual machine technology existed as early as the 1960s,[42] but for the most part, it was supplanted by virtual memory under the control of a single operating system.

Cody Hosterman
Virtualization Solution Architect
"I view so-called 'best practices' as workarounds. It's like saying, 'Here are the things you have to do to make our product work in your environment.' Pure Storage makes the storage easy. Our job as solution architects is to make everything above it easy, so the only best practice you need is 'deploy Pure Storage.'"

As computers became more powerful, however, the virtual machine idea was revived. In 1999, VMware introduced *VMware Virtual Platform* for Intel processors. By the early 2000s, there was a commercial market for virtual machine technology, with VMware and Microsoft offering virtualization software products, and open source available from Xen (subsequently acquired by Citrix).

Data centers have embraced virtualization for its efficient resource utilization, configuration flexibility, and administrative simplicity. It decouples hardware acquisition from individual projects and applications. Virtual machines can be created when applications are deployed or when they need more resources and dismantled when they are no longer needed. Administrators use a GUI to allocate resources rather than installing physical servers.

---

[42] https://en.wikipedia.org/wiki/Timeline_of_virtualization_development

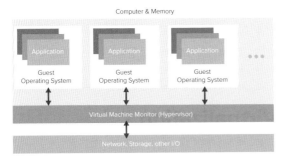

Computer & Memory

A virtualization software architecture consists of a host operating system, often called a *hypervisor*, that interacts with the hardware. The hypervisor schedules processors, allocates memory, and is the gateway to I/O adapters (primarily NICs and HBAs).

A hypervisor manages *virtual machines*, each one a process with its own budget of memory, processing power, and I/O devices. Internally, virtual machines run *guest operating systems*, identical to those that run directly on computer hardware (so-called "bare metal"). Applications run in the context of guest operating systems, but their requests for system services such as memory management and I/O are intercepted and executed by the hypervisor, which controls the actual hardware.

Where Do Virtual Machines Live?

System administrators create *images* of virtual machine system disks and store them persistently in storage managed by the hypervisor. VMware, for example, stores virtual machine images in volume-like containers called *datastores*, formatted with VMware's VMFS file system or with NFS. Each virtual machine image is a file in its own directory. Any additional storage devices are instantiated as files in their virtual machines' directories. The hypervisor presents these as unformatted disks.

Storage topology for a virtualized data center can be quite complex. System administrators can combine physical and virtual disks to create datastores, each having a layout (e.g. concatenated, striped) and a redundancy scheme (e.g., mirroring, RAID), both of which the administrator must specify when creating it.

To some extent, this defeats the flexibility of virtualization—administrators must configure each datastore's properties based on the needs of the virtual machines it will host and the virtual storage devices it will contain, neither of which may be known when it is created. The uncertainty tends to foster conservatism—better to overprovision than to be faced with downtime later when a datastore requires more capacity or a virtual machine and its data must be moved.

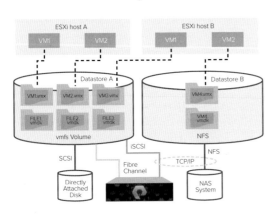

Virtualization software partly compensates for this uncertainty with facilities for moving virtual machines and storage devices to different physical resources (VMware's facilities are called *vMotion*

and *Storage vMotion* respectively), but target datastores must already exist, and moreover, moving virtual machines can be disruptive, time-consuming, and error-prone.

VMware Administrators and Storage

A major portion of virtualized data center administration consists of administering storage for the environment. For example, to create a virtual machine hosted by a volume presented by a storage array:

1. A system administrator requests provisioning of virtual storage with specified capacity, performance, and redundancy.

2. A storage administrator allocates a storage device with the specified properties (e.g., a FlashArray volume) and makes it accessible by hosts that require access.

3. The system administrator directs the hosts' to locate the new device, and creates a datastore on it (e.g. for VMware, a VMFS file system).

4. The system administrator creates a virtual machine image and any necessary virtual disks.

The virtual machine and storage can then be turned over to application managers for application installation and configuration. This workflow has three noteworthy aspects:

COORDINATION

It requires close coordination between system and storage administrators to negotiate storage properties. Policy exceptions must be justified, documented, and implemented.

INFLEXIBILITY

Although virtual, the storage is relatively static. Capacity and redundancy are specified in advance, before the demands of the workload to be run on the new machine are known.

LIMITED SCOPE

Even if the storage matches requirements exactly, it is only valid until the application needs more capacity or migrates to a different host, at which time negotiation starts all over again.

With conventional storage arrays, virtual device creation can itself be complex, especially in data centers that use storage arrays to host many virtual machines. With disk-based arrays, virtual devices are typically configured from slices of storage from each of several physical disks to optimize overall performance by statistical load distribution. If a virtual device is to be redundant, capacity must be allocated for mirror copies or RAID checksums, along with dedicated spare capacity for autonomous failure recovery.

Finally, constraints in the virtualization environments may have unintended side effects. For example, at one time the maximum size of a VMFS file system, and therefore of a datastore, was two terabytes. Administrators had to create and manage multiple datastores because virtual machine images wouldn't fit into one. VMware eventually increased maximum datastore capacity to 64 terabytes, which relieved some of the complexity, but users quickly discovered that disk-based datastores typically could not satisfy the I/O demands of the number of virtual machines that could be hosted by such large devices, so they would revert to the complexity of multiple datastores.

Whatever the configuration constraints, administrators must keep track of which datastores occupy space on which physical disks and which virtual machines they host so that multiple applications with heavy I/O demands don't use the same physical storage and I/O resources. Administrative complexity grows exponentially with the size of the virtualized environment.

It's Even Worse with VDI

VDI is attractive to enterprises with large numbers of knowledge workers that use the same applications. It replaces desktop computers with compact, inexpensive "thin clients"— diskless workstations that load and run operating systems and applications on remote virtual machines instantiated on central servers. VDI clients essentially serve as keyboard, mouse, and video controllers that interact with applications on the virtual machines.

For anyone with many desktop computers to manage, the appeal of VDI is obvious— lower per-user cost to be sure, but more importantly, centrally managed user software. Administrators can deploy new applications and operating system updates from a central virtualization console, keeping all users' environments identical and under central control. New users can be activated by cloning a "golden image" with up-to-date representations of everything needed to do their work. Hundreds of users equipped with thin clients can be enabled rapidly by cloning virtual machine images to serve them.

VDI is also attractive from a security standpoint—centrally managed virtual machine images are less susceptible to malware than individual desktop computers. Moreover, if thin client hardware is misappropriated, the loss is limited to the value of the hardware— no data is compromised.

But while VDI is conceptually attractive, early adoption was slow. As recently as 2013, one industry analyst estimated that the technology was only suitable for 5% to 10% of desktop environments.[43] Market acceptance seemed to bear this out. Starting around 2010, analysts declared each year to be "the year of VDI," but large-scale adoption never seemed to occur.

The barrier to acceptance appears to have been the user experience. Knowledge workers who depend on their computers want them to perform. Their point of comparison for VDI clients is their experience with desktop computers. Sluggish graphics and slow application response compare unfavorably with local desktops. Perhaps the most frustrating aspect of VDI is the start-of-day "boot storm," as hundreds of users power their thin clients on and the virtual machines behind them compete for I/O capacity to load operating systems and applications.

VDI performance issues were partly graphics-related—updating screens over Ethernet was problematic, even with relatively few users. But the biggest performance limitation was access to storage. When hundreds of thin clients vie for I/O from a disk-based array, latencies that would deliver a favorable VDI experience are impossible to achieve.

---

[43] https://searchvirtualdesktop.techtarget.com/opinion/VDI-adoption-is-hitting-its-stride-finally

FlashArray and Virtual Machines

Today, all storage systems are robust. Given that reliability is expected, the primary advantage of FlashArray for virtualization is that they simplify administration of the virtual environment, partly because of flash performance, but also partly due to the arrays' ease of use.

The most important FlashArray performance property that makes administration of virtual environments easier is that it is *array-wide*. Arrays use their resources to deliver the best possible performance on every I/O command, regardless of volume. Because access time is essentially equal for every block of flash in an array, virtualizing the volumes presented to hosts carries no performance penalty. The data in a volume is typically distributed across most or all array storage devices. Since device access times are equal, it makes sense to execute each host command as it arrives, regardless of the volume addressed or other commands being executed at the time.

Equal I/O performance regardless of volume eliminates several concerns for virtualization environment administrators. For example, there is no RAID or spare configuration, no need to locate virtual machines on separate devices to avoid I/O interference, and no reason to create multiple datastores to improve performance. FlashArray protects all stored data with RAID technology that survives dual hard read errors. The arrays encrypt all stored data, with autonomously managed keys, eliminating a source of administrative complexity in secure environments.

Most FlashArray users can operate with a single datastore. The only technical limit is the maximum capacity supported by the environment (e.g., the current maximum size of a VMware datastore, is 64 terabytes).

FlashArray can also relieve environmental constraints. For example, by default VMware limits the maximum number of I/O commands in progress on a datastore to 32. If command arrival rate exceeds average service time, I/O queues build up and virtual machines wait. To circumvent this limit, administrators typically increase the number of datastores. With FlashArray's sub-millisecond average latency, however, commands complete much faster than with disk-based arrays, so datastores can execute more commands per unit time. With FlashArray, queues are shorter, response times are lower, so fewer datastores are typically needed—another reduction in complexity.

Instant Clones

In virtualized data centers, large blocks of data are frequently copied. Administrators instantiate new virtual machines by copying a reference ("golden") image into a datastore. Sometimes, a virtual machine or virtual disk must be duplicated or moved to a different location. Virtualization software provides these functions, but being host-based, they must read source objects block-by-block and write them to target locations, consuming significant time and I/O bandwidth.

Virtualization and storage developers both recognized that storage systems could do better. At a minimum, they could copy volumes internally to eliminate storage network bandwidth consumption. Even better, a storage system able to clone volumes could create and populate an entire new volume with a single host command.

The standards community responded by specifying SCSI XCOPY commands to expose storage system bulk-copy capabilities to hosts, especially virtualization hypervisors. With a single command, a host can direct a storage system that supports XCOPY to copy an arbitrarily large range of blocks to target addresses on the same or a different volume.

Virtualization software providers quickly incorporated XCOPY in their administrative tools. For example, VMware uses XCOPY in their VAAI feature.

FlashArray executes XCOPY commands almost instantly; arrays simply create new mapping structures that represent the target's virtual block addresses but point to the "copied" data. Source and target maps point to the same data image until a host modifies either source or target data, at which point the array adjusts its maps to point to the modified data—unmodified data continues to be represented by the single image.

With FlashArray, an administrator can create hundreds of identical virtual machine images in minutes. Multi-gigabyte volumes can be "copied" instantly for use by unrelated virtual machines instantiated in other datastores hosted by the array. Until a host modifies source or target data, no additional storage is consumed. With FlashArray, using XCOPY to clone virtual machines or copy data volumes saves time and storage compared to other approaches.

Sometimes You Win

Consolidation of parallelized applications is an unexpected FlashArray benefit realized by some users. As processor design shifted from higher clock speeds to more cores per die, many developers restructured their applications as multiple threads able to execute concurrently on different processor cores. Parallel execution delivered better aggregate performance when more cores were utilized, so many developers made licensing and pricing proportional to the number of cores in which their applications ran.

But because disk-based storage performance had not scaled with processing power, individual threads were spending significant time waiting for I/O commands to complete. Users were paying for processing power that was idle much of the time.

With FlashArray, I/O commands complete faster than with disk-based storage. Typical response times are below a half millisecond (compared to 5-10 milliseconds), so application threads spend less time waiting. More work is done by each thread, so fewer threads are needed for a given aggregate performance. Fewer threads means fewer cores, which in turn often means lower application license costs.

FlashArray and Desktop Virtualization

VDI works because typical knowledge workers' computing resource demands are quite low. A thousand users, each using tens of IOPS can easily be serviced by an array capable of executing hundreds of thousands of IOPS. In VDI environments, I/O throughput is not the main cause of user dissatisfaction. That honor is reserved for latency.

I/O latency is a large part of the response experienced by interactive users. For example, an array with 5 millisecond average latency accounts for a half second of response time to a user command that requires 100 I/O operations. With FlashArray's typical half-millisecond latency, the contribution is 50 milliseconds—barely perceptible by a human. Moreover, VDI workloads are inherently random because each user accesses a different virtual disk, so disk-based array latency is likely to be higher than average. FlashArray executes all commands in about the same time, regardless of addressed volume, so the randomness of VDI workloads does not affect performance.

A big benefit of FlashArray storage for VDI occurs at the start of the work day when many users are logging in. Hundreds of users loading virtual machine images at the same time can mean "boot times" in the tens of minutes, or even hours—clearly unacceptable from a productivity standpoint. Reducing I/O latency by an order of magnitude lowers the start of day "boot storm" to a tolerable level and gets knowledge workers going promptly, no matter how many are contending for the storage resource.

A recent VDI deployment trend is *non-persistent virtual machines*. Each time a user connects a thin client, the virtualization manager clones a virtual machine from a "golden image" and boots from it. When the user disconnects, the virtual machine is discarded. This is highly advantageous administratively—every user session is based on a clean, up-to-date guest operating system and applications. Patching and updating is a snap—only the golden image is altered. FlashArray near-instant clones are ideal for non-persistent virtual machines; they enable users to log in and start working immediately.

Non-persistent virtual machines aren't the answer for every VDI deployment—users working with encrypted files or requiring unique software can't take advantage of the technology. But non-persistent virtual machines can simplify many VDI deployments, making the technology applicable in a wider variety of environments, especially when backed by FlashArray storage.

vSphere Virtual Volumes

As storage arrays became more intelligent and feature-rich, it became clear that implementing each datastore as a volume was not the optimal granularity. Using a separate datastore for each virtual machine complicates administration. But most arrays implement features like replication at the volume level, so placing many virtual machines in a single datastore means that they share the same storage properties.

VMware removed this limitation with the *vSphere Virtual Volume* (VVol) construct that enables arrays to integrate their configuration and management features with the vSphere management framework. VVols have the following properties:

VIRTUAL DISK GRANULARITY
Each VVol is instantiated as a separate volume on the array.

AUTOMATIC PROVISIONING
When a VMware administrator creates a virtual disk, vSphere directs the array to create and present a volume. Similarly, resizing or deleting a virtual disk automatically resizes or removes the volume on the array.

ARRAY-LEVEL VIRTUAL MACHINE VISIBILITY

Arrays can recognize associations between virtual machines and virtual disks, so they can manage and report performance and utilization at either level of granularity.

MANAGEMENT BASED ON STORAGE POLICIES

Arrays can take snapshots and replicate at volume or virtual machine granularity. Administrators can manage storage properties either by policy or ad hoc. Storage administrator overrides of VMware policies generate non-compliance alerts.

Purity//FA includes *VMware APIs for Storage Awareness* (VASA) provider software that implements VVol functions. A companion plugin for the vCenter management framework links vCenter and FlashArray administrative functions.

With VASA, arrays represent each virtual machine and its storage as a *protection group*, a management construct that enables common host connection, snapshot, and replication policies to be applied to a set of volumes. Each of a virtual machine's volumes is part of its protection group. The virtual machine and its volumes can be connected to or disconnected from a group of hosts with a single command or can be snapped and replicated atomically.

The FlashArray VVol plugin makes VMware administration of FlashArray storage simple. FlashArray policies can be imported into vCenter so a VMware administrator can apply them to other storage objects. Other FlashArray capabilities that the plugin integrates with vCenter include:

IMPORT DISK

Instantly presents a clone of any VVol or VVol snapshot that belongs to any VVol-based VM in the same array to the selected virtual machine.

RESTORE DELETED DISK

Instantly recovers a deleted VVol-based virtual disk within in the 24-hour period following the deletion.

CREATE SNAPSHOT

Creates a FlashArray snapshot of a specified virtual disk.

OVERWRITE DISK

Overwrites a VVol with the contents of any VVol or VVol snapshot of the same size on the same array.

Once the plugin is installed and configured in cooperation with a storage administrator, VMware administrators can perform most routine storage administration operations on VVols instantiated as FlashArray volumes without involving the storage administrator.

The FlashArray Threat

FlashArray ease of use occasionally elicits a negative reaction from virtualized data center administrators. As one Pure Storage solution architect observes, "25 minutes after I first touched a FlashArray, I knew everything there was to know about configuring it." Because so many of their skills and so much of their time are spent configuring and managing storage, administrators can envision becoming redundant when storage management is all but eliminated. This is almost always a false concern, however.

The pace of change in data centers is such that virtualization environments are constantly changing—virtual machines and disks are created, altered, moved between hosts and datastores, and dismantled, at a pace that almost requires some type of automated orchestration. Orchestration tools exist (VMware's is called vRealize), but with administrators consumed by routine management of the storage environment, there is limited opportunity to develop skill in their use. Virtualized data centers are often managed based on individuals' spreadsheets, or worse, are in perpetual crises.

The FlashArray Promise

FlashArray eliminates most storage configuration and management tasks that require guesswork with conventional storage. For example, volumes are provisioned dynamically as data is written to them. At any point in time, a volume occupies storage for the data it contains and no more. Sizing volumes accurately is therefore much less critical than it is with arrays whose volume sizes are based on physical device capacities.

Similarly, FlashArray executes all I/O commands for a given data block size in approximately the same time, so there is no need for an administrator to stripe datastores across multiple volumes for performance—arrays automatically optimize performance across all of their flash devices.

Likewise, all data stored in a FlashArray is protected by dual fault-tolerant RAID. Administrators do not configure RAID groups, spares, or any other aspects of redundancy reminiscent of legacy storage micromanagement.

This is not to say that FlashArray doesn't require any administrative attention. Administrators must configure multipathing (i.e., paths to both of an array's controllers for each virtual machine host), ensure that storage network zones and VPNs enable the required connections, and that the right hosts are authorized to access each volume. It is significant, however, that these are data center environment considerations, not array requirements per se.

Freeing the Administrator

Relieved of the constant need to micromanage storage, data center administrators can pursue higher-level skills, such as orchestration, that deliver more value to their organizations. For VMware, Pure Storage supports this with a plugin that makes the vSphere management framework FlashArray-aware. For functions that the plugin doesn't support directly, administrators can create REST calls, Powershell (for Windows HyperV), or scripts for the vRealize orchestrator to automate recurring management tasks.

The Pure Storage Knowledge Base contains a wealth of tools contributed by the company's engineers and users that automate common VMware environment tasks. The tool most often downloaded is a best-practices checker that determines whether an array conforms to documented best practices for integrating with VMware environments. Because FlashArray administration is straightforward, the checker essentially verifies that VMware defaults for FlashArray storage are in effect.

There's more than enough work to go around in the virtual data center. As the same Pure Storage virtualization solution architect also observed, "I've seen people automated out of jobs by external forces, but I've *never* seen anyone automate him or herself out of a job. A person who can figure out how to use a legacy storage array in a virtualized environment can learn how to do anything that needs doing in the data center."

With FlashArray storage, administrators spend less time managing storage, so they can use the vRealize orchestrator to provide repetitive services like rapid provisioning, snapshots, backup, and replication to their users.

The Greatest Among Equals

Virtualization software vendors avoid favoritism in dealing with storage vendors. When they add functionality to their products, they typically consult with their storage partners to construct solutions that apply to all of them. For example, when VMware developed their *VStorage API for Array Integration* (VAAI) technology for granular locking and bulk copy offloading, they invited storage partners to comment on the proposed specification and reacted to their comments. The result is an API standard that any storage vendor can implement. Pure Storage has implemented VAAI; FlashArray is able to offload bulk data copying and perform fine-granular locking in VMware environments.

Integration goes beyond reacting to vendor requirements. Cooperative relationships among complementary vendors can often improve integration and simplify administration for their customers. VMware multipathing support is a case in point. Although FlashArray primary controllers *execute* all host I/O commands, both controllers can receive them; the secondary controller relays commands it receives to the primary for execution. The purpose of this architecture is fault tolerance without performance penalty. If a controller fails, hosts can continue to issue commands to its partner and the array continues to operate at essentially full performance.

When both controllers are functional, however, *round-robin* scheduling alternates commands to both controllers, leading to better I/O performance. Originally, VMware left I/O scheduling algorithm selection to its users, many of whom did not specify round-robin for FlashArray, effectively neglecting half the available bandwidth between array and hosts. This was easily remedied with a minor VMware configuration adjustment, but for users unaware of that, disappointing I/O performance often resulted in support engagements. With its cooperative relationship with VMware, Pure Storage was able to negotiate a change in configuration defaults so than when a host recognizes a FlashArray, it automatically adopts round-robin scheduling.

Ongoing relationships with complementary producers are often synergistic. Companies adopt new technologies at different rates. NVMe and NVMe-oF are a case in point. Pure Storage was an early adopter of NVMe—it has been the NVRAM interface in all FlashArray models starting with FlashArray//M. More recently, the company introduced NVMe-oF-connected expansion storage shelves for its arrays. Arguably, Pure Storage is one of the most experienced NVMe adopters. When NVMe-oF began to gain traction as a host-to-storage interconnect, virtualization software vendors naturally turned to the company for guidance and support. As a result, the first all-NVMe "stacks" to reach the market incorporated FlashArray storage.

In This Chapter...

Microsoft Windows Server is one of two operating systems that predominate in mainstream data center servers. It includes several common storage services, such as data encryption and deduplication, but their functionality is limited, they are complex to administer, and they consume significant processing power.

FlashArray performs advanced storage services automatically and transparently to Windows system administrators, with no impact on host performance. Storage configuration and expansion are simpler, I/O performance is uniform across all volumes, and data is secure against access by "rogue" hosts and media misappropriation. Pure Storage provides a comprehensive toolkit that automates many common Windows Server administrative tasks with FlashArray storage.

Realizing that many installed arrays have significant "headroom" (unused processing power and I/O bandwidth), the company has introduced Windows File Services—a virtual clustered file server for Windows clients, whose nodes run in virtual machines within a FlashArray's two controllers. FlashArray users can provide file services to Windows clients without deploying and configuring dedicated physical or virtual servers for the purpose.

FlashArray and Windows

The Windows Server operating system includes storage virtualization, mirroring, RAID-5, asynchronous and synchronous replication, encryption, compression, and deduplication. All services are performed by software running in the Windows Server systems that host applications. Storage services in the application server have two important consequences:

CPU Loading

Advanced storage services require significant I/O bandwidth and processing power. For example, server-based mirroring and RAID-5 cause considerable write amplification—a single application write can result in several operations with corresponding storage network traffic. Encryption, compression, and deduplication are all CPU-intensive; they reduce processing power available to applications.

Administrative Complexity

Each time a server's storage configuration changes—additional storage devices are connected, a volume is resized, encryption is enabled or disabled, and so forth—storage, server, and application administrators must ensure that changes are understood and agreed upon, and that each administrator makes the required changes in his or her sphere of responsibility properly and reacts to others appropriately. For example, when a device is added to a RAID group, the data stored in it must be restriped to make use of the new capacity, and applications must be restarted to recognize the altered storage configuration.

Robert Barker ("Barkz")

"I joined Pure Storage in 2013 as its first Microsoft Solutions Architect. I quickly learned that even the new guy can make an impact.

At the time, there was no PowerShell module for FlashArray, so I began by writing what became the Toolkit as a 'grassroots' open source project. I didn't have to ask permission or build a business case; I just did it.

Customers have used the Toolkit for all sorts of automation. Eventually, I turned it over to engineering, which developed a binary version. The two have been downloaded over 8,500 times!

I am inspired every day being part of the Pure Storage team because of the creativity, forward thinking, and team members. Not a day goes by when I don't have an opportunity to work on something cool. Our road ahead will continue to disrupt the storage industry and I'm pumped to be part of that journey."

Most of the advanced storage services provided by the Windows Server operating system have FlashArray equivalents, and thus need not be enabled at the Windows level. This frees application-server compute power for applications and greatly reduces or eliminates the need for administrative coordination when storage is reconfigured.

Streamlining Storage Design for Applications

Most major Windows applications, such as Microsoft's own SQL Server and Exchange Server, require careful storage layout to optimize I/O performance and provide data resiliency. For example, SQL Server best practices recommend locating logs on separate volumes from the database and multiple volumes for the database itself. Both are aimed at distributing I/O load across as many physical devices as practical for I/O concurrency and so that database volume(s) can be restored independently of the logs.

With disk I/O latencies in the tens of milliseconds, this is necessary advice, but it has consequences. The first is that storage and application administrators must predict the I/O load and design the storage layout accordingly. If they're wrong, they either live with mediocre I/O performance or disrupt operations to correct the layout. The second consequence is that whenever the I/O configuration must change, for example when more storage is required, application, server, and storage administrators must coordinate the configuration change, which often requires lengthy service disruption as databases are copied or backed up and restored onto the new storage layout.

Storage Design with FlashArray

The contrast with FlashArray storage couldn't be more striking. First, the order of magnitude difference between flash and disk performance provides an automatic performance boost. But in addition, the virtualized volume layout prioritizes every I/O request equally. There is no need to partition databases on multiple volumes; whether on one volume or a dozen, performance is the same. This also makes performance independent of I/O load distribution, so there is no need to change database layouts when I/O distribution changes.

FlashArray uses the same form of RAID, called RAID-HA, to protect all data and metadata. Administrators do not have to decide among mirroring, RAID-5, or other options, configure "RAID sets," or reserve "spare" devices.

Similarly, volumes are resized with a single command using the FlashArray CLI, or through PowerShell or Python. Further administrative action is only required if it is necessary for applications to recognize the new volume size. Again, there is no copying or backup and restore needed to re-layout data.

Protecting Stored Data

Increasingly, government regulations are forcing enterprises to look hard at how they protect client (and employee!) data. In the United States, the healthcare and financial industries already face stringent data protection regulation, and the European Union's *General Data Protection Regulation* (GDPR) appears to be a forerunner of things to come across the globe.

Digital data protection is a broad and complex topic, but one important dimension is guarding against misappropriation of "data at rest"—data in storage systems or devices connected to servers. Threats to data at rest may come from two directions:

STOLEN MEDIA

A disk or SSD removed from a server or storage array by an unauthorized party may be "scavenged" to recover confidential data. The data may be fragmentary and difficult to parse, but with sufficient time and effort, confidential information can be exposed.

"ROGUE" SERVERS

Storage networks are nearly ubiquitous in data centers. While they convey tremendous benefit, they "connect everything to everything," at least physically. As Ethernet-based iSCSI storage networks become prevalent, Ethernet's universality increases the danger. Fibre Channel zoning and Ethernet *virtual private networks* (VPNs) restrict access to specific endpoints, but an in-zone server may gain access to volumes for which it is not authorized.

Windows Server includes *BitLocker Drive Encryption* to protect against these threats. BitLocker encrypts the entire contents of virtual or physical storage devices. It requires an encryption key on a readable device such as a USB thumb drive, or in servers that support *Trusted Platform Module*, in the computer's *basic input/output system* (BIOS). The server administrator must enable and manage BitLocker, as well as several ancillary features, including key management. Server-based encryption is compute-intensive. It can impact application performance by as much as 20% in extreme cases.

FlashArray and Unauthorized Access

FlashArray provides defenses against both stolen media and access by unauthorized computers. To protect against exposing data when media are misappropriated, arrays encrypt all stored data all the time. Encryption cannot be disabled. All FlashArray performance results quoted by legitimate sources include encryption of data before it is written and decryption when it is read.

Encryption key management is both an administrative headache and a security risk. Keys must be available to all servers that use the data in any form, including snapshots, backups, and replicas. The number of instances of a supposedly secure key can grow quickly, along with the number of individuals to whom it is exposed.

FlashArray key management is completely autonomous—array administrators have no access to keys, or mechanisms for altering them. They are encrypted and stored on flash devices, partitioned in such a way that more than half of an array's devices must be accessible to reconstruct them.

FlashArray also protects against access to volumes by unauthorized servers. The arrays manage *host* objects, that represent servers identified by their storage network address(es). An administrator must explicitly *connect* a host to a volume for an array to recognize and respond to its I/O commands. A host that issues I/O commands to a volume receives no response unless the array administrator has explicitly connected the two.[44]

---

[44] Arrays support host group and volume group objects to expedite multiple connections.

Data Replication

Replicating production data to remote locations is a common data center practice. Replicas can provide stable data for remote backup, analytics, or development testing, but perhaps their most important use is protecting against disasters that incapacitate entire data centers. With a reasonably up-to-date replica of data at a remote data center, production IT can resume in relatively short order after a severe event.

Replication isn't free. It uses processing, network, and storage resources at both main and secondary data centers. For applications that can tolerate a small amount of production data loss—the most recent few minutes of updates—*asynchronous* replication can tolerate somewhat relaxed network latency. Where no data loss is tolerable, *synchronous* replication that keeps production data in lockstep with its replica is a must, albeit at higher cost.

The Windows Server operating system includes an optional *Storage Replica* feature. A Windows administrator can configure Storage Replica for either synchronous or asynchronous replication of each volume. After configuration and initial synchronization of production and replica data (usually by transporting a production data backup to the replica location and restoring it), Storage Replica sends production data updates individually or in batches to the replica location, where Windows Server applies them to the replica.

Storage Replica does the job, but is somewhat complex to install, configure and administer. It requires specific administrative roles and network ports and limits the types of data that can be replicated. It uses the *Server Message Block* (SMB) protocol for data transfer, so configuring for recoverability from link outages is complicated and error-prone. With asynchronous replication, only the latest completed replication episode is available.

Data Replication with FlashArray

FlashArray capabilities include asynchronous and synchronous replication, both of which are independent of hosts. *FlashRecover* asynchronous replication replicates periodic snapshots of groups of volumes. The snapshots capture the contents of all volumes at a single logical instant. FlashRecover economizes on network bandwidth by transmitting only "deltas"—changes that occur between successive snapshots—to the replica location.

FlashRecover replication can be ad hoc—an administrator can take and replicate a snapshot at any time. The more common usage, however, is "set and forget"—an administrator specifies snapshot frequency and replica retention. With that information, FlashRecover "makes it happen," taking snapshots on schedule and transmitting changes to as many as four target arrays. The targets apply changes and automatically destroy replicas when their retention periods lapse.

An important advantage of FlashRecover is retention of multiple snapshot replicas. For example, if replication is hourly with 48-hour retention, a replica can be cloned to recover a production data set to its state at any hour within a rolling two-day window. This simplifies recovery from corruptions of production data whose times can be pinpointed.

For situations in which every production data update "absolutely, positively has to be there" at the replica, FlashArray offers *ActiveCluster* symmetric synchronous replication between pairs of arrays. Unlike Storage Replica, ActiveCluster has no master-slave concept. Both arrays export a replicated volume group during replication. Every update by a host connected to either array is immediately visible in both.

Like FlashRecover, ActiveCluster is "set and forget." The arrays' administrators establish a secure network connection, specify the volume group to be replicated, and let it happen. Initial synchronization is over the network link; there is no need to transport data to a replication site and restore it.

ActiveCluster eliminates another complexity common with synchronous replication: mediation. Synchronous replication requires mediator to designate a "survivor" if the link that connects replication partners fails. Most implementations require users to set up and maintain a mediation site. For ActiveCluster, Pure Storage provides no-cost, no-configuration Internet-based mediation that designates one array to *survive* (continue operating) when the two cannot communicate.[45]

ActiveCluster requires low-latency communication between replicating arrays; its network requirements are more stringent than those of FlashRecover. Moreover, performing every data update twice exacts a performance cost relative to I/O to a single array. But for high-value production data, ActiveCluster is by far the most flexible, easiest to administer means of synchronizing two instances of data remote from each other in real time.

Both FlashRecover and ActiveCluster are included with every FlashArray. There is no incremental cost, no add-on software to install, and aside from initial setup, nothing to administer. Users sometimes enable one or the other to backstop application replication mechanisms such as SQL Server Always On.

Data Reduction

Once an exotic feature used only in exceptional circumstances, data reduction—removing redundancy from data to reduce storage hardware requirements—has become common in data center storage. Many storage purchasers count on it when budgeting.

Data reduction has two basic forms: compression and deduplication. Compression finds repeated byte strings in a block of data and replaces them with pointers to a dynamically constructed "dictionary" containing an instance of each string. Deduplication does a similar thing with entire blocks of data.

Both forms of reduction are data-dependent. If a data set contains no redundancy, there is nothing to compress or deduplicate. This occurs with digital audio and video, where data is highly irregular, and hardware or software digital signal processing removes redundancy before it is stored. For most types of data, however, reduction provides a significant benefit. Ratios in the range of 2:1-5:1 are not uncommon. In some specialized applications, such as backup and VDI, data (e.g., operating system images) is highly redundant by nature, so much higher reduction ratios are possible.

There are several compression algorithms in common use. All are CPU-intensive to

---

[45] The company also provides a virtual machine image that users for whom Internet arbitration is not feasible can install on their own premises.

some degree, but in general, they balance compression efficiency against the amount of processing per byte they consume. Likewise, several deduplication techniques exist, again typically delivering higher reduction ratios in proportion to the system resources they consume. With deduplication, however, the system resources include not only computation, but also memory to hold block signature tables, and I/O for overflow signatures and for verifying the identity of candidate duplicate blocks.

In disk-based arrays, compression and deduplication are constrained by the universal 512-byte sectors in which data can be written. A 1,024-byte block that compresses to 513 bytes must occupy two sectors; even though the data is highly compressible, no storage is saved. With deduplication, the challenge is finding duplicate sector sequences among many terabytes of stored data. This is often done by caching hash signatures for stored blocks and comparing them with the signatures of incoming data blocks.

Windows Server offers both compression and deduplication options. Compression is a per-file system option for *New Technology File Systems* (NTFS) only—others are not supported—and requires the default 4 kilobyte allocation unit size. Deduplication is a background job that runs periodically to identify files with "chunks" of identical content and replace all but one instance of each. Both compression and deduplication consume processing power that is therefore unavailable to applications. In addition, because they both operate at the file system level, they omit some files (e.g., encrypted ones), Moreover, there are inherent inefficiencies. For example, to move a file from one compressed file system to another, Windows must read and decompress it and recompress it before writing. With deduplication, GC—removal of deduplicated chunks no longer referenced by files—occurs weekly by default, and requires administrative action to change.

Data Reduction with FlashArray

FlashArray reduces incoming data before storing it. As with encryption, data reduction is "always-on"—it is not an option. Arrays reduce data in two stages:

INITIAL
> When data first arrives in an array, it is compressed using a relatively "lightweight" algorithm and deduplicated against the most probable duplicate block sequences.

BACKGROUND ("DEEP")
> Continuous background processes compress data more thoroughly, using more compute power but executing at lower priority. They deduplicate against a realm of candidate duplicates that spans the entire array.

Arrays compress incoming data and stage it in NVRAM before signaling write completion to hosts, so initial reduction is "lightweight" to keep host I/O latency low. Background reduction only reduces data that remains unaltered for an extended period (typically hours or days), so no resources are consumed deep-reducing data that is overwritten or deleted soon after creation.

FlashArray deduplication has two important properties that make it the most efficient on the market:

ARRAY-WIDE SCOPE

Arrays search for duplicate block sequences throughout an array, not just within the volume or file system containing the blocks.

ALIGNMENT INDEPENDENCE

FlashArray aggregates consecutive sector signatures to detect duplicate blocks of eight or more sectors regardless of boundary alignment. For example, if a 64-sector incoming block contains 16 sectors that duplicate data already stored in the array, Purity//FA deduplicates them, regardless of where in the 64-sector block they lie.

Moreover, duplication is not constrained by sector (or any other) boundaries. Each block of data stored in a FlashArray, whether compressed, deduplicated, or stored as received, occupies only as much space as it requires. There is no "rounding up" to sector or block boundaries. Thus, a block that compresses to 513 bytes, occupies 513 bytes of flash (plus a few bytes of metadata that describe it).

In summary, FlashArray always-on data reduction applies to all data in an array, is more efficient than any other form of reduction in common use, uses no server resources, and perhaps most importantly, requires no administrative attention. FlashArray constantly does its best to reduce all stored data.

Bulk Data Copying

Windows Server administrators must often copy large data sets from one server or cluster to another. Windows File Explorer drag-and-drop copies files serially. The RoboCopy utility expedites large copy jobs by multi-threading. In many cases, original and copied data sets are stored in the same array. To expedite bulk data copying, Microsoft implemented its ODX protocol, used by Windows Servers to direct arrays to copy large blocks of data between volumes without server involvement. ODX is similar but not identical to the SCSI XCOPY commands used in other contexts.

FlashArray supports ODX, so a Windows Server can direct an array to copy as much as terabytes of data from one volume to another in the same array. ODX is "always on"—no licensing, configuration, or enabling is required to use it. Copying is nearly instantaneous because Purity//FA creates metadata structures that represent the copied data by pointing to the original. As the copied data is modified, the changes are stored and the metadata is adjusted accordingly. Incremental storage is required only for changes to the copied data set, rather than for a full copy of the data set.

Windows as a File Server

Windows Servers are often used as file servers, replacing servers that use the NFS or SMB network file access protocols. The operating system includes a *File Server* role specifically for this purpose. The role is usually configured in clusters, running on two servers connected to the same storage devices. One server provides file services to clients; the other is a hot standby that takes control of the storage and provides ongoing client service should the first fail.

Many applications are not processor-intensive, so Windows Server *File and iSCSI Services* often runs in virtual machines. Server administrators are responsible for installing and configuring Windows, connecting the virtual machines to storage, and managing both on an ongoing basis.

Purity//Run exploits otherwise-unused FlashArray compute power to run applications. FlashArray administrators can configure virtual machines within an array to run certain types of applications. One such application is Windows Server File and iSCSI Services, called *Windows File Services* (WFS). WFS is installed on a FlashArray's two controllers. One becomes the active file server; the other takes over if the first one fails. FlashArray volumes provide the storage. With WFS, data centers can provide file services without dedicating and configuring physical or virtual servers.

FlashArray is first and foremost a block storage array that exports volumes (logical units, or LUNs) to clients over a storage network, so Purity//Run gives WFS a fixed resource budget for serving files to clients. CloudAssist historical data collected from the installed base indicates that most arrays are less than 50% utilized. Running WFS in a FlashArray both helps users get more out of their Pure Storage investments and makes deployment and ongoing management of file services for Windows significantly easier.

In This Chapter...

New applications for FlashArray storage continue to emerge. Two notable ones are both in the medical field. In the United States, recent legislation has prompted rapid computerization of patient records and integration of provider and insurer databases. Many providers are not sophisticated users of computer technology, so FlashArray ease of use is attractive to them, and to independent software vendors.

Providers must maintain medical record confidentiality. While this involves both technology and operating procedures, FlashArray always-on encryption secures medical data while it is "at rest."

Medical image processing has expanded beyond X-rays to become a key diagnostic tool for many specialties. Rapid, accurate diagnosis assisted by timely image analysis can sometimes be the difference between life and death. Low-cost image acquisition equipment has enabled image-based diagnosis in remote areas that were previously inaccessible to the technology.

Reliable storage is key to successful computer-based imaging. As acquisition technology creates higher-resolution images, I/O performance and storage cost become important as well. Finally, mandated data privacy means that data security is a necessity.

Reliability, capacity, performance, ease of operation, and data security are all FlashArray characteristics. Health care providers are noticing, and arrays are being employed as storage in medical imaging applications.

Emerging Applications

FlashArray was developed for the mainstream enterprise storage market in which storage applications initially fell into two broad categories—databases and virtualization. In the intervening years, some structured data applications, for example medical and core business record keeping, have become specialized and today are regarded as separate categories with unique storage requirements. For these as well, FlashArray provides significant advantages over disk-based and hybrid storage systems.

Electronic Medical Records (EMR)

In 2009, the United States Federal Government passed the HITECH act, which included provisions that incentivized health care providers to computerize and integrate patient records. The act vaulted *independent software vendors* (ISVs) who had been struggling to persuade providers of the advantages of computerizing

Jean-Luc Degrenand
Solution Architect, EMR
"Since joining Pure Storage in 2015, I have watched FlashArray use in the healthcare sector grow from a handful to hundreds of installations.
This is a tribute not only to the company's products, but also to its willingness to understand its customers' businesses and work with them to solve their problems."

to prominence as their *electronic medical records* (EMR) applications were suddenly in high demand. The few ISVs whose applications were ready for deployment quickly gained market share and continue to dominate the space.

EMR is essentially an *online transaction processing* (OLTP) application—medical practitioners record patient histories, treatments, and prescribed medications and therapies. Recently, patients have gained direct access to the systems, which they use to schedule appointments and review treatment regimens and recommendations. In addition, there is a bidirectional information flow between insurers and EMR systems. Insurers communicate coverage details and the systems respond with treatment records and billing information.

EMR is a natural *database management system* (DBMS) application. The leading ISVs in medical recordkeeping all use DBMSs to organize and manage data. Among the dominant providers, about half base their applications on conventional relational DBMSs—Oracle and SQL Server, while the others use various outgrowths of a DBMS called MUMPS,[46] originally developed specifically for medical record keeping.

As the EMR software providers have evolved, some have moved into hosting, while others provide software and recommend computing infrastructures to their customers. Hosting ISVs offer dedicated on-premises solutions to their largest customers, and service the smaller ones from data centers that they own and operate.

FlashArray and EMR Processing

From an I/O standpoint, EMR resembles other OLTP applications that use databases to organize and store data. Accesses are predominantly retrievals, I/O sizes are relatively small (typically 8 to 16 kilobytes), and load is mostly determined by the number of concurrent users. Sub-millisecond response to I/O commands makes FlashArray ideal for EMR. Deploying FlashArray typically doubles the number of users that an EMR configuration supports.

One characteristic unique to EMR I/O loads particularly affects products that use MUMPS derivatives—periodic high-intensity bursts of writes that can interfere with read performance. DBMSs derived from MUMPS persist updates in bulk every 80 seconds. With hundreds of interactive users, a lot can change in 80 seconds, so frequent large bursts of write commands are the norm. Even if a storage system processes I/O commands in arrival order (which FlashArray does), a read command resulting from a doctor's request can be blocked for hundreds of milliseconds. In some instances, that may be an annoyance (medical professionals are not the most patient of computer users), but in others, such as requests for known allergies prior to administering medication, it can be life-threatening.

Not only does FlashArray stage writes in NVRAM as soon as they are received, arrays write data to flash in large sequential blocks, segmented so that a write cannot block a read for more than a few hundred microseconds. Moreover, Purity//FA limits the number of concurrent writes in a write group. Finally, if outstanding write operations block a read, the software uses RAID reconstruction to deliver data with minimal delay. Thus, arrays mitigate the impact of intense bursts of writes and provide consistent fast response to interactive users, even during background database updates.

Two other properties make FlashArray uniquely attractive for EMR:

Ease of Use

Many smaller healthcare providers lack the in-house IT skills common in other fields. FlashArray administrators do not manage RAID groups, spares, data set separation, or other storage details. Providers refreshing customers' first generation EMR systems often adopt FlashArray to eliminate recurring issues with their original deployments.

For ISVs too, FlashArray ease of use is a major advantage. As they configure and manage customer systems, they create fewer volumes, make fewer host-volume connections, specify fewer snapshot schedules, and so forth. Moreover, Pure1 gives the ISV instant access to the performance and utilization of their customers' arrays, allowing them to proactively detect potential issues and assist with capacity planning.

---

[46] Massachusetts General Hospital Utility Multi-Programming System-https://en.wikipe-dia.org/wiki/MUMPS

Data Security

Among its provisions, the *Health Insurance Portability and Accountability Act* (HIPAA) requires that health care data be kept private and secured. For the most part, the act deals with restrictions on disclosure, but it does require institutions to safeguard electronically stored data against theft and unauthorized access. FlashArray "always on" encryption secures data against device theft and does not require administrators to manage encryption keys. Arrays protect against unauthorized computer access by requiring administrators to explicitly make connections between each volume and the hosts authorized to access it. Stored data is secure against threats from within and without.

EMR Directions

ISVs specializing in EMR are gradually developing hardware compatibility lists with the goal of guiding their customers, who often lack IT expertise, in directions that maximize their prospects for successful deployment. Most EMR ISVs do not have rigorous certification procedures; they create tests for vendors to run and report results to them. Pure Storage pursues relationships with all major EMR ISVs, and for some has made arrays in its labs available for their own "comfort level" testing.

The largest healthcare providers are concerned with protecting their electronic records and processing capabilities against disasters. They find ActiveCluster synchronous replication conceptually attractive as part of an overall wide-area solution that includes automated failover of virtualized EMR application servers.

In principle, this is an ideal way to make electronic records continuously available to healthcare professionals, but there is a limitation. Nominally, ActiveCluster requires pairs of arrays separated by no more than 10 milliseconds of round-trip network latency. The constraint avoids application server I/O timeouts resulting from replicating and acknowledging updates. Adding 10 milliseconds to sub-millisecond I/O response times is generally unacceptable, so Pure Storage recommends that EMR deployments of ActiveCluster be in configurations in which round-trip network latency between arrays is a millisecond or less. This typically means within the grounds of a campus—a common layout for large providers—but is not generally practical for smaller providers that operate within the confines of a single building.

Recent events such as the hurricane that struck northeastern United States in 2012, have shown that even several kilometers of separation (e.g., between Long Island and coastal northern New Jersey) can fail to protect against severe disasters. Some healthcare providers have therefore adopted long-distance replication at the application-level to protect medical records.

Healthcare providers and ISVs are realizing that their EMR data is a treasure trove that can be mined to improve patient outcomes. Knowing the results of various treatments on patients with similar symptoms can help doctors treat others more quickly and accurately. ISVs are developing analytics adjuncts to their core EMR applications. As an application that uses storage intensively, analytics is a natural for FlashBlade, where volumes are huge,

Esteban Rubens
Enterprise Imaging Architect
"As a 'storage guy' focused on medical imaging, I was excited to discover how Pure Storage products could make life easier for diagnosticians and accelerate their work."

data is unstructured, and the important performance metric is throughput rather than latency of individual requests.

To date, EMR has been primarily a North American market. Like the United States and Canada, many countries have national laws governing the processing and storage of electronic medical information. Most are smaller than North America and are therefore less attractive to major ISVs. Moreover, in countries where EMR is the norm, local ISVs already dominate, making inroads by larger US providers difficult. Pure Storage deals with several EMR ISVs around the world through its partner network.

FlashArray and Enterprise Imaging

Once dominated by X-rays used primarily by radiologists, digital imaging has spread throughout health care—to cardiology, ophthalmology, pathology, oncology, dermatology, and others. Imaging technology has become so pervasive in health care that its common name is now *enterprise imaging*.

In medicine, the enterprise imaging infrastructure has two parts: the image capture equipment (usually called *modalities*) and the computer systems that ingest, store, render, and deliver them to professionals for analysis and diagnosis.

The medical imaging equipment market is dominated by a few large companies. Many deliver complete systems, including both modalities and data processing systems. In addition, some specialized ISVs offer image handling software. Manufacturers and ISVs have standardized on the *Picture Archiving and Communications System* (PACS) software architecture. Based on the *Digital Imaging and Communications in Medicine* (DICOM) standard of the *National Electrical Manufacturers Association* (NEMA), PACS automates secure storage and organization of digital images, and most importantly, makes them accessible from authorized workstations anywhere in the world. For example, an image captured in the United States can be analyzed by a US board-certified radiologist who has chosen to reside in Australia, an arrangement common enough to have a name—*Nighthawk* service. DICOM conformity means that images can be exchanged among different vendors' PACS implementations.

Computing and Storage for Enterprise Imaging

Processing medical images consists of storing and organizing them and delivering them on demand to medical professionals'[47] workstations. Image capture generates prodigious amounts of data—thousands of "slices" comprising hundreds of megabytes of data from a CT scan or MRI. PACS servers store and index these and send them on demand to

---

[47] There is also a requirement for preserving inactive data on nearline or "cloud" storage that is not discussed here.

PACS workstations for viewing. Storing the output of a procedure takes significant I/O bandwidth, but as an after-the-fact operation, latency sensitivity is minimal.

Historically, the retrieval architecture has been "workstation rendering." A medical professional at a PACS workstation would request the output of a procedure from a PACS server. The server would retrieve the entire output from storage and transmit it to the workstation. The workstation would render (prepare for display) and display slices on operator request. PACS servers required high read bandwidth, but for remote users, the limiting factor was usually network bandwidth.

Workstation rendering has other limitations as well. Among them is cost—to render image slices at speeds acceptable to a medical professional, PACS workstations need powerful processors, large amounts of DRAM, intelligent graphics, and fast local storage. A more important consideration, however, is security. PACs servers are generally in physically secure environments, but physical security is not always possible for workstations. Heightened concerns over medical record security have raised questions about misappropriation of procedure results from workstations, either through network breaches or physical theft.

Data security and cost concerns, along with the advent of powerful multi-core server processors have led to a newer "server-side rendering" architecture. With server-side rendering, a workstation operator requests displays on a per-slice basis. The PACS server reads the information necessary to render a requested slice, renders it, and sends the rendering to the workstation. Workstations need fewer resources—they essentially become display stations (in fact, many display images in an HTML5-capable browser) with minimal processing and storage requirements. Network demands are lower as well. Rendered images are more compact than raw data and they are transmitted only on operator demand rather than in bulk. Most importantly, the data is secure. Since no data is cached at the workstation, none is exposed to compromise. (Obviously, network security is required for "data in flight.") PACS server I/O needs change from high read bandwidth for retrieving large objects to low latency for retrieving individual slices for server rendering.

Why FlashArray?

The properties that make FlashArray attractive for virtually any tier-1 storage application are especially germane to enterprise imaging in medicine:

Reliability

Hospitals, trauma centers, and other medical care providers are increasingly dependent on their IT systems. If an institution's PACS system fails, it cannot function—images cannot be stored or retrieved for analysis. Although excessive downtime can put certification at risk, the impact is not just financial; it can be health, or even life-threatening.

Storage is not the entire PACS reliability story, but FlashArray's "six nines" of availability, continuously verified by the entire installed base, means that an outage will seldom if ever be caused by an array failure.

PERFORMANCE

Overall, PACS server I/O loads are not particularly bandwidth or latency sensitive, but they are characterized by periodic brief bursts of intense activity, for example when a medical professional at a workstation retrieves slices in random order, or when a technician operating a modality saves procedure output. When many professionals are analyzing image slices and multiple outputs are being saved concurrently, bursts can overlap in time, causing high latency and user dissatisfaction.

FlashArray I/O latency is typically less than a half millisecond for reads and writes of 32 kilobytes or fewer. Array throughput can be upwards of a gigabyte per second. These are significantly better than those of disk-based storage systems and are more than adequate for the most demanding PACS server workloads, even those that serve multiple professionals concurrently. FlashArray users often find that their arrays are underutilized, and add other workloads such as electronic mail, human resources, and medical record applications to them.

DATA REDUCTION

Modalities capture images in uncompressed form. Because they are so large, PACS software compresses them before storing. Conventional wisdom holds that already-compressed digital images are not reducible, but arrays deployed in PACS applications show data reduction ratios in the range of 1.5:1-1.9:1. With typical PACS short-term cache storage requirements ranging from 50 (small institutions) to 500 terabytes (large institutions), storage cost savings can be significant.

DATA SECURITY

HIPAA, which became effective in 2003, heightened medical institutions' awareness of the need to secure patient data against loss and misappropriation. The scope of patient data protection is broad, encompassing networks, applications, individuals who handle it, and the storage where it sits "at rest" when not being processed.

FlashArray solves the problem of securing data at rest. All data in a FlashArray is encrypted automatically using the well-known AES-256 algorithm, implemented in software for consistency across all device types. There is no way for an administrator to bypass encryption. Encryption is transparent. Key management, complex and breach-prone in other implementations, is autonomous, with device access keys changed regularly. Keys are stored piecewise on multiple devices, with more than half of an array's devices required to reconstruct them. Thus, even if a device is removed from an array without authorization, there is no way to decrypt the data it contains.

COST

FlashArray may not be the least expensive option for PACS storage, but lifetime cost of ownership is bound to be in its favor. Total cost of ownership is the sum of the advantages enumerated above. Reliability means less downtime and less susceptibility to certification challenges. High performance increases medical professionals' satisfaction and may reduce an institution's overall storage cost by hosting storage for other applications. Data reduction means less physical storage is required for a given amount of PACS data. And transparent always-on data encryption eliminates the cost of acquiring and managing separate encryption facilities for PACS.

FlashArray in Core Business Applications

Although information technology has changed the way many products and services are delivered, since its advent, IT's most important usage has been in core business processes—accounting, finance, human resources, analytics, and so forth.

A few ISVs dominate the core business application software market but, over time, German-based SAP has emerged as one of the, if not *the*, leading business software vendor in the world.

Krishna Satyavarapu
SAP Solution Architect
"As a SAP engineer, I was excited to discover how much Pure Storage could improve SAP and SAP HANA in terms of performance and ease of use."

In part, SAP's market success is based on the universality of its applications. The company has adapted them to all major computing platforms and to work with all major DBMSs. The company has accomplished this by migrating its most important applications to its own *Advanced Business Application Programming* (ABAP) programming language and making the language available to customers for developing custom applications to process SAP data. The language includes a virtual database interface layer that insulates applications from the database in use. This, plus the common language makes it relatively straightforward to move SAP environments to different platforms or underlying databases when users expand or refresh their application infrastructures.

SAP HANA® Architecture

In late 2010, SAP began a gradual transition of its applications (and applications developed by third parties) to a new architecture called High-Performance Analytic Appliance (HANA®). HANA is based on an in-memory database that provides application access at DRAM rather than I/O speeds. Because DRAM is volatile, however, HANA logs every transaction to persistent storage. It copies blocks of modified data to non-volatile backing store at five-minute intervals called savepoints.

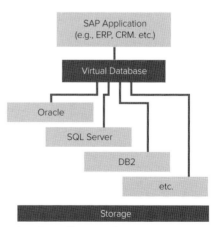

"Traditional" SAP Architecture

The HANA in-memory architecture is advantageous for applications because it supports both column-based and row-based operations from the same data set. Column

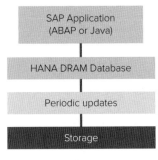

SAP HANA Architecture

operations are common in business analytics ("number of customers that ordered product X in the last six months"), whereas row-based operations usually dominate online transaction processing ("add this line item to customer Y's order"). Data item access at DRAM speed makes it possible to satisfy both query types from a single body of data.

SAP developed HANA to handle the increases in transactional and analytical data access its customers demanded. While it provides adequate application performance for even the largest enterprises, HANA does carry a cost burden. Application servers with the most powerful processors and tens of terabytes of DRAM are not uncommon. HANA mitigates this cost somewhat with "always-on" data compression. Nevertheless, HANA servers must be configured with prodigious amounts of DRAM.

Ignoring server cost, which tends to decrease over time, SAP HANA is clearly advantageous for organizations that prioritize high-performing, accurate, reliable business transaction processing and bulk data analysis. SAP strongly encourages users to migrate to HANA environments by 2025, in part with new HANA-only applications such as geospatial analytics and machine learning. While HANA is conceptually attractive, the complexity and potential disruption of migration cause ongoing customer concern.

SAP Storage and I/O Requirements

Pre-HANA SAP architecture is essentially a database application, characterized by large numbers of small (e.g., 4 to 16 kilobyte) I/O requests, with typical read:write ratios of about 80%:20%. This profile is a FlashArray "sweet spot"—with average latency of under a half-millisecond, the arrays typically outperform disk-based storage by several hundred percent in SAP applications.

FlashArray offers other important advantages in traditional SAP environments. Much of SAP data is character-oriented, and most SAP applications store multiple copies of data to expedite analytics. These properties suggest significant potential for Purity//FA data reduction, and in fact, analysis of Pure1 data indicates an average data reduction ratio in pre-HANA SAP environments of 4:1—a significant storage cost reduction for databases that contain hundreds of terabytes.

FlashArray simplifies administration of pre-HANA SAP databases. Deployments that utilize legacy storage typically expand their databases by adding volumes. Each addition requires configuration, data set redistribution, and adjustment of operating and maintenance procedures. FlashArray requires no such tuning. Moreover, the size of a volume can be enlarged instantly with a single console command.

Because business applications are vital to their operation, organizations are extremely careful about changing them. They test modifications extensively against copies of live data before deploying them in production.

Copying a production SAP data set is a complex, time-consuming, multi-step process. Database volume contents must be captured at a single point in time and used to create clone volumes. The *SAP metadata* that describes application data objects must be adjusted to refer to the clone volumes rather than to production ones.

A single FlashArray can easily host both SAP production data and a clone for testing, analytics, or other purposes. Clone creation is easy, partly because FlashArray-based databases require fewer volumes, but also because FlashArray snapshots are nearly instantaneous, as is cloning new volumes from them. With FlashArray storage, setting up a SAP test environment is as simple as adjusting the SAP metadata to refer to the test database.

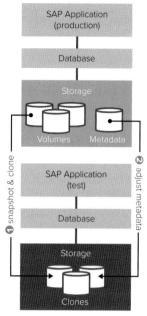

Copying a SAP Database

Storage and I/O for SAP HANA

SAP HANA storage and I/O characteristics differ from those of pre-HANA SAP implementations. Generally, with FlashArray storage, SAP HANA needs only a data and a log volume. Except during recovery, data volume I/O is dominated by large sequential writes because application reads are satisfied from the DRAM database image. HANA writes a log record for every transaction, thus write latency is crucial. FlashArray's half-millisecond average write latency provides higher transaction throughput than legacy storage. Data volume writes that spike at five-minute intervals are also easily within the arrays' capacity.

Although HANA satisfies application reads from DRAM, FlashArray read performance is still important for speeding up system restart. Many HANA users restart their HANA environments periodically, usually during periods of very low activity. To restart a database, HANA reads it in its entirety to its latest savepoint, reconstructs its DRAM image, and replays logs up to the desired recovery point. Most of restart time is in reading the database image. With disk-based legacy storage, restarting a 500-gigabyte database may take upwards of an hour. With FlashArray storage, restoring 500 gigabytes takes five minutes or less.

FlashArray snapshots integrate nicely with HANA's native mechanisms to recover a database from a snapshot of its persistent storage. Using the *SAP Studio* management GUI, an administrator can prepare a HANA database for a snapshot, use the FlashArray CLI or GUI to take a snapshot of its volumes, and catalog the snapshot in the HANA database.

To recover a HANA database, an administrator places it in recovery mode, uses the FlashArray CLI or GUI to restore (overwrite) its data volume from the the desired snapshot, and uses SAP Studio to select the recovery point. Because restoring FlashArray volumes from snapshots is nearly instantaneous, recovery is fast, so downtime is minimal—FlashArray recoveries six to eight times faster than with disk-based legacy storage have been recorded.

FlashArray and SAP HANA

SAP's flexible infrastructure certification process enables customers to build their infrastructures from a selection of server, network, and storage components. The company provides hardware vendors with test suites. Vendors execute tests and return the results to SAP. SAP adds successfully tested hardware families to its *Tailored Datacenter Integration* (TDI) certification tables. Customers select components from the tables to configure supported infrastructures. Utilizing uncertified components relieves the company of support obligations.

FlashArray is certified as a TDI storage component for HANA, both in single-server deployments and for server clusters. In addition, to ensure successful deployment, Pure Storage publishes array sizing guidelines based on anticipated HANA database size and rate of log activity (and in cluster deployments, additional shared volumes).

PART IV

Startup²

The FlashBlade Story

In This Chapter…

In 2012, FlashArray had already started to upend tier-1 storage. John Hayes began to speculate about architectural changes that would make flash affordable for tier-2 storage as well. Tier-1 storage typically serves core applications, whereas tier-2 houses data warehouses, artificial intelligence data stores, digital images and the like. Tier-2 data sets are much larger, less well-structured, and tend to grow monotonically. A scale-out system would be appropriate for tier-2, but cost per gigabyte would have to be much lower.

At the time, the company had a revenue stream, but a major new development would be risky, both in itself and in disrupting FlashArray development. A compromise was reached. The company would fund a "startup-within-a-startup," to develop a low-cost tier-2 storage system but would recruit entirely from outside. There would be no disruption of FlashArray engineering.

A team was recruited, an architecture created, and key components were developed. The team grew, initially by external recruiting, but later by cross-fertilization with the FlashArray team. FlashBlade was delivered and became a market success. Along the way, the FlashBlade team learned a valuable lesson about customers' awareness of their own tier-2 storage needs and refined their market approach accordingly..

Branching Out: A Startup within a Startup

arly arrays were built from off-the-shelf hardware—servers, device enclosures, SSDs, and network interface cards. The hardware architecture was conventional—dual controllers connected to clients via a "front end" storage network and to flash devices via SAS "back end" networks. The Pure Storage-designed FlashArray//M and FlashArray//X series arrays performed better and were more efficient, but their fundamental hardware architecture was the same as that of earlier models.

Could We Do Something *Really* Radical?

In 2012, Hayes began to speculate that a different hardware architecture could reduce the cost of flash storage enough to make it affordable for tier-2—online storage for everything from "big data" to backups. Tier-2 data sets are generally larger and not as structured as databases and virtual machine images. Applications usually read and write entire files or objects rather than individual records, so they typically transfer more data per I/O command. Most tier-2 data is in files or objects, so I/O has high percentages of metadata-only operations such as permission changes.

Hayes concluded that three fundamental changes were needed to make flash affordable for tier-2: higher density flash (at the time, SSD vendors were non-committal about devices larger than one terabyte), less processing power per gigabyte, and fewer of what he characterized as "wires"—movements and transformations of data on the path between client and storage.

FlashArray controllers receive storage network frames or packets, which they transform to a reduced DRAM representation of data. They eventually transform the reduced data to SAS packets which they send to interposers. Interposers transform the packets to SATA and relay them to SSDs, which transform the data to memory images prior to persisting it on flash. Hayes believed that the I/O path could be shorter, and that petabyte-scale flash systems could be made inexpensive enough to disrupt the tier-2 storage market. He proposed forming a new team to develop a second product line.

Can the Company Afford It?

The first challenge to Hayes' proposal was strategic. In 2013, Pure Storage had the beginnings of a revenue stream, but was not yet profitable. Moreover, FlashArray lacked data services like replication that were necessary to be competitive in tier-1. Could the company afford

Peter Vajgel

"Practically everyone in Silicon Valley has good ideas, but only a few can execute. Of those, even fewer succeed in creating a viable product or company. And only a tiny percentage beat the odds and succeed more than once.

Coz and Mike were two of those rare serial successes, so I had no doubt that Pure Storage and FlashBlade would be successful."

a completely new development project? Would it divert key engineering resources from FlashArray?

But Hayes' idea was plausible, and the company's long-term goal was to span the entire enterprise storage spectrum, so it decided to develop a completely new architecture for flash-based big data storage without diverting engineering resources from FlashArray—a strategy described internally as a *startup-within-a-startup*. The plan was to use its strong financial position to fund a separate organization to develop and market a radically new product. The new organization would occupy separate premises, and except for Hayes, who became the principal architect,[48] would be staffed by hiring. As part of Pure Storage, however, it could take advantage of FlashArray technologies such as data reduction and GC algorithms that it would otherwise have to develop. In keeping with the tradition of naming projects after dense natural elements, the project was called *Iridium*.

The startup-within-a-startup structure had two key advantages.

RECRUITING

Pure Storage was a stable employer which nonetheless offered talented engineers an opportunity to participate in a completely new, potentially game-changing development. The separate organization made it possible to recruit and compensate experienced developers who were attracted by the startup mystique but considered nascent startups too risky.

MAINTAINING FOCUS

Separate premises and staff minimized contact between FlashArray engineering and the new organization. Eventually, cross-pollination was encouraged, but in the beginning, isolation allowed the new organization to focus on its project without distraction. Likewise, Iridium was largely "out of sight, out of mind" for engineers working on critical FlashArray projects.

Getting Off the Ground

With simplifying hardware architecture as its driving principle, a small team was assembled. Definition of a low-cost, scalable flash storage system for tier-2 data began in mid-2013. The first team members were Peter Vajgel and Brian Gold. Peter, a file system and storage engineer of long experience, had been an informal technical advisor from the company's earliest days. He joined the Iridium team in mid-year.

---

[48] Partly to emphasize the separation, Hayes relocated his office from Pure Storage headquarters to Sutter Hill for a brief period while the new organization was created.

In early 2013, Doug Mohr had contacted Brian Gold about "a startup company with nearly 100 employees and shipping products." Brian's initial reaction was that if he were to leave his then-current position with a local technology giant, he would prefer to join a company at an earlier stage. Doug persuaded him to visit Mike Speiser, who surprised him with a Pure Storage NDA. He signed, and Mike introduced the startup-within-a-startup concept. The concept was attractive because it combined the "starting from scratch" technical challenge with the security of an established affiliate. The combination of a brilliant technologist (Hayes), a "with it" executive (Mike), and a visionary CTO (Coz), reinforced by several of the company's engineers whom Brian knew and respected, impressed him. Despite his concerns about his lack of storage background he decided to join. As he describes it, he spent his first few weeks scrambling to learn both storage technology and Hayes' novel ideas at the same time and trying to distinguish one from the other.

Several years earlier, Doug Mohr had placed Alex Ho at a networking startup that became quite successful. In 2013, Doug called again, with another startup opportunity, this time with a storage company. At his Sutter Hill office, Mike laid out the Iridium vision. Alex had already experienced a startup, so that aspect wasn't all that exciting, but the challenge of reducing flash storage cost to the tier-2 level was. The financial stability of a company with shipping products suggested that the cost of hardware development would be sustainable and that the team wouldn't be starved for resources. He interviewed with Brian, Peter, Hayes, and Coz, and joined the project in the summer of 2013.

When Alex became the fifth team member, the Iridium offices were at Sutter Hill,[49] and the project was still very much conceptual. The basic goal was to create highly scalable flash storage for file and object data at a cost comparable to then-available tier-2 offerings. Performance could be lower than that of FlashArray but should still outdo that of disk-based products by a wide margin.

Brian Gold
"When I saw that smart, personable acquaintances who weren't storage veterans were at Pure Storage, I began to believe I might be able to contribute meaningfully."

Alex Ho
"Some of us vacationed in Norway during the summer of 2014. I enjoyed it so much that I decided to code name the product Norway. The individual components were named after Norwegian cities—Oslo, Bergen, Alesund, Tromsø, etc.
We built prototypes for the software team and external beta testers that were milestones toward the finished product. They were codenamed Labrador and Greenland, both on the path from Silicon Valley to Norway."

There were obviously multiple approaches. The team considered SSDs for persistent storage—at the time, developing a flash device seemed risky. Several options for what

---

[49] A few months later, the team moved to a more permanent location two blocks away from the company's Castro Street headquarters.

Prototype Storage Unit
"While it is physically more compact, the design of the production storage unit is remarkably close to our original prototype."—**Rob Lee**

"In the early days, I was the (reluctant) FlashBlade internal recruiter. Doug Mohr would identify candidates and I'd help persuade them to join us.
I did everything from feeding real estate leads to a remote candidate to show him that the Bay Area could be affordable, to coaxing an engineer out of retirement to join. It was interesting, but I'm glad we have dedicated recruiters these days."
—**Brian Gold**

eventually became the blade modules were considered, including off-the-shelf small form factor mainboards with multiple SSDs. Packaging was also a variable, but it depended largely on the choices of electronic components.

In mid-2013, Shantanu Gupta, then with a Bay Area semiconductor developer, received his semi-annual email from the indefatigable Doug Mohr mentioning that a small company had just started a hardware-software project that might interest him. Content with his situation, Shantanu disregarded the email, but in the following months, he became disenchanted with his company's direction. Encouraged by a friend who worked at Pure Storage, Shantanu met with Brian Gold, then acting as informal Iridium in-house recruiter. He was encouraged that Brian had a background similar to his.

That initial meeting led to interviews with Hayes, Brian, Peter, and Alex that convinced Shantanu that flash could be practical for tier-2 storage if support component cost could be reduced. He was excited by the concept and impressed by the team, so when an offer followed the interviews, he accepted immediately, joining in late 2013.

Among Shantanu's first assignments was figuring out how to transfer data between storage units and the blade, both in formative stages at the time. So-called "merchant silicon" for NVMe was a ready-made solution for the storage unit side, but cost, power consumption, and inflexibility made him hesitant. Low-power FPGAs cost less, but gate counts were limited; every gate would have to count.

On the blade side, he realized that available drivers would impair blade processor performance with constant user-kernel mode context switching. He solved the problem by developing a user-mode driver that utilized shared memory and a signaling mechanism to eliminate nearly all context switching.

Since his early days on the FlashBlade team, Shantanu has continued to play a key role in evaluating hardware-software design tradeoffs as the product evolves and incorporates new technologies. He spends his "spare time," refining the storage unit data transfer protocol to further improve system performance.

From Whiteboard to Breadboard

When Shantanu joined, the team consisted entirely of engineers. To deliver a product, much more would be required—market research, vendor logistics, package design, beta testing, pricing, promotion, schedule coordination, and so forth. Coz was able to attract former colleague Par Botes (page 301) to become the Iridium general manager. Par joined the team in late 2013, adding a product and market dimension to its technical skills.

The first weeks were spent "making six smart guys into a team"—establishing common context and agreeing on goals. For members accustomed to large, established environments, the "blank sheet" was disconcerting. Some wondered when they were going to build something. Everything was open to debate in the daily architectural discussions. Only Peter had done extensive storage engineering, but each member brought his own experience to bear. Hayes' knowledge of FlashArray architecture helped the team adapt parts of that software (data layout, scheduling, multi-threading, flash management, etc.) to the scale-out design.

The first two months yielded key architectural concepts—a symmetric scale-out system consisting of identical modules. Each module would host "virtual controllers" that managed flash. The modules would distribute data and I/O across the system using the same network that was used for client communication.

The next tier of decisions was more tactical: SSDs vs. custom hardware with raw flash, FPGAs vs. merchant silicon for data transfer to and from flash, the best algorithms for data distribution, session management, data reduction, and so forth.

By early 2014, the architecture had been mapped out. To minimize risk, the team focused on the most challenging hardware component—the storage unit. They acquired off-the-shelf Ethernet switches and servers to use as virtual controllers and built prototypes for software development.

Hayes was well-aware of the shortcomings of off-the-shelf SSDs, so he favored developing a custom flash device. There were multiple challenges, from acquiring flash in volume to designing and fabricating boards, to developing an interface between devices and blades. The team decided on a custom device, which they

Shantanu Gupta
"At Pure Storage, people are truly empowered to take ownership and solve the hardest engineering problems as a team.
As we developed the FlashBlade prototype, we encountered and resolved a number of complex problems that spanned the hardware-software stack.
The experience helped us all become better engineers and technical leaders."

Hari Kannan

"Initially, we tried to fit our storage unit into an SSD form factor, but the supercaps we used were too small, so we added a board with bigger ones wired to the main storage unit.

We began to notice spurious storage unit power failures, but only in the afternoon. It took us a while to figure out that as the lab got warmer during the day, we would turn on a fan to cool it down. The fan caused glitches in the wire connecting the supercap board to the storage unit.

We eventually redesigned the storage unit to eliminate the wire, but that bug sure was hard to find."

called a *storage unit*, in a 2.5" SSD form factor to allow connecting more than one to an off-the-shelf blade mainboard.

Designing a storage unit was a formidable undertaking for the tiny team, but in late 2013, the company acquired the IP of a small company with high-speed interface expertise along with some of its employees. This reduced the risk and allowed the original team to devote more attention to the blade mainboard.

The storage unit needed both a "front-end" interface for communicating with the blade mainboard and "back-end" logic for reading and writing flash.

The Storage Unit "Front End"

The interface between storage units and blades was key. Each page of data sent to flash had to be ECC-protected, encrypted, and checksummed before it was stored, and decrypted and validated when read. Software could not perform those functions at the needed speed. With an FPGA, the team could implement them in hardware, so they favored that approach over (faster) fixed-function "merchant silicon" *application-specific integrated circuits* (ASICs).

But FPGAs have limitations, chief among them being gate count. Most vendors offer low-power devices with modest gate counts and others with more gates, but larger die sizes, greater power consumption, and higher cost. The team needed a low power device with enough gates to ECC-protect, encrypt, checksum, and transfer data. They chose a mid-range device within the storage unit power budget that appeared to have just enough gates.

Shantanu and colleague Zhangxi Tan evaluated NVMe for data transfer. Drivers and firmware were available, but both had issues. It appeared that the available firmware wouldn't leave space for other functions. Zhangxi, however, was able to pare it down to the essentials needed for data transfer, creating the *non-volatile transfer protocol* (NVTP). NVTP used only 5% of the selected FPGA's gates, about 10% of what full NVMe required. There was plenty of room left to implement ECC, encryption, and page checksums. Although close to capacity, the FPGA worked.[50] In mid-2014, the blade processor communicated with storage unit flash for the first time. By end of year, it was storing and retrieving data.

The team added NVRAM to the storage unit, implemented with DRAM and supercapacitors. As an added benefit, FlashBlade NVRAM scales linearly with flash capacity.

---

[50] It has since been replaced by a newer model with more gates.

NVTP and the user-mode driver solved the front-end problem, but in the meantime, the storage unit had outgrown the 2.5-inch SSD form factor, so the team also had to design a custom blade mainboard.

The Storage Unit "Back End"

In the fall of 2013 Hari Kannan was designing CPUs for a large semiconductor house when Doug Mohr contacted him about a unique opportunity with a young company that was creating a new product line by spawning a "startup-within-a-startup." Hari was intrigued, in part because he knew and respected several project team members—John Davis, Brian Gold, and Zhangxi Tan. He interviewed, finishing up with acting Iridium CEO, Mike Speiser,[51] who presented him with an offer.

On the plus side, Iridium would exercise Hari's considerable design skills. Moreover, the project was an opportunity to be a vital part of a small team and work at the system level— two of his career goals. But he did not immediately see how the proposed product could distinguish itself among the numerous solid-state storage startups apparently flourishing at the time. On balance, though, the opportunity seemed positive, so he decided to take the risk. He completed his design project and joined in early 2014, becoming the eighth FlashBlade engineer.

When Hari joined, Shantanu and Zhangxi were developing FPGA firmware and driver software. From his extensive design experience, he convinced the team that they would require exhaustive error-checking before production. After an unsatisfactory engagement with a verification contractor, they were able to add three good verification engineers to the team within the short space of two months.

Hari took on the storage unit "back end" logic for storing and retrieving flash. Flash is inherently error-prone, so robust error detection and correction were necessary. Iridium was able to acquire the IP of a small company with the needed expertise and more importantly, a few of its key engineers, who joined Hari to create robust storage unit data storage and retrieval.

With a Little Help From Our Friends

Low latency and high throughput were musts for inter-blade communication, because blades would be constantly communicating to balance load. Low cost was also important, as was designing for longevity and "non-disruptive everything." The team considered several options—bridged PCIe, Infiniband, and Ethernet—and adopted the latter for its low cost, adequate performance, and strong future road map. Two fortuitous developments made the decision easier. First, 10Gb/s Ethernet had matured—affordable parts were readily available. Second, the blade processor supplier released a multi-core *system-on-chip* (SoC) with two on-board 10Gb/s Ethernet interfaces. FlashBlade was able to use Ethernet (pre-wired on the chassis midplane) for both inter-blade and external communication.

The SoC and the choice of Ethernet met two of Hayes' key goals: low processing cost per gigabyte and minimal "hops" and transformations of data on the path between

---

[51] In its early days, the Iridium project had its own informal board of directors, consisting of Mike, Dietz, Hayes, Coz, and Par Botes (page 273).

Robert Lee ("Rob")

"When I saw the size of Pure Storage and learned what they were thinking of building with Iridium, part of me thought it was just a little bit crazy. But I signed up when I realized it was just my kind of crazy."

"In our first storage unit design, we would occasionally encounter unexplainable data corruptions. After chasing the problem for a month, we noticed that sometimes a byte in the middle of a block would be written twice, throwing the rest of the block off. The problem turned out to be poor signal integrity caused by badly shielded connectors.

The bug was actually a tipping point for us—it convinced us we had to redesign the prototype hardware for the final product."

*—***Hari Kannan**

client and persistent storage. The SoC with built-in Ethernet kept processing and communication cost low, and all-Ethernet communications minimized data transformations during transit.

Dealing with flash vendors had its challenges, both technical and cultural. Fortunately, a team member fluent in Japanese was able to overcome the barriers to dealing with major vendors, and both parties learned from the experience. Today, flash vendors consider Pure Storage an early adopter as they bring new technologies to market.

Moving the Goalposts

As the design progressed, the team realized that product cost would be dominated by flash; the cost of other components would be much less significant. They were able to budget for more powerful processors, switches, and other components with little impact to per-gigabyte system cost. As a result, the project goal evolved from low-cost scalable storage to low-cost, scalable, *high-performance* storage. Latency might not quite match that of FlashArray, but in FlashBlade's target markets, throughput was more important.

Software Has to Run Somewhere

The software being developed concurrently with FlashBlade hardware needed something to run on. The team assembled prototypes from off-the-shelf servers and Ethernet switches for testing storage units and communications. Similar systems were built for beta testing—1RU servers with external "top of rack" switches. Concurrently with beta testing, a packaging team led by Clay Ross was developing what would become the production FlashBlade package—a 4RU chassis housing between seven and 15 blades, each with either one or three storage units. The chassis design was a challenge, particularly for NDU—it had to support blade-by-blade replacement in running systems. It had to be future-proof, and eventually support aggregation into larger systems. Chassis were designed for decade-long lifetimes. Ethernet paths were designed for at least a generation beyond the 10Gb/s ports on the SoC blade processors.

Throughout development, though, the team remained focused on designing for file and object data, for high throughput as opposed to high IOPS, and above all, for cost per gigabyte comparable to other tier-2 storage alternatives.

Enlarging the Software Team

Robert Lee ("Rob") had been with a valley technology giant for a dozen years, involved in both in-house developments and acquisition integrations. He was feeling an urge to develop a significant product from the beginning, and realized that large, disruption-averse companies were unlikely to incubate such projects. Although his employer offered both hardware and software products, he also believed that integrating the two from the outset could be much more effective than combining pre-existing components. With those factors in mind, he contacted Mike Speiser in the fall of 2013 to say he was "ready for a challenge." Did Mike have a deal for him!

Igor Ostrovsky
"Hayes had a pretty complete design in his head. His explanations would be fast-paced and a bit abstract; the rest of us just had to learn to keep up."

Rob learned about Pure Storage and the FlashBlade concept from Hayes and Brian. The story was interesting, but he wondered why, with his minimal storage background, the company would be interested in him. Eventually, he learned that they preferred smart, hard-working people willing to "think out of the box" to individuals with the right resumes. Fortuitously, Hayes' scale-out system vision aligned well with Rob's skills and experience.

Like most candidates, Rob was surprised by how fast Pure Storage operated. His interview round ended with an offer and an expectation that he would start the following Monday. He managed to delay his decision for a week. In late October 2013 he became the sixth member of the team, working in a tiny office suite a few blocks from company headquarters.

Joshua Robinson
"Early on, I worked on controller virtualization and flash management, but frankly, most of my job in those days was trying to figure out what was in Hayes' head."

In its early stages, the organization was extremely fluid. Some members concentrated on hardware, others on software, but the distinction was not a hard one. Quite often, as with the FPGA, software developers would propose hardware changes to simplify software, and hardware developers would do the converse. The open workspace encouraged a degree of interaction that might have been impossible in a more structured organization.

With hardware engineering underway, recruiting turned to software. Through his extensive network, Doug Mohr discovered Igor Ostrovsky, then developing operating systems in the Seattle area. The timing was fortuitous—Igor was interested in working "closer to users," so Doug's description of Pure Storage intrigued him. A meeting with Brian convinced him that smart people were doing good work, and an early-stage project in which people did "what needed doing" was attractive. Like many early hires, Igor did

Par Botes

"My job was to make sure that the product we built was one that people would actually buy."

not have extensive storage experience, but interviewers felt that he was both brilliant and energetic. For his part, he was attracted by the opportunity to participate in a project that might significantly alter the way data centers stored and processed information.

Igor joined Pure Storage in late 2013. In his first few weeks he found himself alternately excited by the quality of his new co-workers, challenged to create an entirely new system to compete in a mature market, bewildered by the combination of unfamiliar technology and the scope and complexity of Hayes' vision, and gratified because the company was supportive and had the patience to endure the uncertainties of a new development.

While working with a Bay Area software giant, Joshua Robinson became aware of Pure Storage through Mike Speiser, who was always on the lookout for talent. Joshua met with Hayes and was attracted by the opportunity to develop the "virtual controller" software for the new system—undeniably the project's most challenging software component.

As co-developer of the FlashArray architecture, Hayes knew it intimately and believed that virtualized controllers using many of the Purity//FA concepts would be an ideal software basis for a scale-out system. The virtual controller software became Joshua's first assignment. The controllers would be stateless to enable non-disruptive expansion and failure recovery. When a blade is added to a FlashBlade system, some of the system's virtual controllers migrate to it. Similarly, when a blade fails, its virtual controllers restart on other blades. Because each virtual controller's state resides entirely in its NVRAM partitions, there is no loss of information or context with migration.

Concurrently with developing virtual controller software, Joshua helped define structures and protocols for blade processors to manage flash, using Shantanu's driver and Zhangxi's NVTP to communicate with storage units.

After about three years with the FlashBlade software engineering team, Joshua made a case for moving to the field, where his intimate knowledge of FlashBlade became an important asset to the technical organization in the EMEA region.

Adding Structure

Early FlashBlade development was communal. Engineers worked on whatever was most urgent. For example, when environmental chambers were needed for heat and EMI testing, Rob and general manager Par Botes bought materials at a local home improvement center and the team spent a weekend building its own chambers.

In general, Brian and Rob acted as technical leaders rather than as "people managers." As development progressed, teams gradually coalesced, and with Evan's transfer from the FlashArray team, the organization took shape. Hardware and software engineering reported to Brian and Rob respectively and Par managed the program as a whole, including the all-important "go-to-market" activity.

Igor recalls the first working version of the software being reliable but very slow. The team was concerned at the time that the system might not perform well enough to be viable. One by one, though, engineers identified and attacked bottlenecks. When the product shipped to its first customers about two years after project inception, the goal of a million NFSops per second had been reached, and systems were delivering a gigabyte per second per blade to hosts and ingesting about 300 megabytes per second per blade, with near-linear scaling.

Procuring Materials for Environmental Chambers

From Project to Program

Early in the Iridium project, Coz had contacted former colleague Par Botes, then working with a networking startup, to ask if he might be interested in leading a program to develop and launch a "super-scalable file server." He was intrigued by the concept, and Coz's leadership meant that there were no concerns about the project's viability, or that of the company. He joined Pure Storage in late 2013 as Iridium general manager. With the startup-within-a-startup nature of the project, he was responsible for everything—office space, equipment and supplies, product definition and management, vendor negotiations, go-to-market strategy, and so forth.

On Par's arrival, the FlashBlade team consisted of Hayes, Brian,[52] Peter, Alex, Shantanu, Zhangxi, Joshua, and processor architect John Davis. It grew to over 30 in short order, with Brian and Rob dividing engineering supervisory responsibilities on hardware-software lines.

When Par became general manager, the system architecture had been broadly outlined. SSDs had been ruled out; the team was designing its own flash storage unit. Prototypes built from off-the-shelf servers and network switches and the team's custom storage units were being assembled.

Environmental Chambers Overlooking Castro Street
"Labrador prototypes were too fragile to transport to test labs, but the smallest commercially available environmental chamber would not fit in our building's freight elevator. We were on the 9th floor, so our only option was building our own chambers."
—**Rob Lee**

"In the early days, a vendor sent us a dual-processor CPU along with Linux support. Try as we might, we could not make Linux recognize both processors. Brian and I finally traced the problem to a bug in the vendor's Linux support module.
We frequently found that we had to fix obscure problems with vendors' components. I describe our engineering culture as 'detailed'—we expect components that we purchase to perform according to specification."
—**Shantanu Gupta**

---

[52] Ironically, Brian was Par's nominal hiring manager.

"In a complex engineering project, some of the less-critical items are inevitably left for 'later.' Controlling FlashBlade fan speeds was one of those.
When we moved our development systems to a CoLo, the fans suddenly ran constantly at maximum speed. On our first visit to the CoLo after the move, we discovered that it wasn't the neatest. Every bit of loose debris in the place had been stirred up and was jammed into the baffles, because we had the fans running so fast they were creating an air current in the room."
—**Rob Lee**

Evan Driscoll
"My management ethos is to surround myself with smart people, remove obstacles, and trust that they will do something amazing.
It works!"

Other aspects of the product were open for discussion. Blade mainboards, interconnects, power budgets, and the system's form factor were all "up in the air." Designing controllers, networks, chassis, midplanes, and storage units, and integrating them into a system was a daunting task list.

Par saw his most important responsibility as matching the eventual product with the potential market. He continuously argued for the lowest possible power consumption, the most compact rack-mountable form factor possible, and the lowest per-terabyte cost, in approximately that order. As the system began to take shape, there was some resistance. The prototype showed promise and *could* be productized quickly with minimal hardware risk. The team felt that hardware and software were challenging enough, and that custom packaging was unnecessary for the first product. But Par argued constantly for "faster, smaller, cheaper." Over the course of three months a team led by Clay Ross designed the FlashBlade chassis—a midplane with 15 blade slots in the front[53] and redundant network switch ASICs, power supplies, and fans in the rear.

The team considered using NVMe to interconnect blades, but the technology was immature and would require significant development, so they opted for 10Gb/s Ethernet, which offered low cost and power consumption with adequate performance.

FlashBlade was delivered as a single-chassis system, but from the beginning the plan was to connect multiple chassis in petabyte-scale systems. Ethernet made that relatively easy. When systems with up to five chassis were introduced in 2017, they included external switches for inter-chassis communication, but they required very little software adaptation.

From Team to Organization

The FlashBlade engineering team grew quickly—within two years, it totaled over 30 engineers, supervised by Brian and Rob, both of whom were fundamentally technologists. Neither had or sought extensive management experience, so with the FlashBlade concept proven and product development well underway, it was time to add structure to the organization.

Par, the overall Iridium program manager, was fully occupied with market research,

---

[53] The width of 52-terabyte blades with three storage units precluded a 16th blade in the chassis.

product alignment, launch planning, SE recruiting, and introducing FlashBlade to potential beta testers and early adopters. An experienced overall engineering manager was needed, so Bob Wood asked Evan Driscoll (page 65) to take the job. Evan had a successful track record with FlashArray, was acquainted with all aspects of the company—operations, marketing, sales, support—and importantly, had a history of successful collaboration with Hayes, who as lead architect was key to FlashBlade's technical success.

Evan was keenly aware that the company had invested heavily in FlashBlade and was eager to see the product ship. It had set a goal of launching (announcing) FlashBlade at its annual Pure//Accelerate™ customer conference in the spring of 2016, and a launch readiness criterion of three beta systems running at customer sites. The general availability date would be announced at the conference. He had to come up with an achievable development schedule.

"The 2016 Accelerate conference was the FlashBlade target launch date. We had to have three beta systems in use prior to the conference, so time was tight.

The first site identified was a FlashArray user in the UK who needed high-performance NFS. Shipping internationally added time to an already tight schedule, but we managed it.

Unfortunately, we shipped that first system in our only certified carton, so when a second site in northwestern US was ready, we had no packing material for their system. We scavenged for cartons that would fit, and finally shipped the system in a server vendor's box with protective packing material that we 'customized' ourselves."

—**Brian Gold**

To meet the launch criterion, Evan proposed shipping prototype hardware, code-named "Labrador," to beta sites, even though the servers and network switches that made up the system occupied more than three times the rack space of the chassis being designed for production. The team universally felt that Labrador would make a poor first public impression, so Evan's proposal motivated them to finish on time. They pushed hard and delivered beta systems in the production package to customers in time to meet the launch goal. FlashBlade was introduced to over 2,000 attendees at the Accelerate conference and has gone on to success in the market.

Evan regarded part of his mission to be, as he puts it, "curating the Pure Storage culture." He emphasized open communication across organizational lines, sharing credit and accepting blame, and celebrating milestones, all aspects of the larger company culture. As the engineering population increased, the organizational structure he put in place supported growth without disruption. Over time, the FlashBlade and FlashArray engineering teams have gradually increased what he describes as "cross-pollination." Engineers move between the two, bringing their experience and expertise to their new assignments.

Listening to Customers

In the fall of 2016, a small group of SEs asked the FlashBlade team to rent a booth at the annual Supercomputing conference in Salt Lake City. The team was reluctant; they saw the conference as a high-performance computing showcase, with little emphasis on storage. But the SEs persisted, and the company rented and staffed a small display. The consensus afterward was that attendees had paid little attention to Pure Storage and FlashBlade.

But a few weeks later, the company received a *request for proposal* (RFP) through a partner for storage systems to support a large Internet company's artificial intelligence project. The team was skeptical—RFPs are often attempts to extract better terms from an already-selected vendor—so they declined to respond. But the partner insisted that the customer had been impressed by the Supercomputing display and was considering FlashBlade for a major "deep learning" project. After some testing against the RFP specifications and a few rounds of negotiation, the customer surprised the team by ordering several FlashBlade systems.

The order was one of the largest FlashBlade sales up to that time, so the team began to consider whether AI might be an important FlashBlade market. Overnight, AI appeared in promotional material and AEs started pursuing AI storage leads. Other prospects emerged, and the team thought it had discovered another key FlashBlade application, until in late 2017, two events occurred.

The first event was a second large order from the same customer, who was provisioning a second data center. That reinforced the team's growing belief that AI would be important to FlashBlade's success. But the second event, following soon after, was receipt of a detailed letter from one of the customer's senior data scientists stating in effect that "FlashBlade performance is abysmal in our application." The team was dismayed, and at the same time puzzled. Why had the customer doubled its order for a product whose performance it found unacceptable?

In the interest of customer satisfaction, the team met with the letter's author to understand his concerns. At the time, it had no AI experts, and the author of the letter, while a skilled data scientist, had minimal computing expertise. After considerable discussion, the team realized that the customer's issue lay with Posix system calls rather than with FlashBlade.

The machine learning infrastructure contained thousands of GPU processors. Most calculations were highly parallel, but certain operations, for example, recursive listings of millions of files, were performed by a single conventional processor. The Posix function that enumerates files makes a separate request for each one. The client requests and FlashBlade responses took microseconds. The overwhelming majority of the time was consumed by network traffic. The customer was comparing FlashBlade to a local file system. With that configuration, there was no network traffic, so enumeration was much faster.

The customer was eventually persuaded that his problem did not lie with FlashBlade, or anything else Pure Storage related. Nevertheless, he expected that Pure Storage would solve it (high-performance computing users tend to be demanding).

The team presented the customer with several workarounds to reduce network traffic in his application. But they realized that other applications that perform frequent metadata-only operations might encounter similar issues, so they developed generalized tools to perform these and similar bulk file management operations orders of magnitude faster than the corresponding Posix functions.

During the course of troubleshooting this performance problem, the team developed a close technical relationship with the customer. Both parties learned from the experience. The customer acquired an appreciation of the workings of computer systems, and the FlashBlade team learned that AI can be as much about storage as computing, and that Posix constructs adequate for hundreds or thousands of files become intolerably slow with millions of files.[54]

This episode taught the company that AI and machine learning scientists may not understand their storage and computing requirements. They may wildly overestimate or underestimate storage, I/O, and even computing needs. FlashBlade configuration flexibility became a selling point—even major adjustments to a storage configuration are easy, and more important, non-disruptive.

Eventually, the customer told Pure Storage that his initial impression of FlashBlade at the Supercomputing conference had been reinforced by a friend who used an NFS file server with FlashArray storage in an AI application. It was primarily the friend who motivated him to request the proposal that ultimately accelerated his machine learning project and as a side effect, made the FlashBlade team aware that AI was a storage market worth pursuing, to the point of developing solutions to deal efficiently with the enormous numbers of files they process.

---

[54] Later, the team encountered other big data users who routinely ran multi-day jobs to change access permissions on large sets of files stored on conventional filers.

In This Part...

In the past decade, new applications including imaging, electronic design automation, analytics, and machine learning have come to the fore. Over the same period, public clouds have matured. Today, users seek a mix of on-premises and public cloud IT for both their core and emerging applications. FlashBlade was introduced amid this period of IT ferment. Three of its most important applications either did not exist or were in their infancy in 2013:

RAPID RESTORE

Disk-based backup is fast but restoring data to primary storage is glacially slow because appliances must reassemble data sets by accessing disks randomly. With FlashBlade, restores are dramatically faster.

ELECTRONIC DESIGN AUTOMATION (EDA)

Semiconductor design involves hundreds of millions of computation steps that manipulate terabytes of temporary and permanent data. FlashBlade accelerates processes, improves time to market, and reduces costs.

ANALYTICS AND MACHINE LEARNING

Enterprises collect and analyze a wealth of data to better understand their operations. They store it in data warehouses optimized for analytics and machine learning. FlashBlade delivers scalable capacity and high throughput, both streaming and random, for machine learning and other analytics.

In these, and in many other applications, FlashBlade capacity, throughput, and operational simplicity make it an obvious storage candidate. The chapters in Part V describe storage challenges in each of these applications and explain why users are adopting FlashBlade for them.

PART V

Where's FlashBlade?

In This Chapter…

The rapid transition from tape to disk-based appliance backup that began in the late 2000's speeded up backup by building each backup of a data set on preceding ones. Unmodified data, protected by RAID within the appliance would not be recopied, saving both backup time and storage cost.

But when a restore was necessary, an appliance would have to reassemble the data set from fragments on its disks, with the seek and rotation delays inherent in random access. Thus, while daily backup would be really fast, restoring a data set could take hours—hours of critical downtime.

FlashBlade capacity made it an attractive backup target, even without deduplication. The insight, though, was that with no seeking and rotation to contend with, restoring a data set from FlashBlade could occur at network speed. Multi-hour restores were reduced to tens of minutes.

Rapid restore quickly became a key FlashBlade application, gradually replacing the prevalent *disk-to-disk-to-tape* (D2D2T) backup paradigm with a F2F2C (*FlashArray-to-FlashBlade-to-cloud*) one.

FlashBlade and Rapid Restore

Backup Is Only Half the Problem

All organizations back up their valuable digital data. Backup protects against environmental disasters, equipment failures, and human errors. It provides input for non-production applications like analytics and software development testing and satisfies internal and regulatory data retention requirements. In general, backup technologies have three important properties:

DISRUPTION

Backup disrupts production IT. Its takes time and consumes processing and I/O resources that could otherwise contribute to production.

PERFORMANCE

Historically, data set backups have generally been assumed to be accessed infrequently if at all. Technologies have therefore been optimized for fast backup creation. Less attention has been devoted to optimizing restoration of data to tier-1 storage for disaster recovery or other application use.

RESTORE PRIORITIES

The most frequent use of backups is recovery of small sets of files that have been destroyed in error. Restoring entire data sets to recover from disasters is less frequent, but more important to accomplish as quickly as possible.

As users attempt to derive value from their data, backups are no longer dormant until disasters occur. Increasingly, they restore backups for analysis, machine learning, forensics, testing software, and similar usages. Restore speed is becoming important for application use as well as critical for disaster recovery.

Why Does Restoring Backups Take So Long?

Restoring data from backups is slow primarily because of the incremental nature of backup tools, especially disk-based ones. For example, successive daily backups of a data set typically differ by less than a percent. Recognizing this, backup system developers have evolved techniques that only copy data items that have changed since previous backups already on file. Catalogs internal to the systems indicate the locations of all items in a set. They point to unchanged items in their locations in previous backups.

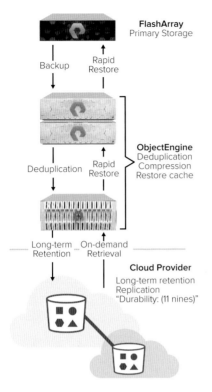

FlashArray
Primary Storage

Backup

Rapid
Restore

ObjectEngine
Deduplication
Compression
Restore cache

Deduplication

Rapid
Restore

Long-term
Retention

On-demand
Retrieval

Cloud Provider
Long-term retention
Replication
"Durability: (11 nines)"

As disk costs have fallen, backup appliances with more dynamic deduplication have largely supplanted file-level incremental backup. They detect byte sequences that are identical to already-stored data, and replace them with pointers to a single instance, a technique not dissimilar to FlashArray's deduplication technology.

Disk-based appliances reduce the impact of backup significantly—backing up the 1% of a data set that changes overnight uses 1% of the time, space, and bandwidth of a full copy. It becomes feasible to take more frequent backups, representing more potential recovery points, and save them longer because the incremental resource cost for each one is a tiny fraction of that of a full backup.

But restoring a data set from an incremental or deduplicated backup means reassembling it from pieces scattered throughout the system's media. Disk-based backup systems access fragments randomly, so restoring at streaming speed is impossible. The majority of restore time is spent waiting for disk seeking and rotation. For multi-terabyte data sets, recovery can take many hours.

Some products offer *synthetic full backup*. The backup client creates an incremental or deduplicated backup, and in the background the backup system assembles a full backup that can be restored at streaming speeds. Synthetic full backups make full data set restore faster, but creating them uses resources that affect system performance. Moreover, synthesizing a full backup consumes the storage saved by deduplicating backup data. Relying on synthetic full backups for disaster recovery is also risky. If a disaster occurs while the synthetic full backup needed for recovery is still being created, it cannot be the basis for restoring destroyed data.

FlashBlade and Rapid Restore

With FlashBlade, there is no mechanical motion to impede data retrieval. When restoring backup data sets, FlashBlade can cut elapsed time to recovery by as much as 90% and make almost any usage of backups viable. Rapid restore is especially important to organizations that rely on service providers for backup.

Initially FlashBlade was a relatively expensive backup solution because without deduplication, each backup retained occupies the space of the full (compressed) data set. Combined with ObjectEngine data reduction, however, FlashBlade systems store deduplicated data, and when connected to a public cloud, can forward data sets to it for long-term retention, a data protection and archiving strategy called *FlashArray-to-FlashBlade-to-Cloud* (F2F2C). Data sets relayed to cloud providers for long-term retention are deduplicated by ObjectEngine and compressed by FlashBlade, so network bandwidth and cloud storage costs are much lower than cloud storage for unreduced data sets.

F2F2C casts FlashBlade in the triple role of initial target for backups, cache for rapid restore of recent backups, and staging area for retrieving older backups from the cloud. With FlashBlade, backup and restore performance scale with data set size. Adding ObjectEngine deduplication makes a user's ability to store deduplicated backups effectively limitless.

In This Chapter …

As semiconductor devices become more complex, so too does the process of designing and verifying them. Hundreds of designers work in tandem. Thousands of processor cores verify logic and routing and produce terabyte-size files that drive the "tape out" process. Throughout the process millions of temporary files are produced and discarded. Typical numbers of clients and quantities of files demand high capacity, high performance file servers.

EDA software is extremely complex and expensive. It is typically leased on a per-user basis. To control cost, it must be fully utilized. But poor storage performance can keep jobs waiting for I/O. Designers sit idle, processes wait for I/O to complete, software leases extend, and time to market is affected. High performance file service is a must.

Scalability and flash performance make FlashBlade ideal for EDA storage. Engineering took care to optimize metadata-only operations because EDA applications use them frequently. Jobs that run for days with disk-based filers complete in minutes when FlashBlade is used for storage.

FlashBlade and EDA

Designing and Building Semiconductors

The complexity of electronic components—processor chips,[55] communication interfaces, sensors, and others—the speed with which they evolve, and the intensely competitive nature of the industry has made design automation a necessity. *Electronic design automation* (EDA) has become a highly specialized field in which a single design may involve thousands of processors running elaborate software and producing millions of files, both temporary and permanent. The industry is dominated by a few very large players who have the financial wherewithal to field the enormous computing "farms" required to develop complex components.

Design houses make heavy use of the industry's own products, especially multi-core processors. They often measure processing requirements in "cores." A single design might require tens of thousands of processor cores working in parallel during five major development stages:

LOGIC DESIGN

As many as hundreds of engineers collaborate to produce a complete design. Because engineers work in parallel on different parts of a design, source control is key. In addition to the final design, the engineers typically create and delete millions of small temporary files as they work.

LOGIC VERIFICATION

Thousands of server cores trace logic paths exhaustively to verify that inputs produce the correct outputs. Logic verification may produce hundreds of millions of temporary files as well as multi-gigabyte files for the next stage.

PHYSICAL VERIFICATION

Thousands of server cores work in parallel to verify that the logically verified design does not violate physical constraints, such as connector lengths and conductor separations. This stage both reads and writes multi-gigabyte files, so it typically requires more I/O bandwidth than the preceding ones.

---

[55] "A high-end processor chip may contain as many as 20 billion transistors.
For example, see https://en.wikipedia.org/wiki/Transistor_count#Microprocessors "

Mask Preparation

This stage converts logically and physically verified designs into photolithographic masks that control fabrication. It reads the files output by the verification stages and produces multi-terabyte files that describe the masks for each layer of the device to be fabricated.

Fabrication

Creates silicon *wafers* that contain multiple copies of the device. It requires gigabytes per second of I/O bandwidth, because it works from the preceding stage's output files.

EDA Software

Just as a few large firms dominate EDA, EDA software has become so complex and sophisticated that a few packages dominate the market. Each is unique, but all are structured as massively parallel applications that share files, so multi-client file servers are the only option for storage. I/O performance with 10,000 plus concurrent clients has been a chronic bottleneck for EDA.

EDA software is the proverbial seller's market. Semiconductor houses need it to survive, but it's too complex for them to produce and maintain. To remain viable, software developers license their software for limited periods and charge by the number of concurrent users. Project delays caused by slow computing infrastructures can be costly, because of software license extensions, idle designers waiting for computer response, and delays in getting new products to market.

EDA and Storage

IT requirements are intense at all stages of semiconductor design, but each stage has slightly different computing, I/O, and storage needs. They differ in the amount of data they process, the numbers and types of files they use, their I/O request profiles, and the number of concurrent clients they serve. Storage system requirements include:

Performance

Verifications typically read hundreds of thousands of input files and produce millions of temporary logs and output files. Storage must be capable of hundreds of thousands of data transfers and millions of metadata operations per second, as well as capable of creating and deleting millions of files quickly.

Amount and Type of Data

EDA generates and uses millions of kilobyte-range files and thousands of multi-gigabyte logs and output files. Its storage must scale to petabytes and be able handle widely varying sizes quickly and efficiently.

Number of clients

With hundreds of workstations during logic design and tens of thousands of server cores during verification, EDA is fundamentally a multi-client shared data application. Its storage must be capable of tens of thousands of client connections to both shared and private files.

EDA and FlashBlade

The amount of data produced and the rate of I/O generated by EDA can overwhelm even the largest conventional file servers. In the best case, clients wait for I/O completions, job run times increase, and schedules slip. In the worst case, overloaded file servers simply collapse, jobs must be restarted, and schedules slip even more. In both cases, costs rise and time to market is affected.

Most of EDA computing is decomposable, so processing can be speeded up by employing more designers, or more cores in the verification stages, but because data is shared among processes at all stages, adding storage systems does not increase I/O performance. A file server must be able to satisfy the demands of the entire complement of workstations and servers used in a design.

The most obvious advantage of FlashBlade for EDA infrastructures is scalability. System capacities range from 120 terabytes to over three petabytes of physical storage, and a conservative compression ratio of 2:1 doubles effective capacity. FlashBlade is a long-term investment that can scale with requirements. As devices become more complex and designs more data-intensive, blades, and even entire chassis, can be added to a system while it is running.

FlashBlade uses its capacity efficiently. Typically, over 90% of the files used in a design are 16 kilobytes or smaller. FlashBlade compression and dense packing of stored data typically consume as little as 20% of the physical storage required by conventional file servers for a given design process. Moreover, FlashBlade file system structures accommodate billions of files, so there is never an artificial need for multiple file systems due to inode limitations.

But perhaps the more important FlashBlade advantage is speed. I/O response at flash rather than disk speeds all but eliminates waiting for I/O to complete. And each added blade increases processing and I/O resources along with capacity. Jobs finish faster, software license costs stabilize, verification is more exhaustive, and ultimately, end products are of higher quality.

High-performance metadata operations are vital to EDA, in large part because of access permission changes to millions of files. Metadata operations may comprise upwards of 70% of the I/O requests in a design process. Performed sequentially, metadata operations can stretch process steps to hours. FlashBlade's parallel metadata operations are a key differentiator—a single system can execute up to 10 million metadata operations per second.

Another important factor in EDA performance is deletion of millions of temporary files created throughout a design process. FlashBlade's fast file delete feature can reduce day-long bulk file deletions to minutes by moving the files to an invisible path and deleting them in the background.

With multi-petabyte maximum capacity, non-disruptive expansion of storage and processing, tens of gigabytes per second throughput, and ultra-fast metadata operations, FlashBlade is a future-proof storage and I/O solution as semiconductors become more complex and designing them more demanding.

In This Chapter …

To derive value from their data, users are implementing data warehouses—historical databases optimized for bulk queries. Unlike transactional databases, which are "pruned" regularly, data warehouses tend to grow over time, suggesting that scalability is an important attribute for their underlying storage. Queries are often ad hoc, and may cause millions of records to be scanned, so high read performance, both streaming and random, is a must.

As disk-based data warehouses grow larger, performance can suffer due to seeking and rotation. To compensate, users often spin off data marts containing subsets of warehouse data. Query performance may improve, but synchronization and management become complex.

Storage attributes for an ideal data warehouse match those of FlashBlade perfectly—capacity that scales to petabytes and performance unhampered by mechanical motion, whether random or sequential.

FlashBlade and Analytics

B usiness intelligence helps organizations understand and enhance their performance and project trends relevant to them. Data warehouses are used to extract business intelligence from data they collect as they operate.

Essentially, a data warehouse is a database, but unlike transactional databases, it is designed to satisfy bulk queries of historical data collected from multiple sources. Data warehouses are optimized for bulk query performance without affecting production database performance.

What's in a Data Warehouse?

Data warehouses are populated by merging data from multiple sources, in a periodic process commonly known as *extraction, transformation, and loading* (ETL). ETL reconciles naming and type disparities,

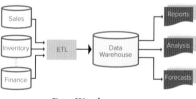

Data Warehouse

aligns items in time, and loads the results into a data warehouse schema optimized for bulk queries, statistical analysis, and reporting to create actionable information for users.

In addition to transaction records, warehouses may include data that varies from web page clicks and environmental sensor readings to multi-megabyte images. ETL converts these into forms that meld with transactional data.

The Data Warehouse vs. the Transactional Database

Data warehouses separate ancillary processing and I/O workloads from transactional production ones. Unlike transactional databases, in which individual records are constantly updated, warehouses are updated in batches during ETL, and almost exclusively read in large blocks during use. The different uses of the two make different storage system characteristics optimal for each.

A data warehouse might be thought of as a single source of reliable information for decision making. It enhances efficiency by eliminating the dilemma of different data sources resulting in different decisions for the same question.

Data warehouses usually contain data acquired over long periods from a variety of sources. Many newer warehouses *extract, load, and transform* (ELT) data, with most or all transformation occurring in the system that hosts the warehouse. Defining the warehouse schema and the ETL or ELT data acquisition process affects the utility of a data warehouse.

Uses of Warehoused Data

Many analyses conducted on warehoused data are time-related. Examples include sales, inventory, and profitability histories, timelines of sensor outputs, event rates over time. But the real value of a data warehouse lies in ad hoc analysis—its ability to provide answers to questions that had not previously been contemplated. A well-designed warehouse should be able to meet ad hoc demands for both aggregated results (averages and other statistics) and "drill-down" details of individual records.

Data warehouses contain the raw material for forecasting and identifying trends. It is here that disparate data sources come into play. For example, combining weather data with sales history might reveal that buying patterns change with temperature or precipitation. Knowing that, a retailer might adjust wholesale purchases or inventory movements.

Mini-warehouses: Data Marts

Data marts are nothing more than data warehouses with limited contents. They typically serve a single department or function. Data can be added to a mart faster than to a full warehouse because its contents are less diverse.

Data marts based on a master warehouse must be constantly synchronized to avoid "information drift" and its consequence: different decisions based on what should be the same data but isn't. *Independent data marts* are loaded directly from source data, preferably that which feeds the master warehouse. They can become information "islands" of questionable consistency. *Dependent data marts* are loaded from a master warehouse, so the risk of inconsistency is less, but loading procedures and usage rules must be carefully managed and adhered to.

A third type of warehouse, the *operational data store* (ODS) is sometimes found between operational data and a warehouse. ODSs typically support operations that involve near-current data—for example, inquiries about the most recent transactions. They are a transitional technology. As computing and I/O power increase, it becomes practical to transform and load a constant trickle of operational data into a warehouse in near-real time.

The Data Warehouser's Prophet

In the 1980s, William Inmon began to develop and popularize data warehousing through a number of books, other publications, and lectures. He described a data warehouse as being *subject-oriented, integrated, non-volatile, and time-variant*:

Subject Oriented

Data warehouses are designed to analyze data about a primary subject. For example, a sales-focused data warehouse can identify the most frequent purchasers of certain items over a period of time, which might be combined with environmental, regulatory, and economic data to predict how and where inventories should be stocked. A warehouse may draw data from disparate sources, but the analyses it can produce have a common focus.

Integrated

Data warehouses *integrate* the data in them. The data they ingest from disparate sources is transformed into formats useful for responding to queries related to the warehouse's focus. ETL (or ELT) resolves naming conflicts, inconsistent measuring units, event timings, and so forth.

Nonvolatile

The data in a warehouse is history; it should not change. Only with unchanging data can analyses be based on actual history.

Time Variant

While a data warehouse may be called upon to answer queries in different dimensions, it is essentially a history of events. An essential element of history is the event timeline. Variations in properties or quantities over time enable data scientists to identify trends, patterns, and relationships in mountains of data. In this respect, data warehouses differ from transactional databases, in which data is "pruned" regularly to limit size and minimize I/O latency.

Storage for a Data Warehouse

A data warehouse is a history, and more complete histories are better at identifying trends and supporting projections. Warehouses tend to grow and hardly ever shrink. When a data warehouse grows, it needs more storage, so its underlying storage environment must be readily scalable. Software technologies for extreme scaling exist, but they are generally difficult to create, and expansion usually requires significant downtime and reconfiguration. FlashBlade's ability to scale from a few tens of terabytes to multiple petabytes makes it an ideal storage candidate for fast-growing warehouses. A data warehouse on FlashBlade storage can grow without disruption by the addition of blades and even entire chassis. The system absorbs the added capacity and over time redistributes data to balance storage and I/O among all resources.

The ideal data structure for a warehouse differs from that of a transactional database. Whereas transactional databases typically consist of tables containing rows of homogeneous records, a data warehouse may contain (in addition to transaction history) temperature, pressure, traffic flow, or other sensor readings, as well as digital images or even video clips. Warehouse schemas must be flexible to accommodate any number of disparate data types.

While transactional databases usually contain little or no redundant data, data warehouse schemas often include multiple copies of data items for faster response to complex queries.

The goal of a data warehouse schema is high ad hoc query performance. Queries against data in a warehouse typically cause large amounts of data to be scanned, so read throughput is usually more important to performance than individual I/O request latency, as it is with transactional databases and their storage.

But data warehouse write performance is also important. The ETL or ELT process that keeps a warehouse current is periodic rather than constant, but it is write-intensive. As ELT uses data warehouse resources to transform data, the load it generates can resemble that on a transactional database—frequent random updates to slot new items into their proper positions. Thus, while the data scientists who utilize a data warehouse typically do not update it directly, storage write performance, both sequential and random, is important.

Data warehouse storage performance requirements vary widely. A single query may retrieve thousands of rows from different tables, so high throughput is a must. But, ad hoc queries may access data in a way that is almost orthogonal to its table structure, so high random-access performance is also necessary.

In this regard, FlashBlade is ideally suited as a data warehouse "hub." First and foremost, all-flash storage means never having to wait for a disk to seek or spin. Reads to satisfy a query occur at electronic, rather than mechanical speeds, and writes are staged in fast NVRAM so they complete almost instantly. Second, the internal data organization balances load across all blades dynamically. Physical locations of files and data objects are completely decoupled from the logical addresses used by clients and randomized so that the largest number of blades possible is active at any one time. Third, the aggregate bandwidth in and out of even a single-chassis FlashBlade system is as much as 40 GB/s, so it can satisfy the demands of high-performing data warehouse servers. FlashBlade makes an ideal hub for hosting a master warehouse and its dependent data marts, thus eliminating bulk data transfers and keeping warehouse and mart in synchronization. In some cases, FlashBlade performance can eliminate the need for separate data marts in favor of virtual views of the master warehouse's schema.

In This Chapter ...

Graphics processor vendors are adapting their products for use in massively parallel computing systems used in machine learning. Typical systems have upwards of a thousand special-purpose processors that process terabytes of data in parallel in jobs that can run for days. A key challenge for system vendors is keeping their machines supplied with data; storage with both high capacity and performance is a must.

Recognizing that FlashBlade makes an ideal companion for these machines, Pure Storage entered a partnership with graphics vendor NVIDIA to deliver ready-to-run *Artificial Intelligence-Ready Infrastructure* (AIRI™) systems consisting of NVIDIA DGX graphics processors, FlashBlade storage, a 100Gb/s network fabric, and the most popular AI application and management software.

AIRI systems are turnkey machine learning environments, ready to take on the growing number of applications in finance, transportation, medicine, and other areas.

Emerging Applications

Artificial Intelligence

Computerized artificial intelligence has evolved from humble beginnings in the 1950s to what today is often called *machine learning* or *deep learning*. It consists of analyzing an input data set against models built from large amounts of historical data. For example, an image of a tumor analyzed against a model developed from thousands of scans of cancerous tumors can quickly focus an oncologist on the most relevant image slices and suggest diagnostic directions. Moreover, each diagnosis can refine the model in a process called *training* or can be used to develop alternative ones. Thus, the accuracy of a model improves over time. AI is deployed in many fields including weather prediction, financial analysis, system and component life prediction, and so forth.

AIRI: NVIDIA DGX Platforms + FlashBlade + 100Gb/s Fabrics

As a computer application, deep learning is extremely resource-intensive, especially when the input to its algorithms is digital imagery. In large measure, the long slow gestation of AI has been the result of insufficient compute power—until recently, it has not been possible to connect sufficient computing resources to a large enough body of data to perform the trillions of calculations needed to develop models that make accurate predictions.

In the last few years, however, a breakthrough has made accurate deep learning-based predictive models more feasible. Processor developers, foremost among them Pure Storage partner NVIDIA, have adapted massively parallel processors originally created for rendering digital graphics to perform more general computations. NVIDIA's flagship series of AI platforms contain either 45,000 or 90,000 processor cores capable of 1,000 or 2,000 teraflops of machine learning calculations.

Training calculations are based on millions of data samples, so massive computational power alone isn't enough. Data must be available to the processing complex. With single-chassis storage capacity of 792 physical terabytes and file and object access performance of up to 1.5 million NFS IOPS over high-speed Ethernet, FlashBlade can meet the storage capacity and throughput needs of multiple DGX series platforms.

Recognizing the emerging need, Pure Storage partnered with NVIDIA to produce the *Artificial Intelligence-Ready Infrastructure* (AIRI) that combines in a single rack two or four DGX platforms, a single-chassis FlashBlade system, and redundant 100Gb/s Ethernet fabric switches that support *Remote Direct Memory Access over Converged Ethernet* (RoCE, usually pronounced "rocky") for high-speed data transfer.

AIRI is a complete AI deep learning environment in a rack. In addition to hardware, it includes a customized operating system, Docker containers for the most popular machine learning tools such as TensorFlow, and a DGX-optimized AIRI Scaling Toolkit that makes it easy to expand computational capacity to multiple platforms as requirements increase.

AI is clearly a technology whose time has come. The ease and plummeting cost of collecting and retaining prodigious amounts of data are enabling applications that would have been impossible to conceive even a decade ago:

AUTONOMOUS VEHICLES

Autonomous (driverless) vehicles need software that can make real-time decisions faster and more correctly than human drivers. Vehicle developers' highest priority is passenger safety, but as the market develops, they must be ready to introduce reliable products. Their engineers base decision-making software on *deep neural networks* that simulate the human brain. These require enormous computational power to process prodigious amounts of data and produce deployable models that "get it right" when faced with unanticipated situations on the road.

QUANTITATIVE INVESTING

Investing at the institutional scale has become less of a "seat-of-the-pants" decision process and more of an analysis-based one. An entire profession of quantitative analysts ("quants") uses AI to guide investors' decisions. Reliable predictions require models based on large amounts of financial, and also climatological, political, and other types of data. Developing the models is computationally intensive, and moreover, they must constantly adapt as new data is gathered and new factors that affect markets are identified.

COMPUTER VISION FOR PATHOLOGY

Pathology is the cornerstone of most cancer diagnoses. With the potential of deep learning, teams of computational pathologists anticipate being able to make cancer diagnosis faster and more accurate by applying the rigor and quantitative analysis of deep learning.

IMAGE-BASED MACHINE LEARNING IN MEDICINE

More generally, AI is being applied to a range of medical applications, not the least of which is using medical images to augment the growing shortage of medical professionals as new modalities (equipment for image capture) make imaging accessible in locations where it has previously been impossible.

Unquestionably, increased use of imaging in the medical field has been beneficial. Diagnosis is faster and more accurate. But interpreting images requires trained, certified medical professionals, most notably radiologists, and therein lies an unfortunate side effect of increased technology adoption: radiologist overload. Frequent press reports note that many radiologists are overstressed; one goes so far as to call physician burnout a public health crisis.[56]

New mobile imaging equipment makes procedures like point-of-care ultrasound scanning possible in remote areas of developing countries. Image capture is fast, inexpensive, and easy, but the shortage of trained professionals to analyze images severely limits its utility. For example, a study led by the World Health Organization found that Nigeria would have to increase its doctor population twelve-fold to reach the per-patient levels of developed countries (and radiologists in those countries are overstressed!), and that it would take the country 300 years to do so![57]

Today, nobody is seriously suggesting that AI could replace medical professionals, but there is significant evidence that it can greatly increase their ability to analyze a variety of data including everything from preliminary diagnosis, dosage recommendations, identification of clinical trial candidates, fraud detection, administrative workflow assistance, and others. Healthcare investment in AI is increasing—over $1 billion was allocated in 2018. In the United States, the Food and Drug Administration (FDA) has approved several AI-based detection and diagnosis software products.

---

[56] https://www.partners.org/Newsroom/Articles/Torchiana-Health-Affairs-Physician-Burnout.aspx
[57] http://www3.wefo-rum.org/docs/WEF_HealthSystem_LeapfroggingEmergingEconomies_ProjectPaper_2014.pdf

Afterword

In This Chapter…

The instant access to resources offered by "public cloud" computing and storage is having a profound effect on information technology and on how organizations approach it. Users can order up whatever is needed in the moment. A new wave of containerized applications can run anywhere. Core applications will be evolving to more virtual, cloud-friendly paradigms that enable movement between data centers and public clouds with minimal adaptation and financial upheaval.

Meanwhile, the cost of solid-state storage is falling, making models that facilitate moving data between cloud and data center even more compelling. IT vendors, including Pure Storage, are adapting their products and services to make it easier to derive value from data wherever it resides. The company is streamlining the interface between on-premises and cloud IT for customers, both present and future.

Where Do We Go From Here?

Skating to Where the Puck is Going

"Skate to where the puck is going, not where it has been" is a quote often attributed to the father of former hockey player Wayne Gretzky. While the adage may be overused,[58] the analogy seems particularly apt for Pure Storage, or for any company intent on leading in a field where both the technology and its uses are changing rapidly. The implication is that for a company to achieve continuing success, it must anticipate change in the technologies it uses, in how users employ its products, and in its markets.

Pure Storage has operated this way since its inception. Even as the company was using consumer-grade SSDs to make flash-based storage affordable, it was developing FlashArray DFMs and FlashBlade storage units to improve flash performance and endurance as well as to reduce cost. Similarly, developing its own controller mainboards and chassis made possible such innovations as reliable NVMe-based NVRAMs, PCIe bridging for controller intercommunication, and faster incorporation of more powerful processors as vendors introduced them.

Starting FlashBlade development while FlashArray was just beginning to gain market traction demonstrated the company's intent to become an across-the-board leader in enterprise storage technology and service delivery. With all-inclusive pricing, ForeverFlash, Evergreen storage guarantees, breakthrough administrative simplicity, and Pure1 Manage the company continues to lead the way in ease of acquisition, utilization, and management of enterprise storage.

Then the Cloud Happened

But while Pure Storage was revolutionizing data center storage, another change was sweeping through information technology: public clouds. Public cloud providers use virtualization technology to deliver subscription computing and storage services via the Internet. Instead of purchasing, deploying, and managing physical resources "on-premises" for every new application, users can lease resources for as long as they need them. They don't have to plan for space, energy, heat dissipation, or in-house data center staff. There is no equipment refresh or residual accounting. If an application needs more computing

---

[58] https://www.canadianbusiness.com/blogs-and-comment/stop-using-gretzky-where-the-puck-is-quote/

power or storage, users order it from the provider. When an application is retired, the user terminates the lease on its resources. When systems are required for software testing or analytics, they can be up and running in minutes rather than months. For critical data, cloud providers offer to replicate across long distances to protect against disasters.

The model seemed irresistible to many users who saw themselves becoming procurers and managers of IT resources, consuming financial and human capital that might otherwise be devoted to their core businesses. Public clouds appeared to promise a respite. By the second decade of the 21st century, it was a rare IT director who did not have an executive mandate to develop a "cloud strategy."

The Good, The Bad, and The Ugly

As with most technology waves, experience with public clouds exposed both benefits and shortcomings. For example, from a technology standpoint:

- Historically, enterprise applications have scaled by clustering computers connected to low-latency shared storage. Clouds on the other hand, are best suited to loosely coupled applications with partitioned or separate data sets and relaxed I/O latency requirements.

- On-premises storage typically presents disk-like volumes with sub-millisecond access times and very high availability. Cloud providers offer multiple options with different properties and associated costs, but none compares directly with the performance and availability of local storage.

There are also economic considerations. For example, on-premises, storage is usually a capital expenditure with planned lifecycle and replacement costs, whereas storage in a public cloud is treated as an operating expense.

For most users, on-premises deployment is preferable for core applications—databases, ERP, CRM, and so forth—that need scalable shared access to data. Core applications are highly interactive; they require low I/O latency and continuous availability, traits that favor on-premises implementation. Because they are among the first functions an organization computerizes, they are generally mature. Operating and maintenance procedures, human use and management skills, and ongoing cost justification are well-established.

New applications tend to be more amenable to cloud implementation. Many of them process large unstructured data sets in a quasi-batch style. They need huge storage "farms" with relatively high throughput potential but they are less latency-sensitive than typical core applications. Their properties favor cloud deployment, although vendor charges for accessing stored data can make deployment for analytics and machine learning quite expensive.

When planning for a new application, however, whether on-premises or public cloud implementation is preferable may not be obvious a priori. But implementers must choose one or the other. Public cloud service guarantees, APIs, management tools, and cost schedules differ from vendor to vendor, so public cloud deployment usually means committing to a provider. If the chosen implementation turns out to be problematic, if requirements change over time, or if the selected public cloud vendor proves to be unsatisfactory, application migration can effectively mean re-implementation.

Public clouds have thus put many organizations' IT in states of uncertainty. Users desire cloud benefits but many have seen and heard enough about the commitments required and the costs to be hesitant about which applications and financial resources to commit to "the cloud."

What's Coming in Information Technology?

There are plenty of computationally intensive problems—weather forecasting, orbital and flight trajectories, genomics, and many others—but overall, IT is becoming increasingly data-centric. A bottomless well of public cloud storage is making it easier for enterprises to collect all kinds of data, which they analyze to improve their operations and predict future trends. Between the prodigious amounts of data being acquired, increasing regulation on data handling, and the need to remain competitive, organizations' IT strategies are increasingly driven by data—what to collect, where and how to store it, how long to retain it, how to dispose of it, and how to derive value from it.

Thus, storage is factoring more heavily in organizations' IT planning. But it isn't as simple as "move everything to the cloud." For some usages—long-term retention of "cold" data, storage for millions of items from myriads of sources (for example, phonehome logs from Pure Storage customer arrays)—public cloud storage is obviously preferable. For others, such as analytics and machine learning, the ideal implementation site is less obvious. On-premises implementation requires careful sizing and large capital expenditures for storage. Public cloud storage requires no capital, but the many repeated accesses to data that this class of applications require can become expensive.

In an ideal IT world, one would choose what appears to be the best deployment style and location for each new application and be able to react quickly and non-disruptively when change became necessary. Of course, the IT world is not ideal, but technology and economics are giving rise to three trends that are likely to fundamentally change the way organizations store, manage, and process their data in the coming years:

Deployment Model Convergence

Today, core application architectures differ significantly from those of applications implemented for public clouds. Clusters of computers with shared storage predominate in the former; containers in the latter. Migrating either of these from its native environment to another can be expensive, time-consuming, and error-prone. In the public cloud realm, implementations are tantamount to vendor lock-ins, whereas on-premises implementations entail significant capital expenditures for storage. There is a need for core application implementation models to become more cloud-friendly, and for homogenization of container-like models to minimize vendor lock-in and make it easier to migrate new-style applications from cloud to data center and the reverse.

New Uses for Old Data

As decreasing local and cloud storage costs make retaining more data affordable, users are seeking ways to extract value from "old" data, such as backups, that historically have only been retrieved to recover from disasters. One important use of data set backups is reducing *recovery time objectives* (RTOs). IT users have realized that while it's important to back up critical data, what's *really* important is how quickly it can be restored to primary storage, so production can resume after a disaster.

NEW FLASH, NEW APPLICATIONS

As information assumes a larger role in all aspects of life, enterprises need to keep much more data readily accessible. But economics still rules. Affordability matters. The cost per gigabyte of flash is below that of high-performance disk and can be expected to supplant even high-capacity disk in the foreseeable future. But higher density, less expensive flash has lower endurance and higher error rates, so challenges remain in the march to completely replace mechanical disks.

Deployment Model Convergence

Application containerization represents a major step toward homogenizing application deployment. A *container* packages an application with all the functional resources (e.g., software libraries) required to run it so it can quickly and easily be deployed on any platform that makes adequate physical (computing, storage, and network) resources available. Coupled with *orchestrators* that match application containers with physical resources drawn from pools, the container model makes application deployment easy. The model works well in public clouds, where virtual processing, network, and storage resources can be quickly and easily configured to order. It is less-suited to data center environments, where the predominant deployment model is virtualization, which requires individual configuration for each virtual machine, guest operating system, supporting software, network, and storage required by an application.

As container technology matures, it promises to make deployment of new applications the same whether in a public cloud or on premises. Orchestration technology will make it possible to manage in-house IT resources as a *private cloud*, much in the same way as users manage public cloud resources—reserve when required and relinquish when no longer required. From a technology standpoint, problem solved. But financially, organizations must acquire the physical resources that comprise their private clouds, typically large capital expenditures that require careful capacity planning. Pure Storage has taken an important step toward making it possible for organizations to implement private cloud storage by introducing *Evergreen Storage Services* (ES2). ES2 is a *storage as a service* (STaaS) model that allows customers to lease capacity as they use it, rather than purchasing it in fixed quantities. With ES2, users can adopt a more public cloud-like approach toward planning and provisioning their private cloud storage, from both technology and financial standpoints.

The Same Only Different

Container technology and the gradual evolution of IT vendor business practices toward more cloud-like equipment acquisition models like ES2 can be expected to provide users with the flexibility to choose between in-house and public cloud implementation for containerized applications. They do less toward making deployment of the huge mass of core (largely transactional) applications that exist in data centers today more flexible.

The dominant deployment style for transactional applications is the tightly-coupled shared data cluster. Application processing power and memory scale by adding computers, all of which have access to data stored in a high-performance array, carefully controlled by locking. The cluster model provides high application availability as well as scaling, albeit in large increments, but it relies completely on high-performance storage that supports advanced functions such as device reservations.

There are major differences between modern arrays and public cloud storage services. The former provides high I/O performance and high availability. Typical public cloud storage offerings are abstracted, so users are generally unaware of physical properties such as physical separation of virtual devices. Public cloud providers typically offer both disk-like virtual volumes and high-capacity object storage for latency-insensitive use. Neither offering's properties closely match those of enterprise storage arrays.

For example, public cloud virtual volumes offer acceptable, if not equal performance to disk-based arrays. But cloud volumes usually have limited capacity and some support only single virtual machine access. Not all vendors guarantee that different cloud volumes will reside on different physical devices. These limitations preclude shared storage clustering for high availability and scaling as a public cloud deployment technique.

Object storage in public clouds offers essentially unlimited capacity with high "durability" (resistance to data loss—*not* guaranteed availability). It can be accessed by any number of clients, both those within and those outside the cloud. But I/O latency can be hundreds of milliseconds, data consistency and availability guarantees are weak, and replication is not guaranteed to be instantaneous.

Public cloud storage must be utilized differently than on-premises storage. For example, with some virtual volume offerings, a virtual machine can't use RAID to protect data because virtual volumes are not guaranteed to occupy different physical devices. Applications must access public cloud object storage using the HTTP protocol—a paradigm not generally used by transactional applications. Not only is object storage latency intolerable, a typical guarantee is "eventual consistency." One virtual machine's update may not be instantly visible to another. Implementing a transactional application in a public cloud requires devising alternatives for high-performing, highly-available shared storage as well as for other common data center services such as encryption, snapshots, and replication.

Similarly, an application developed specifically for a public cloud would likely require extensive re-engineering to be migrated to a data center, or even to be moved to another provider's public cloud.

Flexibility for Core Applications

The most prevalent core transactional applications are widely-available software packages that are not likely to be re-engineered for public cloud deployment any time soon. One way to make deploying them more flexible would be to adapt the shared data cluster model for use in public clouds. In 2019, Pure Storage took an important step toward this by introducing *Cloud Block Store* (CBS), a public cloud-based functional equivalent of a FlashArray. CBS consists of virtual machines in a cloud running Purity//FA coupled to others that use providers' storage services to emulate flash devices. Together, they implement a virtual FlashArray that applications access via virtual iSCSI connections.

With CBS, virtual machines that run applications can create, write, read, resize, take snapshots of, replicate, and destroy FlashArray volumes just as their physical counterparts. On-premise applications that use FlashArray storage can migrate to a public cloud with no architectural changes. CBS provides the same features and resiliency guarantees as physical arrays on premises. Similarly, applications developed for public clouds that use CBS storage can migrate to data centers using physical arrays with no restructuring.

CBS enables on-premises applications to utilize public clouds in additional ways. For example:

- Virtual disaster recovery sites for applications running in data centers can be created in a public cloud without capital expenditure.
- Arrays in a data center can use FlashRecover asynchronous replication to maintain snapshots of production data in a public cloud.
- A physical FlashArray can use ActiveCluster to replicate high-value data synchronously to a virtual FlashArray in a cloud to protect against disasters.

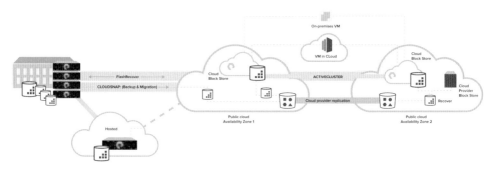

Like all FlashArray models, CBS virtual arrays use thin provisioning and data reduction to keep public cloud storage costs low. They make the full suite of FlashArray data services available in public clouds. Pure Storage customers can choose data center or cloud for disaster recovery, analytics, backup, and so forth, and migrate applications between the two without re-architecting. CBS not only makes deployment of core applications more flexible, it provides mechanisms for blending on-premises and public cloud computing and storage to users' advantage.

New Uses for Old Data

Low-cost public cloud storage has become a convenient repository for all manner of "old" data, from logs to event traces to backed up images of production data sets. Low-cost cloud storage makes it possible for organizations to retain more data set backups, increasing the granularity of recovery point objectives (RPOs).

In the meantime, increased requirements for "always-on" IT services have thrust backup into a more active role in IT operations. With the pressure on to get IT back up and running when a disaster or data corruption destroys production data, rapid restore has become vital for many organizations.

With the ability to retain more backup data at affordable cost, organizations are seeking ways to extract value from it. Public clouds offer very low-cost storage for seldom-accessed data and more expensive, but still-affordable, alternatives for data more likely to be accessed, such as recent backups and data used in analytics. Many users see public cloud backup as a more flexible and less capital and labor-intensive alternative to tape, with its massive infrastructure rquirements. Today, the transition of backup strategies from tape to disk-based appliances that began over a decade ago is being overtaken by a similar one that replaces on-premises appliances with backup to clouds, both public and private.

The First Transformation

Backup underwent a transformation in the early 2000s when efficient techniques for deduplicating data were developed. Because most backups are nearly identical to their predecessors in time, backup is a "poster child" usage for deduplication. For example, if the content of each backup differs from the previous one by less than a percent, 100 deduplicated backups can be stored in little more than the space required for two full ones. As disk-based appliances became popular, they spawned a backup lifecycle in which production data was backed up to appliances, and backups would be spooled off to tape periodically. The D2D2T paradigm quickly became the enterprise backup strategy of choice.

Disk-based backup appliances were great. Backup was fast, because unchanged data wasn't re-copied. Storage cost was low for the same reason. The only disadvantage was restore time. When a production data set must be restored from a backup, faster is better. But a deduplicated backup scatters fragments of data sets on disks throughout the appliance. Streaming is impossible—restore time is dominated by disks seeking and rotating to access the millions of fragments needed to reassemble a data set. Restore times became a major frustration for users, especially those who outsourced backup and restore operations to service providers.

Backup appliance vendors responded by enhancing their appliances to reassemble full backups in the background, but it was the proverbial "bandage on a tumor." More full backups in an appliance negated deduplication space savings, and if a restore was needed while a backup was being reassembled, both restore and reassembly would be slowed even further.

The Second Transformation

FlashBlade did two things to change backup strategies. First, its large capacity and low cost per gigabyte made it an attractive alternative to disk-based appliances. Second, and more importantly, FlashBlade systems can restore backups at streaming speeds. With FlashBlade, random and sequential access are equally fast; the systems can decompress and deliver data as fast as it can be moved on the network. Rapid restore became a popular FlashBlade application, so much so that many users would forego the storage cost savings of deduplicating appliances to lower restore times, in some cases from days to minutes. The team partnered with major backup software vendors to integrate FlashBlade with their products, making rapid restore available to users, whatever their backup software.

FlashBlade systems can expand to petabytes, but there is a limit. Eventually, inactive data no longer justifies online storage, and should be discarded or moved to even less expensive media, the role that tape had fulfilled in the past.

That's where public clouds come in. Cloud storage incurs ongoing cost, but providers' lowest-cost offerings are inexpensive compared to the capital, human, and logistical cost of a tape infrastructure with mechanical libraries and the need for offsite archiving. But there was a limitation to using public clouds to archive inactive data: lack of deduplication. Every backup sent to a cloud occupied the full size of its data set.

In the spirit of "skating to where the puck is going," Pure Storage took steps toward integrating its flash-based systems used for backup with public cloud storage. Following integration of FlashBlade with major backup suites, the company acquired specialized deduplication technology and developed *ObjectEngine*—a scalable engine for deduplicating data stored on FlashBlade systems and pushing it to public clouds for long-term storage.

An ObjectEngine is equipped with flash storage in which it maintains a massive deduplication index and a catalog that it uses to satisfy client requests for deduplicated data. It effectively uses FlashBlade as a cache for recent backups, which are the most likely to be restored. With ObjectEngine, the backup paradigm evolves from D2D2T to F2F2C.

ObjectEngine brings deduplication cost savings to backups in the cloud while retaining the FlashBlade rapid restore advantage. In principle, deduplicated backups cached on FlashBlade systems can be accessed directly, for example for analytics. ObjectEngine effectively integrates public clouds into a cost-effective F2F2C lifecycle.

New Flash, New Applications

In 2011, FlashArray made flash affordable for tier-1. In 2015, decreasing flash cost and advanced engineering brought flash to tier-2 with FlashBlade.

With Cloud Block Store and ObjectEngine, Pure Storage has taken the lead in the long process of unifying public cloud and on-premises data processing and storage. But requirements for online data storage are on the rise as well. The amount of data being captured today is staggering, and a good share of it must be readily accessible to be of value before it ages into irrelevance. Manufacturers' production records and service logs must be instantly available when product issues arise. Digital content producers must keep graphical components online for ready access by artists developing new properties. The demand for affordable online storage is far from abating.

Flash cost has fallen below that of performance disk storage, but it is still too expensive for online storage of the masses of data being collected. Flash itself is evolving, with recently introduced *quad-level cell* (QLC) flash with four bits per cell and 3D flash which stacks layers of cells vertically in a single die. Flash is both competitive and lucrative for producers, so densities are likely to increase and prices are likely to continue to fall over time.

Pure Storage keeps abreast of developments in flash and technologies that might supplant or augment it and continually assesses their implications on its products. For example, with increasing density, flash endurance drops and read error rates rise. The company is actively developing more sophisticated error detection and correction and mechanisms to maximize high-density device lifetimes.

The capacity of flash devices in Pure Storage products will likely increase along with flash density, but in addition, there is room for architectural adaptation. For example, a multi-petabyte "data farm" with much more flash managed by a processor than today's systems could lower storage cost even beyond that of FlashBlade. For Pure Storage, the key to continued leadership is taking advantage of relevant new technologies by adapting its product architectures to incorporate them for the benefit of its customers and to meet the needs of evolving markets.

Son of Flash

Semiconductor developers continually experiment with alternative technologies to improve on flash access speed, endurance, and addressability. "3D XPoint" and "Z-NAND" are two recent developments offered by major vendors. Their access speeds and endurance are an improvement over flash, but cost per gigabyte is much higher, so applications have been limited. While the cost of electronic technologies tends downward over time, flash cost is experiencing the same sort of rapid decrease that began with disks nearly two decades ago. To make inroads on the flash market, a competing technology must offer superior properties *and* be at least as, if not more, cost-effective.

More Worlds to Conquer

A completely different evolutionary direction lies in mainframes, long virtually ignored by the storage industry. While not regarded as a growth market, mainframes still run many applications that represent the backbone of large enterprise IT—credit card processing, social benefit administration, and tax collection, to name three. Just as more modern applications have benefitted from the disk-to-flash transition, these legacy systems could gain performance, reliability, footprint reduction, and ultimately user satisfaction from a transition to flash storage customized to meet their specific needs.

It Never Stops

Even as it explores new directions in data-centric IT, Pure Storage is "running faster to stay even" with its current products and architectures. In-house hardware has made it possible to track processor, DRAM, network, and flash component developers' evolution much more closely. The company routinely develops new systems based on processors and other components before they are publicly available. Typically, before a product generation, such as FlashArray/M ships, development of the next generation (FlashArray//X) is underway. Similarly, two generations of blades for FlashBlade systems shipped in rapid succession. By careful attention to packaging and interconnect architectures (e.g., by pioneering in NVMe or by integrating communications on the FlashBlade midplane), and adhering to its policy of non-disruptive hardware and software upgrades, the company continues to offer storage systems with decade-long lifetimes of uninterrupted service and unparalleled ease of use and administration.